A Ceremonial Ox of India

A
Ceremonial Ox
of India

The Mithan in Nature, Culture, and History

*With Notes on the Domestication
of Common Cattle*

by

FREDERICK J. SIMOONS

with the assistance of

ELIZABETH S. SIMOONS

Illustrations by

GENE M. CHRISTMAN

The University of Wisconsin Press

Madison, Milwaukee, and London

1968

Published by
The University of Wisconsin Press
Box 1379, Madison, Wisconsin 53701

The University of Wisconsin Press, Ltd.
27–29 Whitfield Street, London, W.1

Printed in the United States of America by
Heffernan Press, Worcester, Massachusetts

Library of Congress Catalog Card Number 68-9023

To the giants of the mithan country
J. H. Hutton, J. P. Mills, C. von Fürer-Haimendorf,
and H.-E. Kauffmann

Preface

In 1963–64 we were in southern Asia investigating milk use and dairying from a geographic and culture historic point of view. One of our problems was to locate the present-day groups in the Indian subcontinent who share the traditional East Asians' reluctance to milk their domestic animals and to consume milk as food. The occurrence of such reluctance probably represents the survival of an ancient habit which once was more widespread. The mapping of such groups should, we felt, provide clues to the earlier extent of the "non-milking attitude." While collecting information from the literature on the hill peoples of Assam and adjoining areas, we became aware of the existence among them of a strange-looking domesticated bovine animal—the mithan (*Bos frontalis*)—which was not milked. The mithan, sometimes also referred to in the literature as "gayal," is little known to the outside world. Though specimens have found their way to European and American zoos, the mithan has been completely overlooked by breeders for possible introduction to tropical highlands similar to its homeland. Though our initial effort was intended only to present a brief statement for the dairying study, we became aware of the need for someone to collect the widely scattered material on the animal. This book springs from that awareness.

The senior author is grateful to the Guggenheim Foundation, the Geography Branch of the Office of Naval Research, and the Graduate Schools of the University of Wisconsin and the University of Texas for providing financial support for this research; and to the Geography Departments of the University of Wisconsin (Madison), the University of California (Berkeley), the Louisiana State University (Baton Rouge), and the University of Texas (Austin), for providing office space and other assistance. We also thank Karl W. Butzer, Gene M. Christman, John Emlen, C. von

Fürer-Haimendorf, J. H. Hutton, H.-E. Kauffmann, S. N. Kramer, L. G. Löffler, Jonathan D. Sauer, George B. Schaller, David E. Sopher, Philip L. Wagner, and S. S. Weinberg for their useful comments on all or parts of the manuscript; H. J. Spielmann for providing unpublished village census materials; the University of Chicago Press and G. B. Schaller for making available galley proofs of his recent book, *The Deer and the Tiger;* H.-E. Kauffmann, C. von Fürer-Haimendorf, James Mellaart, and J. H. Hutton for providing photographs and permission to use them; Gene Christman for drawing the sketches and maps; and the many scholars and others who answered our queries for information and who are cited individually in the text. Of our colleagues and associates who have been amused but tolerant of our excitement with "the ox," we are appreciative.

F. J. S.
E. S. S.

Austin, Texas
October 15, 1967

Contents

Part III

The Mithan in Society and Economy
A General View

Part IV

The Domestication of Mithan
and of Common Cattle

Appendices

Illustrations, Maps, Tables

Illustrations

following page 128

Maps

Tables

Introduction

Seven decades ago the German geographer Eduard Hahn argued that common cattle were first domesticated in Mesopotamia to provide sacrificial animals for the lunar mother-goddess. Man, he claimed, was struck by the crescent shape of cattle horns, which resemble the new moon, and thought cattle especially suited for such sacrifice. Many scholars, perhaps most notably those inclined to seek economic motivations for cattle domestication, have rejected Hahn's ideas as fanciful and without merit. Others, among them various cultural geographers, anthropologists, and zoologists, have viewed them with more favor.[1]

Few, however, have thought to look beyond the evidence about common cattle to other domesticated bovines: to methods of husbandry; role in society, culture, and economy; to the probable incentives for, and processes of, domestication; and to the relevance of the newly gained knowledge for the domestication of common cattle. Largely ignored in the discussion have been the water buffalo and the domesticated bovines known only in eastern Asia: the yak of Tibet, the Bali cattle of Indonesia, and the mithan of the Assam border country.[2] The purpose of this study is to treat in detail one of the overlooked domestic bovines, the mithan,[3] and then, in the light of this information, to reexamine theories about the means and motives of domesticating common cattle.

The mithan has remained so little known because it occurs in a limited area in a remote part of the world—the rough, isolated, forested up-

---

1. See, for example, Erich Isaac, "On the Domestication of Cattle," *Science,* 137, No. 3525 (July 20, 1962): 195–204.

2. How the mithan qualifies as "domesticated" is discussed in Part IV, pp. 211–13.

3. Hahn mentioned the mithan briefly in his great work *Die Haustiere* and decried the lack of knowledge about these animals.

lands that border the Indian subcontinent to the north and east (see Map 1, p. 6). In the region are the easternmost arc of the Himalayas, including eastern Bhutan and what today is known as the North-East Frontier Agency of India; the southward swinging jumble of mountains and hills between India and Burma which terminate in the Chittagong Hills of Pakistan and the Arakan Hills of Burma; and the southeastward trending mountains between Burma and China. This area straddles several international boundaries and has long been a no-man's land, marginal to the high cultures of India, Burma, China, and Tibet that flank it on every side. The hill peoples have borrowed culture traits from the neighboring high cultures, but until modern times have remained distinct from them and free of their political control. Their closest affinities have been with other tribal peoples found in India, Southeast Asia, and southern China. Most of the hill peoples have remained tribal and animist, and usually support themselves by shifting cultivation. Their domestic bovines, including the mithan, do not commonly aid in cultivation, but serve principally for sacrifice and meat. In recent decades significant changes have taken place in traditional culture from place to place, especially in the southern range of the mithan. We note some effects of acculturation where they are indicated in the literature; but because available information is limited and not always recent, in most cases it is not possible to determine the precise up-to-date state of acculturation. Because of this and because our primary interest is in reconstructing the traditional role of the mithan, we write usually in the ethnographic present, and generally provide in the text the dates of the sources used.

The approach in this study, it should be emphasized, is not that of the zoologist, but that of the cultural geographer. A balanced view of the mithan will be attempted by following two methods adapted from more general geographic studies. One involves consideration of the mithan by topic. The other treats the mithan within each of several ethnic groups where it is found. We believe this is the first time a domestic animal has been viewed in quite this way, and we use the combination of methods to bring out both the overall position of the animal and the differing roles it plays in different cultural contexts. Part I discusses the physical and behavioral characteristics of the mithan, its distribution and habitat, numbers, and place in the bovine world. In Part II the mithan is observed in several ethnic groups, each selected because it represents a particular relationship between the animal and man. These groups are the Sherdukpen, the Dafla, the Apa Tani, and the Adi—all located in India's North-East Frontier Agency and all of them north of the Assam Valley—and the Lhota Naga and Central Chin of the mithan's southern range, south of the upper valley. Part III treats by topic the role of the mithan in society and economy; while Part IV turns to the domestication of the mithan, and to the broader question of the domestication of common cattle.

Part I
The Mithan in Nature

1

The Animal

Description

The mithan (Figures 1–4) is a heavily built domesticated bovine. In height, bulls rarely exceed 5 feet 8 inches at the shoulder, but the average bull is about 5 feet tall, and the average cow is several inches shorter. Most young mithan are brown, and they darken in color as they age. Adult males are generally black with white stockings on all four legs. Some mithan, however, are piebald or white (Figures 3–4). Other characteristics of the animal are a dorsal ridge on the crest of the shoulders, a small but pronounced dewlap, a generally flat forehead, and horns which extend mainly outward. The horns are of unusual girth. They are straight or gently curving but do not recurve at the tip. The length of a horn on mature males averages perhaps 14 inches, but there is one horn of 22 inches on record. The mithan is an unusually gentle animal, as revealed in the Chin expression "gentle as a mithan." Normally even a stranger is safe in approaching one, and if he gives it a bit of salt, it will usually follow him about. There are, of course, occasional troublesome mithan; the Zanniat Chin believe that if a woman's skirt is thrown over the head of such an animal, it will be shamed "into feminine subservience" (Stevenson, 1943: 56). On provocation the mithan can charge with agility and with its great strength cause serious injury to man or beast.

R. H. Sneyd Hutchinson (1906: 21–22), seeking a bull mithan for the Calcutta Zoological Garden, found a "truly magnificent specimen" among some Kuki in the Chittagong Hill Tracts, and attempted to take it along. The Kuki tied long ropes of creeper around the mithan, and then turned the animal over to Hutchinson's escort of Gurkha sepoys. With Hutchinson joining them, the sepoys took up the ropes and began to lead the mithan out of the village. Suddenly the mithan became aware that

3

he was being taken away. He dropped his head, turned abruptly around and, after a loud bellow, pulled the entire group back through the village, to the great amusement of the Kuki. Hutchinson, the sepoys, and the villagers succeeded in stopping him, but then nothing could induce him to move, except to charge angrily at anyone who approached. Even salt proved useless in attempting to win him over. Eventually the Kuki decided that a sacrifice was necessary if the animal was to be removed, and an old man was called. He sacrificed a white cock before the mithan, put some of the blood and some rice beer between the animal's horns, and chanted, apparently telling the mithan he must leave quietly. Oddly enough, just then the mithan decided to go along, and peacefully accompanied Hutchinson and his group. Some weeks later, however, on the journey down to the lowlands, the mithan dropped dead from the heat. The Gurkha were sure that the old Kuki had put an evil spell on the mithan, and that that was the cause of his death.

Distribution

The mithan is found in the long, curved belt of hill country stretching from the Arakan Hills and Chin Hills of Burma, through the Chittagong Hill Tracts of Pakistan, and the Lushai (Mizo) Hills, Manipur, and the Naga Hills of India (Maps 1 and 2).[1] It is reported among certain Naga groups in the Patkoi Range—though we have not determined its presence generally there.[2] The mithan is found among the Mishmi at the head of the Brahmaputra Valley. From there, its distribution extends westward across India's North-East Frontier Agency (hereafter referred to as NEFA) to its western borders and beyond, into Bhutan, and eastward into the northern hills of Burma.

In northern Burma mithan are few and are found only among peoples of the remote hills; most observers who have worked in the area have neither seen nor heard of it. There are, nevertheless, several brief notices of it there: among Naga living between the Hukawng Valley and the Patkoi Range (No. 48 on Map 1); among the Daru of the Tamai Valley (53); in the Nung Hills (45); in Hkinlum village, whose people presumably are Lisu (47); among the Maru of Magri or Mang-yam village (46); and in Gamhkawn (Hkamhkam) village, where a mithan or hybrid was brought in presumably for a Lashi feast (44). Though four of these ref-

1. Peoples and places mentioned in the text are located on Maps 2–7.
2. Parul C. Dutta, who has studied certain Tangsa of Tirap Frontier Division of NEFA, which includes the Indian sections of the Patkoi Range, writes that the mithan is not found in Tirap (pers. com., Sept. 21, 1965).

erences were for either the 1920's or 1930's, two are for the 1950's, which suggests that mithan may still be present in small numbers today.[3] Though the animal occurs in villages close to the Yunnan border, a search of the literature failed to uncover a single report of one in China, nor is there any evidence that mithan have ever been present in Thailand or elsewhere in Southeast Asia.

Although some deny the existence of the mithan in Bhutan, there is clear documentation of its presence at least in small numbers. The earliest reference is from the account of Samuel Turner (1800: 160–61), who, on his way to Tibet in 1783, saw a fight staged by the Raja of Tassisudon (Tashi Chho Dzong) between two mithan. The animals, said Turner, were foreign to Bhutan and were brought from "a more eastern part of the same range of mountains," presumably what is now the North-East Frontier Agency of India. Additional references to their presence came from the mission to Bhutan under Captain R. B. Pemberton in 1837–38 (Griffith, 1839: 210–11, 269, 281–82; Pemberton, 1865: 67–68). The indications are that mithan were fairly common. The late J. P. Mills noted that in 1945 there was a trade in mithan between certain peoples of NEFA and Bhutan (1946: 10–11), an observation later confirmed by R. R. P. Sharma (1961: 9–10). A photograph of a mithan or mithan/common cattle hybrid[4] (Todd, 1952: 719) in the Ha Valley of western Bhutan adds further confirmation.

The occurrence of mithan in Sikkim has also been noted, and a few were reported even in Darjeeling (O'Malley, 1907: 69–71; 1917: 116–17; Chatterjee, 1926: 178–79; Dash, 1947: 108). Most accounts of Sikkim, however, make no mention of the creature. This, together with specific testimony to its absence,[5] indicates that at best it is quite rare there today.

3. H.-E. Kauffmann (1934: Kartogramm Nr. 3) made the only previous effort to map the distribution of the mithan, basing his map on the literature. Kauffmann indicated mithan present among the Maru and Kachin. He comments (pers. com., Sept. 3, 1965), however, that if he found reports of mithan anywhere among an ethnic group, he made the sign for the mithan over the entire group territory. His subsequent field observations and those of other writers reveal that the buffalo is the principal sacrificial animal of the Kachin and that the mithan is not known in most of the Kachin country.

4. The term "common cattle" as used here and subsequently in this book refers in a general way to both zebu cattle, which in the literature are usually designated *Bos indicus,* and humpless cattle, *Bos taurus. Bos indicus* and *Bos taurus* are completely interfertile and should be considered races rather than species. The common cattle of India are zebu in type, with a more or less pronounced hump.

5. Stonor, basing his statement on first-hand observation, asserts that though breeding stock is traded eastward to the Bhutan-NEFA border, he observed no herds of mithan in Bhutan, Sikkim, or Nepal (pers. com., C. R. Stonor, Aug. 18, 1965). Prof. P. P. Karan, who traveled extensively in the area, did not observe any mithan

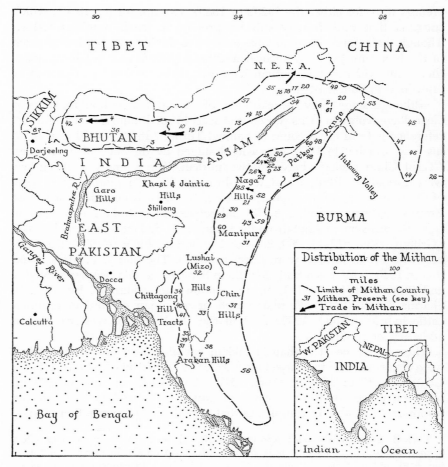

Map 1

Identification of Numbers on Map 1

1 Kunsong's village (Mishmi) (Cooper, 1873: 189–91)

2 Tashalun village (Mishmi) (Bailey, 1945: 158)

3 Dewangiri (Griffith, 1839: 210–11, 282)

4 Tangsa or Tongsa (Griffith, 1839: 282)

5 Tassisudon (Tashi Chho Dzong) (Turner, 1800: 160–61)

6 Chowsam's village (Khampti) (Cooper, 1873: 168)

7 Tangyong village (Khumi) (Tickell, 1854: 110–11)

8? Sikkim (O'Malley, 1907: 69–71; 1917: 116–17; Dash, 1947: 108)

9 Northern Sangtam Naga (Stonor, 1950: 9; but H.-E. Kauffmann, 1939: 218, and pers. com., May 10, 1966, says that the Northern Sangtam do not keep mithan.)

10 Monba of the Dirang Dzong area (Mills, 1946: 10)

11 Aka (Hesselmeyer, 1868: 199, 200; Dalton, 1872: 38; Elwin, 1959: 445; Sinha, 1962: 35–37)

12 Dafla (Stonor, 1953–54: 335; Shukla, 1959: 40, 41)

13 Apa Tani (Fürer-Haimendorf, 1946: 39–42; 1948: 242; 1963: 145; N. K. Das, 1947: 297; Stonor, 1953–54: 332)

14 Hill Miri (Dalton, 1845: 265–66; 1872: 34; Fürer-Haimendorf, 1946a: 52)

15 Gallong (Sen Gupta, 1955: 71, 76; Srivastava, 1962: 34–35, 47)

16 Minyong Adi (Fürer-Haimendorf, 1954: 597; Sen Gupta, 1954: 158, 166; S. Roy, 1960: 151–53, 160)

17 Padam Adi (Dalton, 1872: 25; S. Roy, 1960: 151–53, 160)

18 Pangi Adi (Sen Gupta, 1954: 158, 166)

19 Sherdukpen (Paul, 1958: 156; Sharma, 1961: 9, 37)

20 Mishmi (Griffith, 1838: 239; Rowlatt, 1845: 494–95; Dalton, 1872: 15; Cooper, 1873: 189–91, 234; Mills, 1952: 3–4; Barua, 1954: 129–30; N. Roy, 1957: 131)

21 Angami Naga (Hutton, 1921: 66, 67, 79–80, 84, 106)

22 Chang Naga (Fürer-Haimendorf, 1939: 188)

23 Kalyo Kengyu Naga (Fürer-Haimendorf, 1938: 209; 1939: 159, 188)

24 Ao Naga (Risley, 1903: 212; Molz, 1909: 64; Majumdar, 1924: 51–52, 59; Majumder, 1925: 23, 27–28, 46–47; Smith, 1925: 4–5, 98, 103, 104–5, 189; Mills, 1926: 132–33)

25 Rengma Naga (Mills, 1937: 91, 92)

26 Lhota Naga (Mills, 1922: 61)

27 Sema Naga (Hutton, 1921a: 69, 103; Fürer-Haimendorf, 1939: 188)

28 Konyak Naga of Hungphoi and Wakching villages (Fürer-Haimendorf, 1939: 52, 95–96)

29 North Cachar (Stewart, 1855: 596, 597, 631, 643; Soppitt, 1885: 8, 11; Baker, 1903–4: 228; Livesey, 1931: 201; Milroy, 1934–35: 103)

30 Thadou Kuki of Manipur (Shaw, 1929: 85)

31 Purum Kuki of Manipur (T. Das, 1945: 66, 84)

32 Lushai (Mizo) (Lewin, 1870: 260–62; Woodthorpe, 1873: 87; Risley, 1903: 224; Imperial Gazetteer of India. Provincial Series: Eastern Bengal and Assam, 1909: 457, 462–64; Shakespear, 1912: 31–32; McCall, 1949: 21, 186)

33 Lakher or Mara (Parry, 1932: 164–65, 169)

34 A Pankhua village near Longkar, Sajek region (pers. com., D. E. Sopher, 1965)

35 Bawm-Zo (pers. coms., H. J. Spielmann, Sept. 9, 1965, and D. E. Sopher, 1965)

36 Bhutan (Pemberton, 1865: 67; Fürer-Haimendorf, 1963: 146)

37 Chin (Newland, 1894: 44, 46; Carey and Tuck, 1896, 1: 180–81; Wehrli, 1905–6: 118; Stevenson, 1943: 47–48)

38 Arakan Hills (St. John, 1873: 238; Blyth, 1875: 48; Spearman, 1879–80, 1: 566, 2: 64; Hughes, 1881: 5–6; Imperial Gazetteer of India. Provincial Series: Burma, 1908, 1: 205)

39 Taunglung village (Khumi) (pers. com., D. E. Sopher, 1965)

40 Nilkop village (Pankhua) (pers. com., D. E. Sopher, 1965)

41 Basanta and Lalkin Para or Kuki Para (Pankhua) (pers. com., D. E. Sopher, 1965; Mills, 1935: 122)

42 Ha Valley, Bhutan (Todd, 1952: 719)

43 Ukurul village (Tangkhul Naga) (pers. com., C. Nakane, 1965)

44 Gamhkawn village, Kachin Hills (J. K. Stanford, 1946: 93; pers. com., J. K. Stanford, Sept. 13, 1965; pers. com., H. E. Anthony, Oct. 1, 1965)

45 Nung Hills (Stevenson, 1943: 47–48; Leach, 1954: 144)

46 Magri or Mang-yam village (Maru) (Kingdon-Ward, 1921: 140)

47 Hkinlum village (Lisu?) (Kingdon-Ward, 1956: 82)

48 Area between the Namhpuk Hka, the Tanai Hka, the western edge of the Hukawng Valley, and the inhabited ranges to the north of these limits up to the Patkoi Range (Naga) (Dewar, 1933: 268)

49 Peti village (Mishmi) (Kingdon-Ward, 1930: 430)

50 Chui village (Konyak Naga) (E. T. D. Lambert, 1937: 312)

51 Mru (Mills, 1935: 123; pers. com., L. G. Löffler, Aug. 20, 1965)

52 Phakekedzumi village (Eastern Angami) (pers. com., H.-E. Kauffmann, May 10, 1966)

53 Daru of Tamai Valley (Kingdon-Ward, 1938: 82; 1949: 86)

54 Ayang village (Adi) (Millington, 1912: 155)

55 Janbo village (Adi) (Dunbar, 1932: 233)

56 Kanpetlet area (Chin) (pers. com., F. K. Lehman, March 10, 1966)

57 Nilö cluster of villages (Miri) (Fürer-Haimendorf, 1955: 212)

58 Phom Naga (pers. com., H.-E. Kauffmann, May 10, 1966)

59 Mollen village (Kuki) (Kingdon-Ward, 1952: 108)

60 Langsing Naga (Konyak) of Loglai Shim and Big Pani Shim (Steen, 1948: 275)

61 Miju Mishmi of village at Glo Lake, Kamlang Valley (Kingdon-Ward, 1951–52: 585)

62 Rasa Naga of Hahti village (R. C. Morris, 1935–36: 663)

The mithan through almost all of its distribution is found among hill tribes, and is virtually unknown to the neighboring lowlanders of Burma, Pakistan, and India. Interestingly, it does not occur among the tribal people of Bihar and Orissa or even those of the Garo and Khasi and Jaintia hills, although the habitat in all of the latter hill areas seems suitable and access to the Khasi and Jaintia hills area is easy. Though there are no indications that the mithan distribution in NEFA has shrunk, there are strong suggestions that it has done so in the Chittagong Hill Tracts and certain other areas, for reasons to be considered later (pp. 166–67).

Habitat

The mithan is a woodland animal and usually is found at elevations of from 2,000 to 9,000 feet. In the Chittagong Hill Tracts and in the Mishmi country, however, it descends to 1,000 feet and lower; and in Bhutan it has been reported as high as about 10,000 feet. At lower elevations the mithan overlaps the distribution of common cattle and water buffalo; at higher elevations in the Himalayas it overlaps the range of the yak. Though it seems to do well in European and American zoos, it does not flourish in the hot, open lowlands of Assam and Bengal.[6] When taken to the lowlands, it seeks out shade and, while it does not wallow in mud like the water buffalo, it does get into pools for relief from the heat.

The hills and mountains of mithan country are dominated by the monsoon circulation of India. The northeast monsoon winds, which blow from December through March, have relatively cool temperatures and bring little precipitation. Following the northeast monsoon period is a hot season during April and May, brought on by the lengthening days and

in Sikkim or western Bhutan in 1961 or 1964. He asserts that one does see the animal east of the Black Mountain Range in central Bhutan and that they appear to be more common eastward along the Bhutan-NEFA border (pers. com., Sept. 28, 1965).

6. Mr. Chatterjee, superintendent of the Zoological Garden, Alipore, Calcutta (pers. com., Dec. 30, 1966), has kindly provided information on eleven mithan possessed by the garden at one time or another. The information did not, unfortunately, include estimates of the animals' ages at the time of arrival. Of six female mithan, all were dead within four years of arrival. The males fared better. One survived for two years; a second for six; a third, a calf on arrival, for fifteen years; and two others, still alive at the time of writing, had been in the garden for six years and were thriving. The mean age of survival for the mithan which had died was less than five years. The experience of wild animals under zoo conditions is, of course, not the same as in the wild, nor is that of domestic animals in zoos the same as under village conditions. For this reason, the figures above cannot be taken to support the oft-repeated assertion that mithan do not long survive in the lowland.

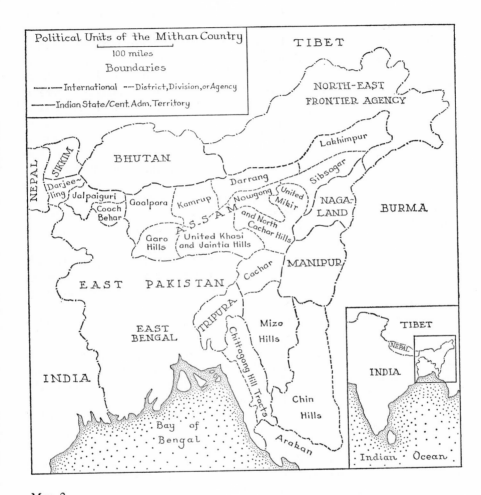

Political Units of the Mithan Country

100 miles

Boundaries

—·— International --- District, Division, or Agency
—— Indian State/Cent. Adm. Territory

TIBET

NORTH-EAST
FRONTIER AGENCY

Lakhimpur

NEPAL

SIKKIM

BHUTAN

Darrang

Sibsagar

Darjee-
ling

Jalpaiguri

Cooch
Behar

Goalpara

Kamrup

Nowgong

United
Mikir

NAGA-
LAND

BURMA

A-S-S-A-M

and North
Cachar Hills

Garo
Hills

United Khasi
and Jaintia Hills

MANIPUR

EAST   PAKISTAN

Cachar

EAST
BENGAL

TRIPURA

Mizo
Hills

TIBET

NEPAL

INDIA

Chittagong Hill Tracts

INDIA

Chin

Hills

Bay   of
Bengal

Arakan

Indian Ocean

Map 2

higher sun's rays. This is followed by the southwest monsoon, which is at its peak from June through September, and which brings abundant rain. In the mithan country, rainfall generally is between 60 and 150 inches annually, though some stations experience 200 inches or even more.

Precipitation is particularly heavy in places where moisture-bearing winds are forced upward, as along south-facing slopes such as the Himalaya foothills. There is, however, a decrease in precipitation above a certain elevation. This is especially notable in the Himalayas, where at higher levels precipitation ranges from 20 to 40 inches; these are conditions of aridity approaching those of Tibet. The topography of mithan country also leads to some striking rain shadow situations: windward slopes receive heavy rain, while leeward slopes are notably drier. The Sherdukpen valley, one rain shadow situation at from 5,500 to 6,500 feet in elevation, receives only 30 to 32 inches of precipitation, which has important implications for both agriculture and animal husbandry.

The prevailing conditions of steep slopes and heavy, concentrated precipitation have contributed to some remarkable erosional features in mithan country. The rivers of NEFA have cut particularly deep gorges southward to the Assam Valley, and constitute barriers rather than aids to contact. Since there is commonly insufficient level land for farming, cultivators find it necessary to clear steep hillsides, which can suffer severely from sheet and gully erosion.

The heavy precipitation characterizing much of the mithan country is accompanied by cloudiness and high humidity. Cloudiness and altitude combine to moderate the summer temperatures of the region. Though there are striking differences in temperature with altitude, in general summer temperatures are among the more moderate of the Indian subcontinent. Even at lower elevations, mean July temperatures are generally no more than 80° to 85°F. Winter temperatures show great variation within the region. In the southern margins of mithan country, a mean January temperature between 65° and 70°F. is common, whereas at 7,000 feet elevation in NEFA it is likely to be about 40°F. Frost is most common in NEFA; where it occurs, in NEFA or elsewhere, it is typically found at higher elevations and in winter. Snow is common in NEFA but is seldom found elsewhere.

Areas below about 3,000 feet in mithan country are usually covered either with tropical evergreen rainforest or semievergreen forest. In the higher areas vegetation cover consists chiefly of subtropical wet hill forest (from 3,000 to 5,000 or 6,000 feet), and of wet temperate forest (from 5,000 or 6,000 to 9,000 feet). The latter two forest types are composed mostly of broadleaf evergreen species, though deciduous species occur, too. Among the important trees are oak, chestnut, maple, alder, birch, magnolia, and laurel. The tallest trees are commonly between 60 and 100 feet high, but there is a second story of medium-size trees. Epiphytes, climbers, and mosses are found on the trees; and there is an undergrowth of shrubs and, in some places, bamboo or ferns. There are generally few grasses in the forests, except in abandoned clearings and on the banks of streams. From the Naga country southward, however, open grassy areas, commonly on hillsides or crests, are widespread. At elevations from 9,000 to 12,000 feet, into which the mithan ventures, is an upper level of wet temperate forest in which conifers dominate. And in NEFA, where mountains rise above 12,000 feet, there is a zone of alpine vegetation which, in turn, gives way, on higher peaks, to permanent snow cover. The general description above applies best to NEFA. In the Naga Hills, Manipur, and in Burma, there also occur, between about 2,500 and 8,000 feet, subtropical pine forests, which include broadleaf trees as well as pines.

Unlike common cattle, the mithan is a browser. Given a choice, it will seek out the tender shoots and young leaves of the forest rather than the grasses of more open country. Presumably forage for a browser is much better in secondary forests, such as those springing up in the abandoned fields of shifting cultivators. Thus the world of the shifting cultivator offers special advantages favoring the keeping of mithan; and their keeper is saved considerable work: he need not clear forest to make pasture available as he would have to for common cattle. This is doubly fortunate in that it reduces the soil erosion that occurs under the prevailing conditions of heavy rainfall.

Numbers

Most livestock censuses do not distinguish the mithan, and no estimate of its total numbers has ever been made. Using what census data are available, together with information on the distribution of the animal, human population estimates for the tribal people among whom the mithan occurs, and statements of mithan numbers in several places, we would estimate that the total number is 100,000 to 150,000.

The only relevant census materials we have uncovered are for the Chin Hills, Burma, collected in 1953 (*Union of Burma, First Stage Census, 1953*, 1957: 20, 28, 76). For the Chin Special Division, excluding Paletwa Subdivision which was occupied by rebels, 184,000 Chin were enumerated and 14,500 mithan, roughly one mithan for every 12.7 people. Among the other domestic animals were 231,000 chickens, 66,000 pigs, 15,400 common cattle, and 6,700 goats. Only about 17 percent of all households actually owned mithan, and these households averaged two mithan each. By contrast 79 percent owned pigs and 86 percent owned chickens.

One detailed local survey of mithan population was done by H. N. C. Stevenson (1943: 47) for the Zahau Chin village of Klauhmun in Falam Subdivision of the Chin Hills. There were 121 mithan in the 165 houses sampled, an average of less than one (.7) per household. The 121 mithan were actually owned by 36 men, only 8 of whom had more than 3 animals. One of the 8, the village chief himself, owned 30 animals, and another man owned 14. On the basis of general observation elsewhere in Falam Subdivision, Stevenson concluded that the average percentage of mithan owners was roughly the same for other villages as for Klauhmun and that it was unusual to find a man with more than 5 mithan. In contrast to mithan, pigs were numerous; Klauhmun had about 2.5 times as many pigs per household. Though Stevenson's data were collected in the late 1930's, they resemble figures obtained from the village headman of Lente, near Falam, in 1954 (pers. com., Theodore Stern, Dec. 9, 1966). At Lente approximately 400 people lived in 100 houses. They owned 200 adult fowl, 120 adult pigs, and 40 mithan (the latter owned by only 10 of the households). Lente thus had three times as many pigs per household as mithan; it had an average of less than one mithan per household (.4); and it had only one mithan for every ten people. As at Klauhmun, the mithan were concentrated in the hands of relatively few men. Another survey is that of Hans J. Spielmann (pers. com., Sept. 9, 1965), who in 1964 attempted a census of 42 Bawm-Zo villages in the Chittagong Hill Tracts. The 22 villages for which exact data were obtained had a total population of 2,179 persons and 199 mithan. This is not quite one mithan per ten persons.

Considerable differences in the numbers of mithan occur from village to village and from one part of the mithan country to another. In the Bawm-Zo village of Tuizung, for example, there were 20 mithan for 73 people, more than one for every four humans, far greater than for many nearby villages. In the Chin Hills of Burma there was, in 1953, an average of about one mithan for every eight people in the southern subdivisions (Kanpetlet, Matupi) but only one for every 16 in the northern ones (Haka, Falam, Tiddim). Fürer-Haimendorf (1962: 37) estimated that in 1945 the Apa Tani of NEFA, who number only 11,000 people or so, had 2,000 to 3,000 mithan. This makes one mithan for every four or five people. The Apa Tani, moreover, live in a densely settled valley not suited to mithan keeping. Their neighbors the Dafla and Hill Miri, shifting cultivators who have vast amounts of forest at their disposal, probably have many more mithan per person. The Dafla number about 40,000, and thus may have at least 8,000 to 10,000 mithan. Stonor (1964: 1697) notes that "in the wild mountain tracts [of NEFA] a rich man can often boast (and never fails to do so) of a herd of several hundred" mithan! He contrasted this with the Naga Hills where, he says, most men own only a few mithan. Certainly it contrasts with most sections of the Chin and Chittagong hills.

2

The Mithan's Place
in the Bovine World

This chapter is intended to define the mithan's position among the bovines of southern Asia and to cast light on its origins. First the taxonomic and linguistic confusion surrounding the mithan will be dispelled. Then the mithan will be compared with various bovines of the region, the nature and extent of crossing with them considered, and the patterns of fertility and sterility of the hybrid offspring examined. Hypotheses advanced for the origin of the mithan will be viewed in the light of this information, in order to reach a tentative conclusion.

Taxonomy and Terms

Synonymy: *Bos frontalis*, Lambert (1804); *Bos gavaeus*, Colebrooke (1808); *Bos sylhetanus*, Cuvier (1824); *Urus gavaeus*, Swainson (1835); *Bison sylhetanus*, Jardine (1836); *Bibos frontalis*, Lambert (1837); *Gavaeus frontalis*, Hodgson (1847); *Bibos gavaeus*, Rütimeyer (1867); *Bos (Bibos) frontalis*, Lydekker (1898); *Bos gaurus frontalis*, Lydekker (1912); *Bibos gaurus frontalis*, Bohlken (1958).

The taxonomy of the bovines (used throughout this book in the sense of Bovinae) has long been confusing. Some writers have included mithan, gaur, banteng (embracing the wild form and the domesticated Bali cattle or Bali banteng), and sometimes kouprey (Figures 1, 5, 6, and 7) —all of southern Asia—within the genus *Bos*. Others join them in a separate genus, *Bibos*. We will follow the later work of Herwart Bohlken (1961: 247–48) in viewing *Bibos* as a subgenus of *Bos* (Table 1). Generally, however, we will designate the mithan simply as *Bos frontalis*, and will leave the *Bibos* subgenus designation as understood.

From the early mentions in English of the animal that is now generally

TABLE 1

Living Relatives of the Mithan
(generally after H. Bohlken)

Subfamily Bovinae	Genus Bos	Subgenus Bos	1.	*Bos taurus: European domestic cattle and
			2.	*Bos indicus: Zebu cattle (properly the above two should be a single species)
		Subgenus Bibos	3.	Bos (Bibos) gaurus: gaur
			4.	*Bos (Bibos) frontalis: mithan
			5.	Bos (Bibos) javanicus, Bos (Bibos) banteng, or Bos (Bibos) sondaicus: banteng
			6.	*Bos (Bibos) javanicus domesticus: Bali cattle
			7.	Bos (Bibos) sauveli: kouprey
		Subgenus Poëphagus	8.	Bos (Poëphagus) mutus: wild yak
			9.	*Bos (Poëphagus) grunniens: domestic yak
	Genus Bison		10.	Bison bison: American bison
			11.	Bison bonasus: European bison
	Genus Bubalus		12.	Bubalus arnee: wild Asiatic buffalo
			13.	*Bubalus bubalis: domesticated water buffalo
			14.	Bubalus depressicornis: anoa
	Genus Syncerus		15.	Syncerus caffer: African buffalo

*Domesticated species.

called mithan there has been confusion of terms, which has not ended today. The wild bovine, *Bos gaurus,* occurs or formerly occurred throughout the range of the mithan. In addition, *Bos gaurus* is found in peninsular India, on the Himalayan slopes as far west as Nepal, and in Burma and mainland Southeast Asia. In English, *Bos gaurus* is now called gaur, a word introduced from Hindi.

In the earliest English language accounts of the mithan, the Bengali and Hindi word *gayal* was used for both the domestic animal and the form from which it was supposedly derived—the wild animal which we now call gaur. Unfortunately a recurring notion developed that there were not only domestic and wild forms of "gayal" but still another wild form. Many Europeans thus believed that there were three animals, and not, as is now known, one domestic animal, the mithan, and one wild one, the gaur.

To confuse the matter further, the word "mithan" or "mithun," apparently taken from Assamese,[1] has also sometimes been applied in English to the gaur. And a final difficulty is European hunters' use of the word "bison" or "Indian bison" for the gaur, though the creature is closely related neither to the European nor to the American bison. Such hunters also commonly refer to the mithan as the "domestic bison."

When at last it was understood that two and not three animals were involved, some of the confusion was cleared away. The terms "mithan" and less commonly "gayal" have generally come, in the English literature, to refer to the domesticated animal, *Bos frontalis,* and the term "gaur" to the wild animal, *Bos gaurus.* The mithan is not found truly wild, though feral individuals occur. The gaur is not found in a domesticated state—unless one views the mithan as a domesticated gaur that should have the gaur name *Bos gaurus domesticus* or *Bos gaurus frontalis.*

"Gaur" will be used here for the wild animal (*Bos gaurus*) found in India and mainland Southeast Asia. "Mithan" as used is synonymous with "gayal" and will refer to the domesticated animal, *Bos frontalis.* Since there are many hybrids and no accepted terminology for referring to them, they will be designated as hybrids or hybrid mithan. In this we follow the common usage.

Mithan and the Genus Bos in Southern Asia

In South and Southeast Asia there are the three wild *Bos:* gaur (*Bos* [*Bibos*] *gaurus*); banteng (*Bos* [*Bibos*] *javanicus, Bos* [*Bibos*] *banteng,*

1. The transliteration of the Assamese word should be "mithun," but the spelling "mithan" has come into more general use in English. For further information, see the section "Names for the Mithan as Clues to Its Domesticators" (pp. 225–27).

or *Bos* [*Bibos*] *sondaicus*); and kouprey (*Bos* [*Bibos*] *sauveli*). The kouprey of Cambodia (Figure 7), which first became known to the outside world in the 1930's, seems too distant in occurrence and too distinct in appearance (see Urbain, 1936–37: Plate X; also Coolidge, 1940, especially pp. 430–33, 478–79) to have contributed to the ancestry of the mithan. The banteng (Figure 6) in the wild state ranges through the hill woodlands of much of Southeast Asia as far west as Burma and adjacent bits of the Chittagong Hills. From the appearance of the Burmese race, typically reddish-brown with white stockings and a white spot on its rump, the vast majority of naturalists have doubted any direct relation to the mithan. The banteng is also known in a domesticated state, especially in Bali and Lombok.

Overlapping the distribution of the banteng, and sometimes meeting it to fight or on more amicable terms, is the gaur (Figure 5).[2] Called "king of the wild bovines" by some, the gaur is believed to be the largest and most powerful of existing wild bovines. In distribution, it ranges from peninsular India and Nepal through Southeast Asia (including part of southern Yunnan) as far east as Malaya, but not to the islands.[3]

Mithan and Gaur Compared

Though similarities and differences in physical characteristics of mithan and gaur frequently have been noticed and commented upon, the most thorough comparative studies have been those of E. C. S. Baker (1903–4: 227–48) and Hubert Schumann (1913). Baker spent thirteen years in Assam, including about a decade in North Cachar, in the heart of mithan country. For much of that time he lived within a few hundred yards of a village where a herd of mithan was kept; and he took every opportunity of seeing other herds. Gaur were plentiful in the area, too, and he killed 54 bull gaur, 4 cows, and 1 calf.

Baker made detailed comparisons of gaur and mithan skulls and horns as well as of other qualities. He emphasized that the most important difference between the two animals is in size, and the greatest similarity is in coloration. The gaur is considerably larger in body and skull. Average gaur bulls stand perhaps 5 feet 8 to 10 inches at the shoulder, and the largest bulls in India stand 6 feet 4 to 6 inches—as against mithan bull

2. Fighting between bull banteng and bull gaur is documented by W. S. Thom (1934–35: 110–11). There are also reports of a lone banteng cow, whose herd was decimated by disease, joining a herd of gaur; of the skeletons of banteng and gaur herds, killed by disease, being adjacent (Antonius, 1934: 184); and of gaur cows in herds of banteng (Edmond-Blanc, 1947: 247–48). Kouprey and banteng also sometimes intermingle (Edmond-Blanc, 1947: 247; Wharton, 1957: 61–63).

3. For a map of present-day gaur distribution in India, see Schaller, 1967: 176.

heights of 5 feet and 5 feet 8 inches. F. T. Pollok reported bull gaur shot in Burma up to 6 feet 11.5 inches, a size which he attributed to the abundant food available in the vast hill forests of Burma (Pollok and Thom, 1900: 88). When on rare occasions the Kuki or Naga capture a young wild gaur and raise it in captivity, it is of very small size compared to those growing up in the wild (Baker, 1903–4: 242). In coloration mithan and gaur are remarkably similar. Cows and young bulls generally have dark brown bodies with white stockings; adult bulls usually are black with white stockings. There are reports of light-colored gaur and, for south India, of "white" gaur. White mithan also occur, as do piebald individuals.

Other physical qualities that have commonly been used to distinguish mithan and gaur are 1) shape of horns, 2) shape of forehead and presence of a bony ridge between the horns, 3) dorsal ridge, and 4) dewlap. Almost all observers agree that horn shape differs strikingly between the two forms. While mithan horns spread outward and are straight or gently curving, gaur horns are more strongly curved, with the tips pointing inward over the forehead. The forehead of the mithan is flat or nearly so, with no pronounced elevated ridge between the horns. The forehead of the gaur is noticeably concave, with an arched ridge between the horns (Figure 8). Both animals have a dorsal ridge, formed by an extension of certain vertebrae; the ridge, however, is not so well developed in the mithan. The mithan has a well-developed dewlap, whereas in most gaur it is slightly developed.[4] Baker, after carefully examining animals for the four physical qualities above, noted a considerable variation within the gaur group on one hand and within the mithan on the other. He also found overlapping in form between gaur and mithan.

Other resemblances between gaur and mithan are an oily sweat and similar odor said to occur in both animals, and a call peculiar to both. The oily sweat, lacking in banteng, is said to have the qualities of an insect repellent (pers. coms., Oliver G. Young, Sept. 30 and Oct. 17, 1966).[5] This would make both animals unusually suited to tropical conditions. Some writers say the gaur has five sounds, others three. The call in question is a high-pitched sound, a rutting call, which sounds like "iiiii . . . ."[6]

4. Many writers have stated that the gaur has no dewlap at all, but this is not true of all gaur. In Travancore, Burma, Malaya, and elsewhere, gaur bulls, or some of them, have well developed dewlaps (Inverarity, 1889: 296; Pollok and Thom, 1900: 89–90; Lydekker, 1907: 56, 60–61; Thom, 1934–35: 109; Baker, 1903–4: 236–37, 246; Hubback, 1939: 9; see also the discussion in *The Field, The Country Gentleman's Newspaper*, Aug. 13, 20, 27, and Sept. 3, 1898 [pp. 270, 364, 372, 440]).

5. Schaller (pers. com., Oct. 20, 1966), however, examined two gaur at Kanha Park and found ticks on both.

6. Antonius (1932: 188) and Pizey (1932–33: 243) both apparently refer to this

In preference of habitat too the gaur and mithan are quite similar. Though it may be found in open grassy country and in the lowland, the gaur is essentially a forest-dwelling animal which prefers hill country. In peninsular India, for example, its favored elevations are from perhaps 2,000 to 6,000 feet. In Sikkim and the Himalaya slopes, it is found up to the Tibetan border in summer (Hermanns, 1952: 137). The elevations favored by the gaur coincide with those where the mithan is found.

Detailed studies of the food habits of the mithan have not been carried out, and information on the gaur, too, is scanty. The gaur, it is clear, is both a grazer and a browser.[7] The mithan, say most writers, is more a browser than the gaur. Others add that, given the choice, the mithan will choose browse rather than grass.

Another parallel is the craving of both mithan and gaur for salt—a trait shared with most other large hoofed animals.[8] This craving can get the mithan into serious trouble. Among the Falam Chin, when saltpeter is being boiled within fenced areas, mithan continually break in to drink the brew, and thereby poison themselves. Attracted by the salty residue of sweat, a Chin mithan occasionally is discovered eating a valuable cloth, an offense which may bring on a stoning, beating, or spearing (Stevenson, 1943: 58). The mithan's craving for salt is useful in getting the animal to return from the forest to the village. This is recognized in the story of Macrae in 1802 (reported in A. B. Lambert, 1804a: 303–5) about the Kuki of Chittagong taming "wild gyalls" through the use of salt. On finding a herd in the forest, they make balls of a certain earth, salt, and cotton. They drive their domestic "gyalls" toward the wild ones, and the herds mingle. The balls are scattered about the woods in places where the animals are likely to pass. The animals, attracted to the balls, lick them and stay in the locality until the balls are gone. Meanwhile, the Kuki prepare more decoy balls and for six weeks or so keep the animals supplied. After a day or two, a man gradually makes his presence known, but does not approach the herd. By degrees he draws nearer, as the animals become

---

sound and state it is common to both animals. Schaller (1967: 195) considers in detail a gaur call that seems to be the same one.

7. Schaller observes that gaur have a long, prehensile tongue well adapted to browsing and are skilled in their browsing techniques. Nevertheless, gaur prefer green grass. When it is not available, they eat coarse dry grasses and many kinds of forbs and leaves. There are seasonal differences in feeding, but in four rumen samples taken during the hot season Schaller found an average of 85 percent coarse semidry to dry grass and only 10 percent browse by volume. One rumen, however, contained 33 percent browse (1967: 183–84).

8. "Theories for the use of salt licks are: hunger for a specific mineral; to obtain sodium chloride; to obtain some vital trace element; to alter intestinal flora and fauna, and to eliminate internal parasites" (Wharton, 1957: 88; for a discussion of the literature on the theories involved, see 33–38 therein).

accustomed to his presence. He strokes the domestic animals, without frightening away the wild beasts. Finally, he extends his hand to the wild animals and caresses them, too, while giving them decoy balls to lick. He is able at last to drive all the animals, tame and wild, to his village. The "wild gyalls" of Macrae's account were probably mithan which had been in the forest so long that they were not readily approachable. It does not seem possible that a man could get near to gaur in this way— though their love of salt is well documented.

Macrae (Colebrooke, 1808: 518–19) also reported that among the Kuki mithan learned to return home each evening because they relished the salt they were regularly fed. The Kuki settlement, presumably of shifting cultivators, was periodically abandoned and a new one started. At such times the villagers had to burn the houses lest the mithan return to the old settlement before they became as strongly attached to the new one. We will consider the question of salt again later, for not only is it a key element in establishing ties between mithan and man but it may have been important in bringing about the domestication of the animal.

In other behavior too there are striking similarities and differences between mithan and gaur. The most noticeable difference is the suspicious alertness and liveliness of the gaur and the placid indifference of the mithan. Though this difference has been noted by many, it is perhaps best illustrated in the experience of Otto Antonius, director of the Schönbrunn Zoo in Vienna (1932: 188–89). He approached a zoo enclosure in Amsterdam containing zebu cattle, water buffalo, mithan, and one female gaur, at a time when no other humans were in the area. Immediately sensing his presence, the gaur jumped to her feet and tensely took a defensive position; the mithan and other cattle continued their rumination undisturbed. This behavior is especially interesting because this gaur had been born in captivity and was thoroughly accustomed to the presence of humans. In the natural state, too, the wariness of the gaur has often been commented upon. It is common for an unattached male gaur to join a herd of mithan in the forest. When the time comes for the herd to return to the village, however, the gaur remains in the forest. When such a gaur is with the mithan herd, people are fearful of approaching. It has also been noted that the hybrid offspring of gaur and mithan have the wildness of the gaur.

The wariness of the gaur is matched by its tremendous strength and courage. When attacked, an adult can handle most predators (apart from man) in its habitat. Most dangerous to it are the giant felines, especially the tiger, and packs of wild dogs (*Cuon alpinus,* Pallas), which can bring down almost any solitary animal. G. B. Schaller, in his study of gaur in Kanha National Park in Madhya Pradesh, central India, in 1964, reports that the main cause of mortality among gaur that year was attack by tigers. The attacks were principally on calves, for tigers seldom attack adult gaur. Schaller's discussion of the relations between gaur and tiger, and observations by other writers, strongly suggest a standoff; the way a gaur responds to a tiger, Schaller says, depends on the circumstances of their meeting. In one case he saw a gaur bull and cow simply watch with alertness as a tiger moved by. In another he observed a tigress walking, followed at a distance of 150 feet by eight gaur. In a third he saw a gaur cow become aware that a tiger was stalking the herd; she gave a snort and fled, followed by the herd. In still another case he saw a mature but badly limping gaur bull facing some trees where there was at least a tigress; the bull showed signs of agitation but did not move off hastily; indeed, he came within 90 feet of the trees but then, on hearing a tigress growl, he turned and moved slowly off (Schaller, 1967: 181–82, 186–87). H. V. Blackburn (1935: 950–51) found the bodies of a mature bull gaur and a tigress which had killed each other in a terrific fight. C. S. Ogilvie (1953–54: 168–69) observed a herd of gaur in Malaya standing against a tiger; his feeling was that the tiger would have been destroyed if it had chosen to attack. Thom (1934–35: 111) claims that a tiger is no match for a mature bull gaur, that only when a gaur is old, diseased, or wounded does he fall prey to attacks by the tiger. On the other hand, Schaller reports that a tigress at Kanha killed an adult bull gaur that seemed in excellent condition (pers. com., Oct. 20, 1966).

The mithan, of course, is far more vulnerable to predators than the gaur, although it can protect itself well enough to be permitted to browse freely in the forest without herdsmen guarding it.

Antonius (1932: 188; 1939: 274–75) noted lateral display by bulls in both zoo mithan and gaur and believed it to be a prelude to attack. Schaller (1967: 192–94), however, points out that among the unconfined gaur of Kanha Park the display behavior was a substitute for fighting; the bull successful in his display gained the superior position without the need of fighting. The instances Schaller observed involved the displaying bull standing parallel to but perhaps 10 to 30 feet away from his opponent, with head lowered and back arched. Sometimes the opponent assumed a similar position. "One [bull] may start to circle, moving very slowly and stiff-legged, while the other stands in one spot but shifts his position to keep his broadside toward the opponent. The animals sometimes continue to display for five to ten minutes, and in one instance for fifty-five minutes, until one is intimidated and accepts the subordinate position. Bellowing and horning the soil or bushes may precede or succeed the display." Lateral display is found among quite a variety of bovines (Schloeth, 1958: 135); one cannot simply conclude that its occurrence among gaur and mithan indicates a close affinity between the two. However, differences in display detail from species to species may be revealing, and should be given more study. Antonius, who observed display techniques of animals carefully, knew of nothing similar to gaur and mithan display among other bovines; on the other hand, Schloeth feels that the lateral display of the Camargue cattle bears a close resemblance (Antonius, 1939: 276; Schloeth, 1958: 127; 1961: 585–86).[9]

In sum, the mithan and gaur resemble each other in coloration, presence of a dorsal ridge, preference for shady woodland at elevations above 2,000 feet or so, oily sweat and odor, and rutting call, as well as in craving for salt and in lateral display by bulls. They differ principally in size, shape of horns and forehead, and presence or absence of a pronounced bony ridge between the horns (in these three characteristics, however, there is considerable variation and overlapping); possibly in feeding habit; and in tameness as against wariness.

Scarcity of Gaur

Throughout its range in India the gaur is becoming less numerous. In part, decline in numbers results from the expansion of cultivation, which increasingly restricts the gaur's habitat. Proximity to domestic cattle, moreover, has introduced rinderpest and foot-and-mouth disease and caused high mortality among herds of gaur. Finally, hunters exact an increasing toll. It is true that the gaur, as a bovine, is safe from Hindus, and that in some parts of its range it is now a protected animal. On the other hand, the thinly settled hills are impossible to police, and the tribal peoples are usually not deterred by religious sensibilities from killing gaur. Within the mithan country proper the gaur is extinct or virtually so in some sections, and its numbers small in others.

The Common Cattle of Mithan Country

A glance at a map of densities of cattle population in India[10] shows few common cattle in the homeland of the mithan, though most groups having mithan also possess common cattle.[11] There are suggestions that in much of the area common cattle are recent introductions.[12] It seems

9. For more information on display among common cattle, see also Fraser, 1957: 48–49; Hafez and Schein, 1962: 280–82.

10. See, for example, map facing p. 3 in *Report on the Marketing of Cattle in India* (Delhi: Ministry of Food and Agriculture, 1956).

11. See H.-E. Kauffmann, 1934: 110, for a table showing the occurrence of these and other domestic animals among the hill tribes of Assam and north Burma.

12. The cattle of the Apa Tani, which are regarded as less valuable than mithan, are said to be of the small Assamese lowland breed and almost certainly descended from imported animals (Fürer-Haimendorf, 1946: 41; 1962: 39). At the present

reasonable to suppose that a combination of factors acted to exclude or limit their numbers in the mithan country: meagerness of pasture; the existence of predators that would make the keeping of cattle hazardous, especially under the characteristic loose system of herding; the traditional plowless agriculture; and a dislike of milk, which has not been overcome entirely even today.

The common cattle of mithan country are mostly of two types. The plains cattle, imported from the lowlands of Assam, are small and generally red animals. The hill cattle, at least in Naga country, are somewhat larger and are often black. Accounts of the breeds of Indian livestock include a category of "small hill cattle," in which the hill cattle of mithan country would be placed; they are smaller and have a much less marked hump than the large white breeds of western India. In general there is little resemblance to the purebred mithan in the appearance or behavior of either of the breeds of cattle of the area. They do not usually have the white stockings of the mithan; they have a hump instead of a dorsal ridge; their skulls show slight resemblances in construction; they have horns quite different in form; they are grazers rather than browsers; and they lack certain behavioral traits of the mithan.

---

time the Apa Tani purchase calves in the lowlands and drive them home. Among the Dafla, common cattle generally are found only in areas that have close connections with the Assamese plains; and among the related Hill Miri, Fürer-Haimendorf (pers. com., Oct. 16, 1966) feels, common cattle are fairly recent. This seems borne out by Dalton's nineteenth-century observation (1872: 34) that mithan are the only "horned cattle" among the Miri. The common cattle of the Gallong are similar to those of Assam (Dunbar, 1915: 43), which suggests that is their origin, and are said to "have been domesticated [introduced?] but not long ago" (Srivastava, 1962: 34–35). They are limited in number, though with the recent introduction of plowing among certain Gallong the number of bullocks has been increasing. Among the Adi (formerly Abor), the mithan is the most important animal, but common cattle are kept [only?] in the lower section of the Adi Hills for plowing (S. Roy, 1960: 151, 160).

Though most Naga groups apparently keep cattle, the Eastern Rengma rarely do, for they suffer severe losses from tigers and prefer to buy cattle as needed (Mills, 1937: 92). The Lhota Naga buy large numbers of common cattle of the ordinary humped Assamese breed in the lowlands. Some they keep for breeding or for eating, but most are traded to the Ao and Sema Naga. To the south, cattle are said to have been unknown to the Lakher of the Lushai Hills before British times (Parry, 1932: 164–65). Among the Purum Kuki of Manipur two decades ago, cattle were kept, but only by individuals who had valley fields; they were used just for plowing and for their flesh (T. C. Das, 1945: 65–66, 275–90). For the Chin of the Falam Subdivision of the Chin Hills District in Burma, Stevenson indicates that mithan, pigs, and goats are indigenous, whereas buffalo, common cattle, and ponies are relatively recent importations from the plains. In the Nung Hills of northeast Burma mithan are common, but common cattle have been "introduced within living memory" (Stevenson, 1943: 47–48, 53).

The Crossing of Bos

Largely unnoticed in the literature is the remarkable series of domestic bovine hybrids that occurs in the Eastern Himalayas, and marks that as the foremost area of bovine hybridization in the world. The striking examples found in one small section of NEFA provide a vivid illustration. The Monba, a tribal Buddhist group living at elevations of 5,500 feet and higher in Kameng Division, have access to common cattle of the plains, to mithan of the rough, wet country of NEFA, and to yak of the high country of Tibet. They cross common cattle with yak, a practice that is customary in Tibet; the hybrids, or dzo, serve as transport and plow animals, and as dairy animals as well (Mills, 1946: 11; 1947: 9; Bower, 1953: 154). They are said also to cross mithan with yak (pers. com., S. Roy, Feb., 1964). There are reports of a hybrid animal between mithan "and something else," which one informant told Mills was a mithan/dzo hybrid; it was used by the Monba for both milking and plowing (Mills, 1946: 10). Thus, if reports are correct, the crosses among the Monba include hybrids of common cattle/yak,[13] mithan/yak, mithan/dzo, and presumably mithan/common cattle.

In addition to the extensive crossing reported for the Monba, hybridization in which the mithan occupies the central position occurs throughout its distribution, with mithan crossing with both gaur and common cattle. Inquiry into the nature and frequency of such crossings—and particularly whether they are encouraged or discouraged by man—may throw some light on the origin of the mithan species.

Mating of Mithan with Gaur

The mating of mithan and gaur, a common phenomenon in the past, has always been of one sort: gaur bulls with mithan cows. There is no record of mithan bulls mating with gaur cows. It may be, as Baker says, that "no wild cow would ever accept the services of a tame bull when, as is *always* the case, those of a finer stronger wild animal were available" (1903–4: 234).

The gaur bulls that mate with mithan cows are likely to be solitary rather than associated with a herd. It is common for gaur bulls to leave

13. For a discussion of the genetics of yak/common cattle hybrids developed in the Zoological Park at Moscow, see M. M. Zawadowsky, "Zebu-Yak Hybrids," *Journal of Heredity*, 22 (1931): 296–313. A discussion of the role of hybrids in Tibetan social life and ecology is included in James F. Downs and Robert B. Ekvall, "Animals and Social Types in the Exploitation of the Tibetan Plateau," pp. 169–84 in Anthony Leeds and Andrew P. Vayda, eds., *Man, Culture, and Animals*, Publication No. 78. Washington: American Association for the Advancement of Science, 1965. 304 pp.

the herd to wander alone or in the company of other males for various periods of time. Certain of these bulls are old. Others are not. Some say that the master bull drives others away, but Schaller, who studied the changing composition of gaur herds, did not find this to be so (1967: 188–90). Solitary life is rather a matter of preference and usually not permanent.

Since mithan range far into the forest, and gaur bulls temporarily join mithan herds close to human settlement, mating with such gaur is readily accomplished. Sometimes mithan bulls remonstrate against their wild rivals. Because gaur bulls are significantly larger and stronger, however, their wishes seem certain to predominate. Shaw observed (1929: 135) that among the Thadou Kuki gaur bulls often kill or seriously injure mithan bulls.

The incursions of gaur bulls are favored not only by their greater size and strength but by the human preference, in sacrifice, for mithan bulls rather than mithan cows. In North Cachar Baker noted several herds of mithan without full-grown bulls; all had been sacrificed before they were three years of age (1903–4: 242). In the herds in question, nineteen of every twenty calves born were estimated to have wild fathers. Herds regularly visited by gaur bulls were noticeably larger and more sturdy. They were also wilder. This is also noted in India where wild buffalo cross with domestic buffalo.

People from place to place in mithan country differ in their view of the desirability of crossing mithan with gaur. Sometimes the very presence of the gaur is regarded as a problem. The British hunter W. S. Thom was urged by villagers in the Arakan Hill Tracts to shoot a bull gaur which was consorting with their domestic mithan. The gaur was a nuisance because, snorting and tossing his head, he repeatedly frightened village women on their way to draw water (Thom, 1934–35: 109). Others have noted that various mithan-keeping groups discourage such crossing because the hybrids would be wild and difficult to handle, might damage fields, or for other reasons.

Undoubtedly the decline in numbers of gaur has significantly decreased the amount of crossing with mithan.

Mating of Mithan with Common Cattle

Mithan have bred with local common cattle (*Bos indicus*) in various places to give rise to hybrids.[14] Though such crossing has been reported

14. In addition to interbreeding in the natural habitat of the mithan, certain experimental crosses have been made, especially in Europe. For a description of mithan/common cattle hybrids developed at the University of Halle, see W. Spöttel, 1932: 302–5.

frequently, it remains to be investigated how widespread the practice is and what its genetic influence on the mithan may be. In most cases interbreeding is not encouraged by the hill people; in a few it is sanctioned.

Perhaps most interesting among the encouraged mithan/common cattle hybrids are those of Bhutan, a region too arid and cold for mithan to do well. At the same time the cattle of Bhutan are small, and the great strength of the mithan is valued. So the Bhutanese trade their surplus of common cattle eastward through intermediaries until they reach the Dafla of NEFA. Dafla bull mithan eventually reach the Bhutanese, who mate them with common cattle to provide a hybrid which has the strength of the mithan and the adaptability to the environment of common cattle. A few mithan have even found their way as far west as Darjeeling, where they were crossed with the Siri breed of common cattle (Chatterjee, 1926: 178–79). However, the people of the area were said generally to object to such crossing, apparently on a religious basis.

In NEFA proper there appears to be some crossing, too. The Mishmi have many hybrid mithan/common cattle (Bailey, 1945: 158). The Apa Tani also have a few, but do nothing to encourage such crossing; and since cattle and mithan keep apart naturally, there is little opportunity for them to meet (Fürer-Haimendorf, 1946: 41; 1962: 40). It is likely that such hybrids occur among the Dafla and Hill Miri, too, for Fürer-Haimendorf indicates that they do not direct the breeding of mithan.

In the Chin Hills and parts of the Naga Hills there has been significant bastardization of the mithan through interbreeding with common cattle. Though common cattle were only occasionally present in Chin Hills villages, Carey and Tuck in the late nineteenth century noted at Haka and certain other places a sizable partly wild herd which included mithan and cattle "in all the various stages of the cross" (1896, 1: 180–81). In more recent times Stevenson observed (1943: 48) that the Chin allowed "promiscuous breeding" between their common cattle and mithan and that there were numerous piebald and skewbald hybrids; and T. R. Livesey (1931: 200–201) reported that every stage of cross between common cattle and mithan might be seen in the Chin Hills. Mills in his book on the Lhota Naga (1922: 59) mentions that, through breeding with common cattle, Naga mithan have become "hopelessly contaminated";[15] Hutton (pers. com., Sept. 8, 1966), on the contrary, doubts that this applies for the Naga Hills other than the Lhota country. Apparently everywhere the usual pattern is for bull mithan to mate with common cows. Bulls of common cattle are often too small to cover mithan cows, and in

15. Crosses with common cattle are indicated for the Sema, Angami, Lhota, and Western Rengma Naga (Hutton, 1921a: 69; 1921: 80; Mills, 1922: 59–60; 1937: 92).

any case, the mithan bull is likely to drive away any intrepid common bull approaching the mithan cows.

L. G. Löffler provides interesting information on crosses between common cattle and mithan among the Mru of the Chittagong Hill Tracts (pers. com., Aug. 20, 1965). The Mru neither encourage nor discourage such crossing; it simply occurs. Common cattle among the Mru are of two types. The first, known to the Bengali as *goru* and to the Mru as *ratca*, is a humped animal with slightly curved horns. The second, known in Bengali as *tong-goru* ("hill cow") and in Mru as *mangchang*, is humpless and has shorter straight horns. The two types of cattle interbreed freely, and more often than not it is difficult to say whether a given animal belongs to one type or the other. The mithan, known in Mru as *cia-nöm* ("the true *cia*"; all ratca and mangchang are also cia), crosses with the mangchang; it is not known whether it crosses with ratca. The hybrid cia-nöm/mangchang is known as *cia-nöm-mangchang*. Crossing these hybrids, cia-nöm-mangchang, with mangchang produces a creature which falls within the mangchang group. Crossing the cia-nöm-mangchang hybrids with cia-nöm (mithan) gives animals which belong with the mithan group. Thus among the Mru the mithan breed and the mangchang breed of common cattle are not necessarily true breeds. One suspects that in certain other areas second generation hybrids are classified in a similar way, with either mithan or common cattle, and that there is a lively exchange of genes between the two species. Perhaps this is what Mills had in mind when he wrote that the black Naga cattle may have been influenced by the mithan. Cases of interspecific crossing, deliberate and otherwise, among other domestic animals are not uncommon in Asia, as, for example, between dromedary and Bactrian camel and between yak and common cattle; this results in a similar exchange of genes between what are commonly designated as distinct species.

Though the record is too scant to permit safe generalization, it seems that crossing of common cattle and mithan is most frequent, with the exception of Bhutan, in southern mithan country, especially in the Chin Hills, parts of the Naga Hills, and the Chittagong Hills. In other areas, notably perhaps in NEFA but elsewhere too, the mithan species remains relatively unsullied.

Mating of Common Cattle with Gaur

There are virtually no indications in the literature of common cows being encouraged anywhere by man to cross with gaur bulls. The sole exception is a questionable nineteenth-century account by Carey and Tuck (1896, 1: 180), their interpretation of what was related to them by Chin informants in Burma.

Nor is there documented evidence that natural crossing between common cattle and gaur has taken place in mithan country, though the possibility cannot be denied. Matthias Hermanns (1952: 38), for instance, suggests that such crossing occurs in Sikkim and Nepal. Somewhat related is Hauxwell's account (1911–13: 1072–73) of a banteng bull joining a herd of common cattle grazing in fallow paddy fields near a village in Upper Burma; the bull took charge of the herd and became tame enough so that he paid no attention to the villagers caring for their cattle. At the end of the season the banteng retired to the forest, but reappeared some time later and resumed his position with the herd. Subsequently he disappeared into the forest with a young cow, to which he had been paying special attention. There is no record of offspring.

Interfertility among Mithan, Common Cattle, and Gaur

In determining the position of the mithan with respect to common cattle and other bovines, the patterns of mithan hybrid sterility and fertility may provide clues. It is widely recognized that hybrid sterility is not necessarily an indication of species distinction. Among the bovines, however, it may be a helpful criterion. Both types of common cattle, *Bos indicus* and *Bos taurus,* for example, are completely interfertile. They should more properly be considered races than species. The European bison (*Bison bonasus*) and American bison (*Bison bison*) are also completely interfertile. When common cattle are crossed with yak (*Bos grunniens*), however, the female hybrids are fertile and the male hybrids are sterile. A similar pattern of female fertility and male sterility generally prevails in hybrids of *Bos taurus/Bison bison, Bos taurus/Bison bonasus* (wisent), *Bos taurus/Bos javanicus* (banteng), and *Bos indicus/Bos javanicus.* More pertinent to our study is the fact that the same pattern occurs in controlled crosses of *Bos taurus/Bos gaurus* (gaur) and *Bos taurus/Bos frontalis* (mithan).[16] Various writers indicate that a pattern of female fertility and male sterility also prevails among hybrids of *Bos indicus/Bos frontalis* (Lotsy, 1922: 60; Hertwig, 1936: 128–29; Haldane, 1922: 101; Lus, 1938: 838; Shrode and Lush, 1947: 242–46; A. P. Gray, 1954: 60–69).

The earliest record bearing on the fertility of mithan/common cattle

16. Although Kühn's crossings at Halle, to be discussed shortly, showed that six half-breed males of *Bos taurus/Bos frontalis* were infertile, one was fertile. In fact, the one fertile hybrid sired eleven calves. In addition, one of the infertile male hybrids was found, on being killed, to have motile sperm (Lotsy, 1922: 33; Nathusius, 1912: 33–34).

hybrids dates from 1808 (Colebrooke, 1808: 521). A certain Mr. Bird living in Dacca (now East Pakistan) obtained a mithan cow from Chittagong. Since no mithan bull was available in Dacca, Bird had the cow blindfolded and had a zebu bull mate with her. The F_1 hybrid calf was a female which resembled her mother. In time the F_1 hybrid was mated with another zebu bull and bore a female calf. At the time of writing the F_2 hybrid in turn was in calf, again by a zebu bull. This record clearly established that the female hybrid of mithan cow and zebu bull is fertile.

Somewhat more extensive efforts to cross mithan were made in the London Zoological Gardens (reported in Bartlett, 1884: 399–400). Again the first crossing was between a mithan cow and a zebu bull. The F_1 hybrid offspring, born in 1868, was a female, and she in turn gave birth to five calves by the same zebu bull. Then she was crossed with a male American bison and bore a female calf. This F_2 calf in time was mated with a bull bison and bore female offspring which could not be distinguished from a purebred bison of the same age. This series of crossings involving *Bos frontalis, Bos indicus,* and *Bison bison* in every case resulted in female hybrids which proved fertile.

The most thorough series of experiments was carried out by Julius Kühn, director of the Landwirtschaftliches Institut at the University of Halle. A pair of mithan was obtained from Chittagong in 1880. The male was mated with cows of various breeds, mostly European, of *Bos taurus.* By 1885 nineteen hybrids had been born of these crossings, nine males and ten females. Later an attempt was made to determine the fertility of the surviving hybrids. Crossings of female hybrids with bulls of common cattle proved fruitful. The four surviving hybrid males, however, sired no young when crossed with their hybrid sisters and with domestic cows. The experiments involved a variety of animals and repeated attempts at impregnating full-blooded and hybrid cows by the hybrid bulls, all to no avail. The conclusion was reached that the hybrid bull is entirely sterile. Kühn took the point of view that two forms of animal which gave fertile hybrids were the same, and two forms which gave no offspring or gave infertile hybrids were distinct species. On these grounds, he concluded that the mithan is not so closely related to common cattle as is supposed by many (Kühn, 1883: 126–27; 1885: 59–61). Subsequent crossings by Kühn over a thirty-year period essentially confirmed his initial results. Just one of seven F_1 half-breed males that were repeatedly bred sired calves. Backcross males, however, showed greater fertility (Nathusius, 1911: 62–64; 1912: 33–34).

A final record, which simply supports what was already known, is that of J. C. Higgins (1931: 445). Higgins noted that at the Kuturi Tea Estate in the Nowgong District of Assam a hybrid cow, descended from a mithan bull and a common cow, bore a calf after mating with a common bull. Though one might expect additional information on the fertility of mithan/common cattle hybrids from the ethnographic accounts, most are too casual to be of much use. Hutton, however, writes (pers. com., Jan. 25, 1966) that he introduced a hybrid bull to his herd of true cows for a year without issue. When he spoke of this to his Naga handyman, the latter replied, "Oh, we did not expect there would be offspring"—clearly indicating native belief that male hybrids are infertile.

If hybrid fertility-sterility patterns are taken to reveal affinity among species, one may wonder what the results of gaur-mithan crossings have been. The zoological literature unfortunately provides no certain answer to this question. At the Schönbrunn Zoo in Vienna a young female mithan, mated with a young bull gaur, produced a female hybrid calf. The calf, however, was born prematurely and died within a week (Antonius, 1932: 181). Schumann (1913: 54) also refers to fruitful crossings between gaur and mithan in zoological gardens. There the record ends. Turning to the ethnographic literature, we find only a few references. Shakespear (1912: 31–32), for example, believed that the hybrids produced in the interbreeding of domestic mithan with "wild mithan" (gaur) among the Lushai were fertile. More convincing are communications received from Hutton and from Lehman. Hutton (pers. com., Sept. 8, 1966) says he is quite certain that mithan/gaur hybrids are fertile; and Lehman (pers. com., March 10, 1966) writes that Chin villagers in Burma insist that mithan/gaur hybrids are fertile. That the Chin have experience with such hybrids is indicated in Lehman's statement that the Haka Chin have special words for different degrees of mixture between mithan and gaur from pure mithan to one-eighth mithan. They also use the words metaphorically to refer to mixtures between Chin aristocrats and commoners. What is greatly needed is a series of crossings, under controlled conditions, between gaur and mithan, which would establish the extent of mithan/gaur interfertility.

Hypotheses of Origin of the Mithan

There are three hypotheses about the origin of the mithan: that it is a domesticated gaur; that it is of hybrid descent, from the crossing of bull gaur and common cow (*Bos indicus*); and that it is an independent race descended from a wild Indian bovine which is now extinct.[17] The first

17. Among those advocating the view that the gaur is the ancestor of the mithan are Julius Kühn (in Riebeck, 1885: Sec. 4, p. 3); the tea planter, hunter, and naturalist E. C. Stuart Baker (quoted in Lydekker, 1912: 176); the British naturalist Richard Lydekker (1912: 176–77; 1916: 108, 175); and the hunter G. P. Sanderson

hypothesis commands the support of most of those who have conducted detailed zoological investigation of the question. The second continues to be held by some. The third receives little serious support today but nevertheless merits consideration here.

Proponents of the view that the mithan species originated from crossing between gaur and zebu have relied heavily on Carey's and Tuck's report (1896, 1: 180) that the Chin in Burma believed that their mithan result from such crossing, and deliberately herded domestic cows in the gaur's habitat. The first generation hybrid, however, was not the mithan; only in the fourth generation was the mithan stage reached. To be acceptable for sacrifice the animal had to be "quite black" and "four breedings removed from the common cow." If the Carey and Tuck account is correct, the mithan thus produced were of hybrid origin though the genetic contribution of common cattle was slight. The entire sequence, moreover, was directed by man.

J. H. Hutton, who has had wide experience in mithan country, questions the accuracy, for a variety of reasons to be considered later, of the information recorded by Carey and Tuck. He thinks it much more probable that the Chin were describing deliberate efforts to encourage crosses between gaur and mithan—rather than between gaur and common cattle.

There is small likelihood that the mithan, a domesticated species, originated through natural hybridization between gaur and common

---

(1912: 250–51). Support for gaur ancestry also has come from the ornithologist and ethnologist Charles R. Stonor, who has field experience in Assam (1953–54: 333; 1964: 1697; pers. com., Aug. 18, 1965; also quoted in Zeuner, 1963: 254–55); and the German zoologist Herwart Bohlken (1958: 146; 1958a: 168), who has done extensive morphologic study of wild bovines. The ethnographers J. H. Hutton, W. C. Smith, and H.-E. Kauffmann also briefly indicate their belief that the mithan is the domesticated variety of the gaur (Hutton, 1921a: 69; pers. com., Jan. 25, 1966; Smith, 1925: 4; H.-E. Kauffmann, 1934: 63, and pers. com., Aug. 19, 1966).

The first statement we have uncovered of the possibility that the mithan is a hybrid between bull gaur and common cow is by L. Rütimeyer in 1867 (106). Another is that of W. Gwynne Hughes (1881: 5–6), who saw the mithan in the Arakan Hill Tracts; and the German hunter Oscar Kauffmann (1911: 183–86) also argued for a hybrid origin. The modern stimulus for this hypothesis apparently comes from T. R. Livesey (1931: 201), who had experience in the Chin Hills as well as knowledge of the Carey's and Tuck's report of the Chin encouraging gaur–common cow mating (1896, 1: 180). W. S. Thom, a hunter and former police officer (1934–35: 109), supposes that the mithan is a hybrid; and the late S. H. Prater (1937: 435; 1948: 201), once curator of the Bombay Natural History Society, presents the view with great certainty. The ethnologist Matthias Hermanns (1952: 134–40; 1954: 78–80) is the principal present-day advocate of this position. It is interesting to note that a hybrid origin has been postulated for the kouprey (see Edmond-Blanc, 1947: 247–48; Bohlken, 1961).

cattle. As Schumann has argued (1913: 55), in nature, without human assistance, crossing between remotely related animals rarely occurs. Should such crossing have occurred, it seems improbable to us that the hybrid offspring, living in the company of common cattle in human settlements, would continue to cross in such a way as to develop a new, distinctive species. There is the further argument that if the mithan originated from a natural crossing, it might be expected to occur far more widely, for gaur and common cattle have been in close proximity in areas from peninsular India to Malaya. Mithan nowhere occur in these places.

Also bearing on the probability of hybridization, both natural and assisted by man, is the evidence that in much of mithan country common cattle are of recent introduction and may not have been available for the hypothesized mating with gaur.

Certain physical evidence—the occurrence of piebald and white mithan —is often advanced in support of a hybrid origin. Mithan of such colors are viewed as throwbacks to the supposed common cattle ancestors. Other explanations of this phenomenon are possible. Since hybridization between mithan and common cattle is widespread today, such coloration in mithan may derive not from the time of mithan origins but from subsequent crossing with common cattle. Some of the coloration may be simply a result of mutations that occurred within the mithan species after domestication; many animals have, since their domestication, undergone similar changes in coloration. Indeed, because piebaldness is rare in wild animals and common in domestic ones, where ancient man has pictured animals as piebald this is taken as evidence for domestication (Zeuner, 1963: 67).

Physical and behavioral comparison of purebred common cattle and mithan reveals nothing to suggest a hybrid origin of mithan. There are notable differences between the two in coloration, form of skull and horns, and occurrence of a dorsal ridge or hump. There are also marked differences between mithan and common cattle in feeding habit and other behavioral characteristics. If the mithan in fact had a hybrid origin, the genetic contribution of common cattle was slight and cannot be proved with presently available physical and behavioral evidence.

Though Schumann rejects the idea of a hybrid origin for mithan, the differences that he finds[18] between gaur and mithan in skull structure and other characteristics seem to him too great for the mithan to be a domes-

18. Altogether Schumann examined 15 mithan skulls (7 male, 4 female, and 4 immature) and 23 gaur skulls (16 male, 7 female). Unfortunately not a single gaur skull came from mithan country; most were from south India (Malabar, Mysore, Cochin, North Kanara), and some from Nepal. Schumann argues, however, that there is no difference among them that would justify classifying the gaur involved in separate races.

ticated gaur (1913: 59). The skull of the gaur, he points out, is longer and heavier. The forehead is concave, not flat. The back of the head, particularly the parietal area, is notably larger. The gaur's nasal bones are longer. Its horns differ. Schumann then is an advocate of the third hypothesis; in his opinion the mithan must have had a separate ancestor, now extinct.[19]

Heinrich Gans (1915–16: 118–19), who made a careful study of the banteng, claimed that the differences Schumann found between gaur and mithan are also either present in wild and domestic banteng or are of little significance. Turning to the question of relationships among these four bovines of southern Asia, Gans found Schumann's hypothesis improbable. Can one assume, he asks, 1) that there were four distinct wild species involved, 2) that two of them were distinguished by small size, 3) that man tamed these two because of their small size and slight wildness, and 4) that the ancestors of the tamed forms both became extinct? He views an affirmative answer as unlikely. There were two wild forms in the area, he argues: gaur and banteng; both were domesticated; and mithan and Bali cattle are the result of domestication. Their small size he attributes to the growth-hampering influences of domestication. Gans's view was endorsed by Otto Antonius (1922: 156–58), who presented sketches of skulls of wild and domestic yak, wild banteng and tame Bali cattle, and gaur and mithan (see his Figures 81, 82, 84, 85, 87, 88) supporting this position.

Further support for the hypothesis that the mithan is a domesticated gaur comes from Baker. After carefully comparing the physical characteristics of gaur and mithan and noting both the variations within each species and the overlapping between the two species, Baker concluded that the differences are the result of domestication.

Various writers, noting the wildness of the gaur, have contended that it cannot be the ancestor of the mithan, one of the tamest of animals. The gaur can hardly be tamed even today; how then, they ask, can the primitive hill peoples of Assam have tamed and domesticated it? Such an argument could be advanced to support an ancestry separate from the gaur, for example in a similar but more gentle animal. The argument, however, has little merit, for the ancestors of most other domestic animals were wary, wild, or both. If primitive man in Southeast Asia or India domesticated the water buffalo and banteng, why not the gaur?

19. There is a somewhat similar hypothesis, involving extinction of an earlier wild bovine, for the kouprey. C. H. Wharton suggests that the kouprey, originally wild in Cambodia, was domesticated by the Khmer 800 years ago; later its wild relatives became extinct. With the fall of Khmer civilization, he says, the domestic animal became feral and spread its range outward (1957: 86).

The evidence presented so far favors the view that the mithan is a domesticated gaur, now mixed in some places with common cattle. The general appearance of the mithan—dark brown or black in color, with white stockings, and dorsal ridge; its oily sweat, odor, and rutting call; its occurrence within the same altitudinal limits; and such information as we have of crossing and interfertility all point to gaur ancestry. The smaller size of the mithan, its gentle quality, and differences in skull and horns are explicable as results of domestication similar to those which have occurred in other domestic animals. Occurrence of piebald forms may also result from domestication, or may come from later crossing with common cattle.

Many points need additional study. Notable differences in feeding habit, for instance, seem unlikely if the gaur is ancestor of the mithan; but detailed information is not yet available. Serological and new osteological studies should also be of value in throwing light on the origins of the mithan.

We will save for Part IV of this book consideration of further evidence —from archeology, history, native tradition, and language—on mithan origins. There, too, we will consider whether the mithan is a recent or ancient domesticate; and why, how, and where man may have brought about its domestication. Let us turn our attention first to the roles the mithan plays among the various ethnic groups who keep it.

Part II
The Mithan in Selected Cultures

3

The Mithan-Keeping Peoples

For our purposes mithan country can be divided roughly into northern and southern parts. The northern part includes the mountains between northernmost Burma and China, as well as those north of the Assam Valley which are part of the Eastern Himalayas. Since we have found few references to mithan in the Burma-China borderlands and in Bhutan, and know virtually nothing about mithan keeping there, we will exclude those areas when we use the terms "northern range" or "northern mithan country," and refer only to the area north of the Assam Valley that is in the North-East Frontier Agency of India. Until the 1940's the northern range was virtually unknown and little touched either by the Western world or by the ancient civilizations that border NEFA to the north and south.

The southern range of the mithan embraces the mountain and hill regions extending south from the upper reaches of the Assam Valley; specifically, the Patkoi Range and the Naga, Lushai, Chin, Chittagong, and Arakan hills. It straddles the international boundaries between India and Burma, India and East Pakistan, and Burma and East Pakistan. The peoples of southern mithan country have long been affected by outside influences, by Burmese from the east and Assamese and Bengali plainsmen from the west. British penetration here was also relatively early; and for various reasons British officials and Christian missionaries increasingly became involved with the tribal peoples of the southern range, whereas those of the northern range were left pretty much to themselves. As a result, there is a larger literature on the southern mithan country and it is better known than the northern. Today, moreover, the southern peoples are changing more rapidly than the northern.

The culture history of the mithan country, both northern and southern, has yet to be investigated systematically. The region has experienced repeated migrations of peoples and introductions or inventions of new

37

culture traits which have affected the various groups in different ways and to differing degrees. Today there is an overall similarity in race, language, and culture among mithan-keeping peoples, except for those who have been acculturated to the ways of the outside high civilizations. There are also differences, some of them striking.

The mithan itself does not occupy an identical niche among all groups, but relates to the individual societies and cultures in a multitude of ways, sometimes with strong contrasts in its position among groups that are only short distances apart. Hence no single group can be viewed as typical of the mithan-keeping peoples as a whole. We have chosen six groups from among the mithan keepers in order to present a sample from all sections of the mithan country on which there is information. Detailed treatment of the six groups will indicate the variety of uses of the mithan that occur. It will show how certain neighboring groups in different eco-logical situations contrast in their mithan keeping and how they relate to each other. It may also provide clues as to the means and motives of mithan domestication, which in turn would have implications for the domestication of common cattle and other bovines.

From the southern range we chose one group of some 26,000 people, the Lhota Naga, from among the 478,000 Naga who traditionally were known by more than twenty tribal names. To represent the 600,000 hill Chin of India, Burma, and East Pakistan, we chose the Chin tribes of a single area in Burma, who number about 85,000. One sample from each of these large populations cannot, of course, give an adequate view of the position of the mithan among the Naga and Chin peoples as a whole, but they do provide a base for making broader generalizations and con-trasts relating to the mithan.

Numerically the northern mithan keepers are far fewer than those of the south, but the concentrations of mithan are considerably greater than in the south. The selection of northern groups for detailed treatment pre-sented problems because so little is known of them. The few studies that have been made, however, reveal interesting differences among NEFA peoples and differences in the position of the mithan among them. We have chosen four groups for consideration: the Sherdukpen, Dafla, Apa Tani, and Adi. Each of the four selected is unique in some aspect of its mode of life which is reflected in its attitude toward the mithan and in the role the animal plays in society, culture, and economy.

4

Peoples of the Northern Range
Introductory

The northern range of the mithan lies within an area now a union territory of India. Today, after various political designations by the Government of India, it is known as the North-East Frontier Agency, or NEFA. For administrative purposes, NEFA has been divided into five frontier divisions: Kameng, Subansiri, Siang, Lohit, which lie north of the Assam Valley; and Tirap, which is entirely south of the valley (Map 3a). These five divisions together encompass about 30,000 square miles.

NEFA is dominated by the Eastern Himalayas, and is characterized by exceptionally rough terrain. Steep foothills rise sharply to the north and east from the plains of the Assam Valley. Above the foothills ranges rise in tiers and together form a great arc that sweeps northeastward across all of NEFA to bend abruptly southward at the borders of Sikang and Burma.

Three concentric environmental zones can be distinguished in NEFA: the rough foothills on the edges of the Assam plain, a broader central band that rises to heights of 9,000 or 10,000 feet, and a third higher region of snow ranges which ultimately joins the Great Himalayan Range. Rainfall in the foothills and the central band in some places exceeds 200 inches a year. The vegetation roughly reflects differences in altitude and precipitation: rainforest on the foothills, subtropical flora in the middle zone, and alpine vegetation in the high country.

The intricacy of the mountain system itself has been enhanced by the numerous rivers dissecting it. Each frontier division has at least one major river, most with large and important tributaries and many lesser streams. The NEFA rivers generally rise in the high mountains and empty into the Brahmaputra in the plains. The Dihang River of Siang Division (the Tsangpo of Tibet and the Brahmaputra of the Assam Valley) is the only known river of NEFA that rises beyond the Himalayas.

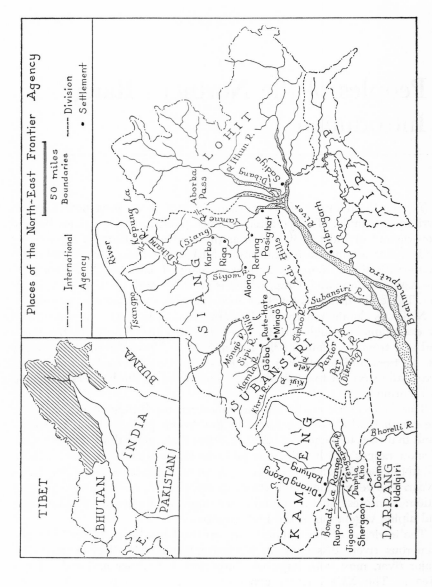

Places of the North-East Frontier Agency

50 miles

--- International
--- Agency
--- Boundaries
--- Division
• Settlement

Map 3a

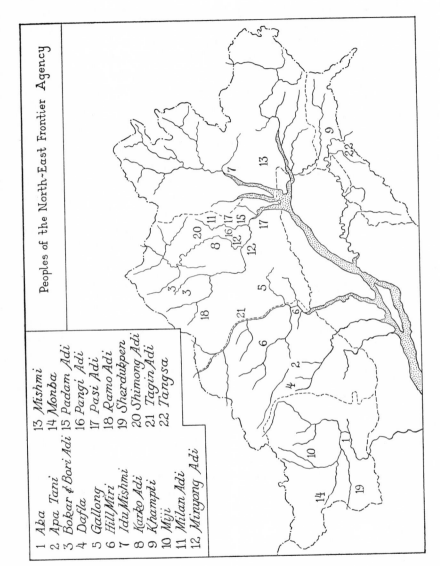

Peoples of the North~East Frontier Agency

1 Aba
2 Apa Tani
3 Bokar & Bori Adi
4 Dafla
5 Gallong
6 Hill Miri
7 Idu Mishmi
8 Karko Adi
9 Khampti
10 Miji
11 Milan Adi
12 Minyong Adi
13 Mishmi
14 Monba
15 Padam Adi
16 Pangi Adi
17 Pasi Adi
18 Ramo Adi
19 Sherdukpen
20 Shimong Adi
21 Tagin Adi
22 Tangsa

Map 3b

Few, if any, of the rivers are corridors permitting easy access to the country back from the Assam Valley. On the contrary, they knife through the mountains and hills and often cut virtually impenetrable gorges, with sides so steep that in many areas even pack trails are impossible. Until the late 1940's all transportation of goods in the hills of NEFA was done on the backs of porters. Now, since India's independence and the recent great interest taken by the Indian Government in this area, certain parts of some divisions have become more accessible. The upper reaches of the rivers remain isolated, however, and some are as little known as ever. In all five frontier divisions the people tend to cluster near the rivers. Some groups locate villages in the river valleys, where this is possible; others, on the valley slopes; and others, on the hilltops nearest the river.

Culturally, the NEFA peoples are unusually situated. Though virtually surrounded by Hindu and Buddhist groups, most of them have maintained their traditional animist beliefs and ways of life.

The NEFA peoples consist of an unknown number of distinct tribal groups speaking about fifty different dialects. Classification of the NEFA languages has not been completed; and controversy over them, and indeed over the entire Sino-Tibetan family continues. Among those who still follow the traditional division of the Sino-Tibetan family into two subfamilies, Tibeto-Burman and Siamese-Chinese, there is a general agreement that most of the NEFA languages fall within the North Assam branch of the Tibeto-Burman subfamily. Robert Shafer, who is supported by several scholars who have worked in the area, takes strong exception to the traditional division. In his classification of Sino-Tibetan languages (1955), he replaces the customary two subfamilies with six "divisions" (Sinitic, Daic, Karenic, Bodic, Burmic, and Baric). Shafer does not definitely classify the NEFA languages he considers, but puts them tentatively in the Bodic division (languages of Tibet and much of the Himalayas). He adds a note saying that they probably are Bodic, but possibly Burmic (Burmese, Chin, and related languages) and certainly not Baric (Garo and certain other minor languages of Assam). Thus, insofar as the NEFA languages are considered in either classification, they are viewed as belonging to the same linguistic stock. We accept simply the position that these languages constitute a related group within the Sino-Tibetan family.

As to racial origin, though all of the peoples of NEFA are not yet known, it is clear that most of the groups are predominantly Mongoloid in physical type. A tradition recurs among many of these peoples that they came to their present areas from the north or northeast. Some claim Tibet itself as their place of origin, others the high country just south of the main Himalayan range. In spite of the persistence of these beliefs and, for one of the groups, a traceable drift from north to south, both Fürer-Haimendorf and Sachin Roy dismiss Tibet as the original home of the northern Assamese hill tribes that they know best (Fürer-Haimendorf, 1962: 6; S. Roy, 1960: chap. 6). They point rather to certain similarities found in the hill cultures on both sides of the Assam Valley, and the striking differences between these and Tibetan culture.

All the NEFA hill people are agriculturalists. With the exception of the Apa Tani, who occupy one small valley in Subansiri Division, all groups about which there is information practice shifting, or *jhum*, cultivation. Rice, millets, and maize are the principal crops grown. Rice is the staple for most hill groups, supplemented with greens and tubers. Domestic animals of various sorts are important to all hill peoples, though they fill differing roles. All groups keep fowl and pigs. Some also keep goats, some keep common cattle, and some keep mithan.

5

The Sherdukpen

The Sherdukpen, a group of only about 1,200 persons, are settled mainly in the valley of the Duphla Kho in the southwestern part of Kameng Frontier Division. Their three important villages—Rupa, Jigaon, and Shergaon—are all situated in the valley, but numerous hamlets are scattered on the slopes of surrounding steep hills. Rupa is at an altitude of 5,500 feet; other parts of the valley rise to 6,500 feet; and the nearby hills are about 2,000 feet higher. The hills form a rain shadow area, and rainfall in the valley (30 to 32 inches a year) is much lower than in other parts of NEFA. The terrain is rocky, with a top layer of sand which retains water poorly.

Like the other peoples of NEFA, the Sherdukpen are Mongoloid in physical type. They have a precisely articulated tradition linking them with Tibet, and many of their cultural practices and religious beliefs connect them with peoples to the west and north rather than with other tribal groups in NEFA.

The Sherdukpen are primarily agriculturalists. They gain only a bare subsistence for their efforts, however, in spite of the fact that in certain ways their cultivation is more complex than that of other NEFA groups. They have permanent fields as well as the usual jhum (shifting) fields, and they use a plow drawn by bullocks. In the jhums they grow maize and various millets, but in the permanent fields they follow a system of crop rotation involving first wheat and barley and then maize and millet. They fertilize the fallow fields by keeping cattle in them. They also have small fenced vegetable gardens, where animal droppings and household garbage are applied as fertilizer. Since they usually do not practice irrigation at all, years of scanty rain bring serious food shortages.

Source: This chapter is based on Sharma, 1961.

Ponies and common cattle are their most valued animals, although they keep goats and chickens as well. Mithan apparently are not kept regularly, though they pass through Sherdukpen hands as trade items. The Sherdukpen are one of the few NEFA people who milk domestic animals. They use the milk of common cattle as such, and also make and consume butter. Animals, however, are reared chiefly for purposes of trade rather than for food. For religious reasons they do not eat beef, pork, fowl, or goat flesh; and orthodox individuals refuse eggs as well. Certain wild animals and fish, however, are acceptable as food.

Two main classes occur in Sherdukpen society: the Thong, descendants of the first Sherdukpen king who settled in Rupa; and the Chhao, descendants of the porters who accompanied him. Traditionally the two groups occupied different villages. The strictures pertaining to food are more rigorous for the Thong. The Chhao are permitted for example to eat mithan flesh, which is forbidden to the Thong (Sharma, 1961: 52). This is the only indication of mithan flesh being used by the Sherdukpen.

Because food production is so precarious, the Sherdukpen also depend in large measure for their support upon an extensive trade. In this the mithan is an important item. "Cows" (females of common cattle?) are traded to the Aka on the east for mithan bulls, and for these the Sherdukpen find a ready and profitable market among the Monba and Bhutanese to the west and north. Both of these peoples value the mithan as a breeding animal from which to obtain sturdy hybrids for plowing.[1]

Besides trading in common cattle, mithan, and other items with their neighbors, the Sherdukpen travel seasonally to lower country to trade. Every year they leave their valley during the three cold months from mid-December to mid-March, when agriculture is impossible, to settle in a temporary camp at Doimara near the Assam plains. They take with them not only the products they want to trade (various home-manufactured items, dried garden produce, and chickens) but also their "cattle." An important Sherdukpen ceremony, the Ba Jung Khloba, performed just before setting out for the winter camp, is for the express purpose of assuring that the cattle, especially the cows, will be protected from epidemics during their stay in the lowland. No mention is made of mithan being taken along and we suspect that they do not participate in this migration. Mithan do not do well outside their forest habitat, they are not found in the lowlands of Assam, and might not readily accommodate themselves to the migration.

1. The Monba and Bhutanese are not considered in this survey of mithan-keeping peoples both because information on their use of the mithan is scanty and because their use is quite limited compared with that by the peoples of the mithan country proper, which starts east of the Sherdukpen in NEFA.

The Sherdukpen traditionally were involved in payment of tribute on one hand and collection of taxes on the other, with various of their neighbors. They paid tribute to the Miji, the Aka, and the Monba for the sake of maintaining peace, and collected taxes from certain Kachari and Monba villages, as well as from Bhutanese immigrants to their territory. The tribute was paid in kind: salt, certain spices, rice, cloth, goats, cows, bullocks, fowl, and other goods. The taxes apparently were paid in Indian rupees. In all these exchanges, mithan are mentioned just once. A group of Sherdukpen near Shergaon paid a Bhutanese official nine mithan as a sort of "ransom" to enable eight Bhutanese immigrant families to remain among the Sherdukpen, instead of returning as the official demanded. This single instance of mithan serving in such payments is in marked contrast to most of NEFA, where it is common for similar obligations to be calculated and paid in mithan.

Sharma gives no indication that mithan are useful to the Sherdukpen as currency. A bride-price is customary, but is paid in cows, sheep, cloth, and scarves. Land, other than jhum land, is bought for cash or paid for with common cattle. Jhum land is distributed to individuals after general consideration by clan members, and depends upon need and convenience, not on ability to pay.

The mithan apparently is of no significance, either, as a sacrificial animal. Sherdukpen religion is a combination of Buddhism and belief in local deities and spirits, perhaps with Buddhist influence dominant. The Buddha is greatly revered, and Buddhist shrines and temples are a common feature of the Sherdukpen landscape. Whenever possible, Buddhist temples are presided over by local lamas who have been trained at Tawang Monastery, in the northwest corner of Kameng Division. The Sherdukpen maintain contact with and appease local spirits and deities through local priests, who offer sacrifices when necessary. It is striking, however, that in the ceremonies described by Sharma, some presided over by lamas and others by a priest, only one sometimes involved sacrifice—of goats and fowls offered in addition to the usual vegetal offerings (1961: 85). This is in sharp contrast to the importance of sacrifice among other peoples of NEFA and those of the Assam-Burmese border. Perhaps another reason the mithan has not found more favor among the Sherdukpen is that there is no important need for it in sacrifice.

6

The Dafla

Perhaps 40,000 in number, the Dafla are concentrated in present-day Subansiri Frontier Division: along the Panior River and its tributaries, and along the middle Subansiri River and its western tributaries, especially the lower Kamla and Khru rivers (Maps 3a and 3b). The area is forested hill and mountain country. In the midst of Dafla country, along one river valley, live the Apa Tani, a distinct ethnic group.

Most Dafla have the usual physical characteristics of the paleo-Mongoloids, though a second, less common, physical type also occurs. The original home of the Dafla is not known. They have a tradition of being descendants of a mythical person called Teni or Abo Teni and of living in the far Eastern Himalayas. Their traditions have them crossing the Subansiri River and then moving to the Kamla and Khru rivers, and finally southward to the Panior area. This is in keeping with Fürer-Haimendorf's report (1955: 160; 1962: 8) of a modern southward drift of the Dafla, from the Khru River to the Panior, then to the Par (Dikrang) River and down that valley into the foothills. Dafla tradition also says that they brought with them to the hills they now occupy the mithan and pig, the arts of weaving and agriculture, as well as articles of value such as Tibetan bells, large metal plates, and beads.

The people live in villages of from two to thirty longhouses located in or near the numerous river valleys that cut through Subansiri Division. The longhouses generally are scattered over the hillsides, the site selected for each being confirmed by omens. The Dafla are polygynous, and each longhouse is occupied by at least one man, his wife or wives, and their unmarried children. Often the longhouse is also occupied by a man's

Sources: This chapter is based principally on Fürer-Haimendorf, 1955 and 1962, and Shukla, 1959; also on Stonor, 1957.

married sons and their wives and children, and sometimes by his brothers or cousins and their families. On the average a Dafla longhouse shelters about twenty persons, but sometimes many more—up to sixty or seventy —representing ten or twelve families. In Dafla society the longhouse is practically autonomous. There is little allegiance to the village, and no political structure with authority over the village as a whole. The long-house and its inhabitants, rather than the village, is the basic political and social unit. Though one man, usually a person of age, position, and power, is head of the household, each elementary family within the longhouse is independent to a considerable degree. Quarrels are frequent within the longhouse, and a man may then move out, taking his immediate family to the house of another relative, or he may establish a house of his own. He may stay in the village or move away to another. Thus the composition of Dafla longhouses and Dafla villages is in a constant state of flux.

Though the Dafla are accomplished hunters and fishermen, jhum cultivation and animal husbandry are their primary concern. They produce one crop a year, growing principally dry rice, millets (*Eleusine coracana* and *Setaria italica*), and maize but also other crops, among them various tubers, chillies, squash, beans, cotton, and tobacco. Rainfall averages between 80 and 100 inches annually and the Dafla generally do not need to resort to irrigation. Fürer-Haimendorf (1962: 47–48) says that the Dafla lack knowledge of irrigation and terracing except in a few villages near the Apa Tani, where they have attempted it with the aid of Apa Tani hired help.

Animal husbandry, at which the Dafla are proficient, is of unusual importance to them, especially as it concerns the mithan. They rear mithan, pigs, a few common cattle and goats, and chickens. Common cattle generally occur only in the areas that have close connections with the Assamese plains. Common cattle and goats are kept primarily for their meat, whereas mithan and pigs are most important as sacrificial animals. Mithan are not only the highest sacrificial animals but are the measure of a man's wealth; they are essential in bride-price, and are often required in concluding friendship pacts and in paying fines and ransoms. Chickens are important both in sacrifice and for taking omens; they are rarely killed simply for their flesh. Dogs are considered pets; they are useful in hunting and for guarding fields. They also are sacrificed, but only on occasions involving witchcraft. The Dafla do not commonly eat dog flesh.

The Mithan among the Dafla

The Dafla turn their mithan loose in the forest near their villages to wander where they will. This brings little risk to crops since the jhums generally are well fenced. Often the animals remain at large for long periods, their owners going into the forest every few days to look for them. In some villages, especially those in the foothills, mithan are brought to the village in the evening and are tied beneath the owner's house (pers. com., Fürer-Haimendorf, Oct. 16, 1966). Shukla (1959: 40) reports that mithan are taken once or twice a month to special water holes which are thought to be particularly good for their health. Each animal is given a name and, as is common with herding people, certain of them—especially female mithan—become favorites of the owner.

In Economic and Social Life

Conforming to the general pattern found among mithan keepers, the Dafla utilize the animal in very limited ways. They neither milk it nor use it for draft or for packing. The meat is prized, but eaten only when a mithan dies or is sacrificed. Mithan hides are used to some extent, despite lack of knowledge of how to tan and dress them with fats. They are crudely prepared and used for sitting on around the hearths and for sleeping. Sometimes Dafla men wear a piece of mithan hide as a chest covering. Mithan hide is often made into small carrying bags used to hold tobacco and a pipe. Shields, belts, and slings are also made from it. The blood of sacrificed mithan apparently is of ritual significance; its use will be discussed briefly below with other aspects of mithan sacrifice.

Mithan horns, although not generally put to any practical use,[1] yet serve a purpose in Dafla life. Skulls and horns of sacrificed mithan are hung up inside the houses, along with skulls, horns, or bones of other domestic animals that have been sacrificed, and trophies from the chase. Such displays probably are the possessor's visible record of achievement and wealth. They are hung on the most important house wall, that along which the hearths are ranged. Mithan horns found hanging among the pottery and baskets on the opposite wall, which is used mainly as a storage place for seldom-used household articles, are those of animals that have died of illness. Though important enough to be saved and displayed, they are apparently not in the same category as the remains of sacrificed and hunted animals. Still another custom points to the special significance of the displays on the main wall: among the few restrictions placed on Dafla women during their menstrual periods is one that pro-

---

1. One practical use of a mithan horn was noticed by Fürer-Haimendorf (1955: 154–55) while in a Dafla house observing the negotiations involving a death settlement. When certain items first offered as compensation were rejected, the person making the payment sent his wives to find something more suitable. They went to a storage place in the roof and pulled down a very large mithan horn. In it, held for safekeeping, was an impressive collection of Dafla valuables.

hibits touching the ceremonial horns and skulls hanging on the hearth wall.

As a Measure of Wealth and a Means of Social Achievement

As slash-and-burn cultivators, the Dafla have no concept of individually owned land and take no interest in its permanent acquisition. Their houses too are temporary possessions, lasting only about three years. They do value and accumulate a certain wealth in such movable items as *majis* (Tibetan tongueless bells), *talus* (metal plates), and *kojis* (Tibetan bangles of bronze or brass, sometimes worn by women); and they are interested in increasing their mithan herds both as an absolute measure of wealth and a means of achieving the other things considered of value in Dafla society.

Because of the lack of village political and social cohesion, the Dafla is thrown upon his own resources for assuring security, for winning recognition and prestige, and for redressing grievances. As he is able to muster kinsmen and friends to his causes he raids for revenge or for profit, and settles his disputes as he sees fit. A man's strength and status are enhanced by the individual bonds or alliances that he forges with others. These occur in three common ways: purchase or exchange of Tibetan bells, friendship pacts (*dapos*), and marriage. Mithan are usually needed in payment for Tibetan bells and in concluding friendship pacts, and they are essential for bride-price. Wives in turn are important in welding additional alliances which give a man power. The ambition of a Dafla thus, as he reaches maturity, focuses more and more on increasing the number of mithan and valuables he owns, and marrying as many wives as he can afford, for these assure his prestige, power, and influence.

In Bride-Price

Bride-price among the Dafla is obligatory and high, and mithan always figure in it. Disputes growing out of claims and counterclaims over bride-price are common and often lead to feuds that are carried on through several generations.

Marriages are generally arranged by the parents; the price finally agreed upon places firm commitments on both sets of parents, but especially on the parents of the girl, who, having received payment for her, are responsible for her performance. If that falls short, or if she dies soon, the groom's parents claim return of part or all of the price paid. If the girl's parents are rich in mithan, this may not be a problem. For a poor father, however, the mithan he receives for his daughter may be difficult to replace. Such payments often are soon used for buying another wife for himself or one for his son, and thus are not available for return. The difficulty of divorce among the Dafla grows out of these firm commitments. A woman cannot leave her husband unless someone can restore the bride-price to his family. Divorce is not lightly undertaken by a man either; if he takes the initiative and puts his wife out he loses entirely the price he paid for her, and has not even her labor in the fields for compensation.

Because Dafla marriage is based upon economic considerations, there are differences among rich and poor in the normal age of marriage. The rich man can at any time spare the mithan needed for bride-price for wives for his sons. A poor man, however, has too few mithan to do this, and his son may have to wait until his sister is married before the father has sufficient mithan to pay a bride-price. Thus the sons of the rich tend to marry earlier, the sons of the poor later; often, too, the daughters of the poor marry sooner than the daughters of the wealthy, so that their bride-price may be used to obtain wives for their brothers and sometimes for their fathers.

The ceremonies of marriage center on the giving and receiving of the bride-price, rather than on the union of the bride and groom. When the bride-price is finally settled, after lengthy negotiations, the groom's father, accompanied by the prospective groom and various relatives, brings a mithan and various other items to the bride's father. The bride's family prepares a feast to honor the guests, who stay in the bride's village for several days. The groom's party then returns to his village, bringing the bride and gifts given by her father. It is customary to perform a special ceremony, the Yulo, involving the sacrifice of a mithan and a feast, a few days after the bride comes to her husband's house.[2] The kinsmen of the groom participate in the feast. The bride-price often is paid in yearly or half-yearly instalments. As he accepts each payment, the bride's father returns token gifts of much less value.

In Death Ceremonies

While the birth of a child is not celebrated among the Dafla with feasting or sacrifice, death is marked with all the ceremony and sacrifice the deceased person's family can afford. The Dafla are torn between grief for the person who has died and fear that his ghost will return to trouble them. Thus the family offers the corpse as many mithan, pigs, or lesser animals as it can, in an effort to keep the ghost contented and away from them. A structure of bamboo is built near the grave, and on this are displayed the heads or horns of the animals sacrificed. Formerly, especially for wealthy persons, very large feasts were held. Even today, when the feasting is less lavish and the body is usually buried the day

2. The Yulo is also performed when a sick person recovers.

after death, the number of mithan heads hung on the grave-side structure indicates a man's wealth and status.

In Feud and Ransom

The Dafla are easily provoked and squabble among themselves constantly. Many of their quarrels arise from claims and counterclaims on bride-price. Alleged theft and accusation of carrying disease are two other common causes of disputes. The usual and approved means of settling wrongs is to raid the enemy, which may lead to counterraids, and finally to feuds. Besides their internal bickering and retaliation, the Dafla raid the Apa Tani. With that settled agricultural group who dwell in the midst of their country, the Dafla carry on an extensive trade which is mutually beneficial. Many disputes, some leading to generations-old feuds, grow out of these trading associations.[3] Though a man gains no special prestige from raiding, he is recognized as being able to settle his affairs.

Sometimes a man setting out on a raid feels himself so wronged that only the death of his enemy will suffice. If he succeeds in killing him, the body of the slain enemy is left for the relatives. One hand of the victim, however, is brought to the victor's village for certain ceremonies. These are followed by the sacrifice of a mithan provided by the slayer. He and his fellow raiders share in the feast, but the ceremony is held to honor the *wiyus*, or spirits, who had made the successful foray possible, rather than to bring recognition to the slayer.

Often raids are undertaken to capture people and mithan. The motive of the action may be to avenge a wrong, or to profit. When Dafla raids result in taking captives or animals, whether from among themselves or outsiders, the raiders expect to hold their prizes for ransom. After protracted discussion carried on by paid intermediaries, a payment in mithan, bells, brass plates, and other items is agreed upon. The price is paid in full and the captive released. The ransoms are high. Fürer-Haimendorf (1955: 138–39) tells of one dispute between Dafla in which fifteen mithan were paid to ransom seven captured men and women. In another case the ransom paid by Apa Tani for the release of two men was two mithan, three long swords, five daos (machetes), four Apa Tani cloths, four hoes, four axes, three brass plates, three Assamese silk cloths, and one white cloth. Besides this, the Apa Tani paid substantial fees to the Dafla negotiators, of whom there were eight, and more moderate fees to the four Apa Tani negotiators (Fürer-Haimendorf, 1962: 128; see also 1955: 42).

---

3. For further discussion of Dafla–Apa Tani trade, disputes, and ransom negotiations, see especially pp. 72–75.

The first-mentioned case became quite complicated because in a subsequent raid a woman inadvertently was killed. This loss initiated a feud that had lasted four years. It was finally settled with the son of the dead woman being paid a death price which included one mithan. The final negotiations and payment took place in the guilty man's village, where also a special ceremony was held to mark the end of the feud formally. The offender provided two mithan which were sacrificed, some of the meat going to the man being compensated and to his followers. This rite, called Pakhe, reestablished friendship between the two rivals and permitted them to accept food and drink from one another again. At a later time the offender would take still another mithan to the other's village for a similar ceremony. If the two former enemies then wished to enter into a more binding relationship, they could continue with a *dapo* ceremony. The dapo is a nonaggression pact of perpetual validity. Mithan or pigs are essential for the sacrifice, and Shukla reports that "once performed, [the dapos] have never been known to be violated" (1959: 90). Besides dapos between individual Dafla, leading Dafla men of specific villages enter dapo pacts with specific Apa Tani villages to ensure, as far as possible, mutual protection of traders venturing into each other's territory.

The character of the dapo may be brought out by comparison with the *thumona* of the Aka, western neighbors of the Dafla. The Aka, a communally oriented people with a strong tradition of hospitality, practice a formalized system of guest-visits, or thumona, which bind the participants in friendship. In the thumona there is an exchange of hospitality and gifts, which may include mithan. The thumona creates firm feelings of loyalty at the individual level, which, within society, contribute to group solidarity. The individualistic Dafla, however, enter into dapos primarily to gain allies needed to support their social position, which is measured in part by their ability to protect themselves from their enemies, carry out raids, and avenge wrongs.

If captured persons or animals were not ransomed they became the property of the raider. The people became slaves, and the owner had absolute rights over them. They could be, and often were, sold. The slaves were valued as laborers, but their lot was not always unduly hard. In the fluid Dafla society, where a hard-working, agreeable slave easily could gain the support and loyalty of his master, many rose to considerable wealth and influence. They were permitted a hearth in the house and clearings in the forest; they could even own animals, if they were enterprising enough to acquire them. Fürer-Haimendorf (1955: 145) tells about a slave of the Dafla village of Talo who was allowed by his master to go to the plains to work during the off-season. He bought cloth and beads with his earnings, traded them for pigs, and with profits from his pigs was able to buy mithan. His master had paid the bride-price for his first wife, a free woman; with his growing affluence, the slave himself had acquired three more wives. Shukla (1959: 93) indicates the value of slaves in a discussion of compensatory payment due relatives of a person murdered; certain payments were reckoned in slaves, but a guilty person unable to pay in slaves could substitute six to eight mithan for each slave.

In Fines

In spite of the apparent lack of codes of law even for single villages, a sort of customary law exists and is the basis for the fines and punishments that are declared and collected. The sentences depend upon the strength and influence of the injured party and the means of the offender (Shukla, 1959: 90–93). Mithan are one of the usual assessments.

Yosinee, or illicit sexual activity of a varying degree of seriousness, is a common occurrence in Dafla society. It becomes a problem or a "crime" only if the persons involved are discovered, and then the collection and payment of the fines still remains an individual matter. One mithan is the usual fine for sexual congress; lesser valuables are assessed for lesser transgressions. If a Dafla is caught stealing a mithan, the usual fine is a mithan in addition to return of the one stolen, and a pig for a ceremony to reestablish friendship. The fines for murder are compensation item by item for various parts of the body, plus two mithan for feasts for the relatives of the murdered person and for a friendship ceremony.

In Buying Tibetan Bells

In addition to alliances made through marriage contracts and dapo treaties, the Dafla have the other way of forging friendships that has already been mentioned: the purchase or exchange of Tibetan bells. Ownership of the bells has a particular significance for the Dafla, and the exchange of one often is accompanied with considerable ceremony. Fürer-Haimendorf (1955: 198–200) describes the ceremonies he witnessed in the northeastern part of Subansiri Division in 1945 in a village of the Hill Miri, considered by Fürer-Haimendorf as close relatives of the Dafla. The Dafla of the Panior and Kiyi valleys, in the southwest, he says, value the bells to the same extent; exchange of bells for mithan and other articles of value creates a bond between the persons involved as binding as a marriage alliance.

In the Miri case a bell which was known by its own name and had come from the Khru Valley was to be exchanged for four mithan and some pigs, cloths, and salt. The two men participating lived in villages about eight miles apart. Two mithan were paid before the bell was handed over; and the two families visited back and forth, entertaining each other as lavishly as possible and becoming well acquainted. For the ceremonies at the time of the exchange, which took almost two days, one mithan—its horns decorated with streamers made of bamboo shavings— and a mithan calf were brought to the house of the seller. The first evening the seller provided beer for the guests; the second day the buyer was host. Two priests officiated, chanting praises to the bell and purifying the food and beer. They touched the beer containers with their bamboo whisks, then poured a little beer on the mithan and on the floor of the house before the beer was served. The purchaser of the bell gained social status through his new possession, as well as widening and strengthening his network of friendship pacts, which with the new alliance penetrated to nine villages and encompassed an area about twenty-five miles in diameter.

In Religion

Stonor was impressed with what he described as the "extraordinary intensity" of Dafla religion and its "all-pervading effects on every aspect of life" (1957: 3). The Dafla, like many of the NEFA peoples, believe themselves to be confronted on every side by spirits, or wiyus, most of whom are evil. These wiyus live everywhere, from the tops of the mountains to the depths of the dark forested ravines. Many dwell around and in the Daflas' houses. All manner of difficulties, from raging storms to sickness and death, are caused by displeasure of the wiyus. Ancestral ghosts, *orums*, also abound, coming back from the Land of the Dead to collect things they had forgotten, and to harm the living by causing illness and other problems. The Dafla protect themselves from the wiyus and orums by offering animal sacrifices to them. A priest frequently is needed to identify the angry supernatural being and to determine which animal must be sacrificed to appease him.

Mithan Sacrifice

According to both Shukla and Stonor, the mithan sacrifice is by far the most important one for the Dafla. It pleases everyone, the spirits to whom the mithan is offered, the feast giver who hopes to achieve a specific end, and the relatives and guests who share the meat, which they relish. No other sacrifice is so effective and in no other are the rites so elaborate or carried out with such care (Shukla, 1959: 101). Stonor goes so far as to say that "in some respects [this animal is] the corner-stone of Dafla life" (1957: 16).

For each occasion of mithan sacrifice the Dafla build an elaborate bamboo structure, a sort of altar. The structures are decorated in various ways, with bamboo shavings, bamboos engraved with designs, and thin flat carvings, and are said to represent the spirits being appeased (Shukla, 1959: 99–100; Stonor, 1957: 16–17). Both Stonor and Shukla state specifically that the structures are only of importance for the sacrifice for which they were built, and thereafter are left to rot away.

Stonor (1957: 18–21) describes in detail a mithan sacrifice performed in 1947 for a man who had been ill for some time. The ceremony lasted for two days, of which the first was spent at various preparations, including building the sacrificial structure. When all was ready, on the second day, a mithan, accompanied by a chanting priest, was tied to three posts in front of the structure. A priest stayed with the mithan, chanting and singing to it during all of the ceremony, which moved between the altar and the inside of the feast giver's house. A relative of the feast giver at length approached the mithan with a bow and two arrows, one with an iron point and one with no head. He shot both of them into the side of the animal, from very close range, and then the master of ceremonies pole-axed the mithan with a metal ax, and stabbed it in the shoulder with a long knife. He gathered the first blood into a sheaf of bamboo shavings which afterward was hung on the altar. The liver was removed and omens taken, as with other sacrificed animals. The mithan finally was divided according to custom, the head and neck and one hind leg going to the feast giver, one side and one front leg to the chief priest, and various other parts to relatives and friends who had helped with the feast.

Shukla's information on the manner of killing the animal is similar but he does not mention the bow and arrows. He makes a point of saying that the method of slaying varies for different kinds of animals and for different ceremonies. He observed that mithan are struck unconscious with a blow of an ax to the neck. A dao is then driven into the heart, and finally the chest is cut open. In the sacrifice of pigs and mithan, the blood is put into bamboo containers, and is heated and eaten by members of the feast giver's clan. If the ceremony is the Yulo, being performed after a marriage or when a person has recovered from an illness, the blood goes to the chief priest, who hangs the bamboo tube in which it was collected on the front of his house.

Specific Spirits and Their Requirements

Among the Dafla spirits is the benevolent Ane Duini, the sun-mother. She is responsible for all the good things in Dafla life: good crops and full granaries, children, slaves, mithan, pigs, Tibetan bells, plates, and beads. No day or special ceremony is set aside for her, but when an offering is made it is the highest sacrifice, that of mithan. She is praised with songs at other important ceremonies, such as marriage, but is not reviled, as are other wiyus, at times of disaster.

Of the numerous malevolent wiyus of the forest, the most important two cause serious illness and sometimes death, and must be offered mithan and pigs. There are two river wiyus too, who require mithan or pigs if they are not to become angered when people trespass on their territory as in fishing.

Rokpeh, the deity of the chase, is a kindly spirit, and success in hunting comes from his benevolence. He is offered a separate sacrifice at all important ceremonies, but the proffered animals are pigs or chickens, not mithan. Stonor found it odd that the most important domestic animal, the mithan, was not offered to one of the major spirits. He speculates that perhaps Rokpeh is very ancient, and that the mithan, possibly a later domesticate than either pig or chicken, was not linked with him in those early times (Stonor, 1957: 5–6).

Spirits cause most kinds of illness suffered by the Dafla. When a person has been ill for a time and none of the minor offerings seems to help, a priest is called to identify the particular spirit that is at the root of the trouble. The spirit is then promised the appropriate sacrifice, often a mithan, which he is begged to accept and to depart from the sick man. Many eggs and chickens, for taking omens, are required at such undertakings.

Stonor (1957: 15) also reported what he thought to be a sort of scapegoat ritual, performed every several years by the Dafla he visited, for the purpose of preventing evil, including illness. The ceremony is for the benefit of the whole community, which contrasts with usual Dafla custom, where each individual acts alone. A bull mithan is bought cooperatively with contributions from the entire village. The killing in this ritual differs from the usual method too, in that an ax is not used. Only arrows and spears are permitted. In the other rituals women participate, but in this one they do not. The meat, however, is divided according to custom, and the original owner of the mithan gets the horns.

Stonor came across one ritual in which the sacrificial altar was not used. This was the sacrifice made to an especially powerful spirit, called Tamün, who required a mithan for propitiation. Tamün is believed to ambush men and eat them. For his sacrifice, instead of the bamboo structure, the Dafla put up a large Y-shaped post, which is said to be his special symbol. Stonor added that the Y-shaped post was often used when an animal was killed to "seal a bond or to conclude a treaty," which he apparently took to mean marriage or trade arrangements (1957: 6–7); but he was not specific in the latter cases about whether the post served along with, or instead of, the usual bamboo altar. Fürer-Haimendorf was surprised at the informality of a sacrifice he saw in the Panior Valley to mark the end of a feud and a death settlement, which had been very costly. For this rite, the two mithan to be slaughtered were tied to a forked post. A

priest officiated, but the ceremony was short, the animals killed quickly
with a sword, their blood rubbed on the post, and the sacrificial meat soon
cooked and eaten. Fürer-Haimendorf makes no mention of any structure
other than the post; and since haste and simplicity were the striking
features he noted, it seems unlikely that the usual elaborate altars were
made (1955: 155).

In Agricultural Rites

Stonor, although he did not see any ceremonies related to agriculture,
inquired about them. He was told that every fourth or fifth year in winter
after the crops were harvested the Dafla held one general ceremony at
which a mithan was sacrificed. The festival was called Mlokum, similar
in name to the annual agricultural festival of the Apa Tani, the Mloko.
All the villagers participated. Stonor (1957: 14–15) concluded that agricultural rites were not very important.

In Black Magic

Black magic is practiced by the Dafla, but evidently is not common.
Shukla (1959: 85) describes the ceremonies performed after a successful
raid, when a murdered victim's palm was carried back to the village. At
the end of the ritual involving the palm but before the sacrifice of the
mithan and the feast, a dog was killed with a spear and its body thrown
into the forest to the Sotung Wiyu (spirit of witchcraft) as a protection
against subsequent witchcraft. Stonor (1957: 21) reported one rite that
involved black magic. When a man is ready to start out on a mission of
revenge, Stonor was told, he calls a high priest to take omens to determine
the method of procedure. Commonly a mithan has to be sacrificed. At the
conclusion of the sacrifice the priest goes alone, except for a dog, into the
forest at night. He ties the dog to a specific kind of tree, kills the dog by
decapitating it with a sword, and cuts down the tree, chanting the correct
incantations. When he gets home, he purifies himself of the close contact
with evil spirits by sacrificing a chicken. If the magic works and the
revenge is successful the priest charges a high price for the risk he took
by involving himself so closely with the spirits. His satisfied customer
happily pays a live mithan along with other valuable items.

In Dreams

Dreams among the Dafla have meaning and are taken seriously.
Mithan appear in them in various ways, sometimes portending good,
sometimes evil. Shukla gives a number of the common notions about
dreams. To dream of mithan sacrifices means that someone in the family
will die. If someone dreams that he is carrying mithan horns, he will be

captured and put into a stockade by an enemy. Dreaming of killing a snake or of removing leeches from one's legs means that one of the big mithan owned by the dreamer may die. Dreams are not often taken to have sexual connotations, but there are a few, one of which concerns mithan. If a man dreams of mithan engaged in the sexual act it means that the man's wife is indulging in sexual relations with a slave.

Status of the Priest

In a society so permeated with malicious spirits, most of whom require a priest as intermediary between them and man, one would expect to find that Dafla priests enjoy a special and respected position; and they do. There are three grades of priests. Priests of the two higher grades attain their knowledge and position through special training and by performing sacrifices. Those of the third grade, the most numerous, perform only simple cures and take simple omens. Though they qualify with minimal preparation, they, like the others, are believed to have been visited by a wiyu while yet in their mothers' wombs, and told that they would become priests. All priests earn their living by performing highly valued services, for which they are paid at specified rates. The chief priest officiating at a high sacrifice in which a mithan is killed is by custom paid one side and one front leg—including the shoulder blade—of the animal. Thus he generally is assured a good food supply. Even at lesser sacrifices the priests are generally entertained with food and drink. If a sacrifice brings a cure or solves a problem, the priest is often given additional payment, such as cloth, later, when the result of his effort can be seen.

Dafla priests are as prestige-conscious as other Dafla. They keep the mithan shoulder blades, each of which represents a separate sacrifice, and display them in various ways for all to see. Sometimes the bones are decorated with charcoal drawings. Shukla found such bones hung up inside the priest's house with the special items of his profession, such as head-dresses and ceremonial fans (1959: 103–4). Stonor reported mithan shoulder blades as part of the paraphernalia on shrines built on the front verandahs of the houses of chief priests of the western Dafla. He saw one shrine on which hung some forty mithan scapular bones, each etched with wavy lines; more were piled on a shelf behind the shrine, along with ceremonial items used in past sacrifices. Hanging at the side of the shrine was a collection of bamboo tubes, decorated with the same kind of wavy lines. The tubes are used for catching and preserving some of the blood of sacrificed mithan. A new bamboo is used at each mithan sacrifice, so the number of bamboos as well as the scapular bones indicates the number of sacrifices at which the priest presided (Stonor, 1957: 13–14). Shukla, too (1959: 102–3, 129), discussed the bamboo tubes, which he reported simply as decorating priests' verandahs; he did not mention the shrines. Clearly the priests display these relics for much the same reason that ordinary Dafla display the heads and horns of mithan, as a record of achievement.

7

The Apa Tani

The Apa Tani, like the Dafla, live in Subansiri Frontier Division, but are a much smaller group. The entire population of about 11,000 live in seven villages located in the small valley of the Kele, a tributary of the Panior (Map 4). This valley, which is only two by six miles, lies at an elevation of about 5,000 feet among mountains that rise to over 8,000. It is possible that at some ancient time the valley was a lake, which was filled in gradually with silt carried down by streams from the nearby mountains. According to Apa Tani tradition, the first arrivals found the valley a swamp, which they drained and turned into the productive place it is today. Indeed, it supports the group at a level of prosperity unmatched elsewhere in NEFA. Rainfall is abundant, and mountain streams that flow into the valley are so numerous, that it is no problem to keep the rice terraces in the valley bottom flooded most of the year. That there are no fixed rules about water rights, and no system of buying or selling them, indicates that the water supply is easily adequate for the system of cultivation the Apa Tani employ.

The Apa Tani differ greatly in language and culture from the other mithan-keeping peoples of Subansiri Division. Their speech, for example, cannot be understood by the Dafla, whereas all Dafla and Hill Miri groups, in spite of differences in dialect from place to place, can converse with one another. The Apa Tani have three dialects; five villages speak the same one, and two, Hari and Hang, each speaks its own. All three dialects however are easily understood by all Apa Tani.

The seven villages act as three units for certain ritual purposes, but the ritual grouping does not correspond with the dialectical grouping. Hang, the southernmost village, acts alone in these ceremonies; Hari and

Source: This chapter is based almost entirely on Fürer-Haimendorf, 1955 and 1962.

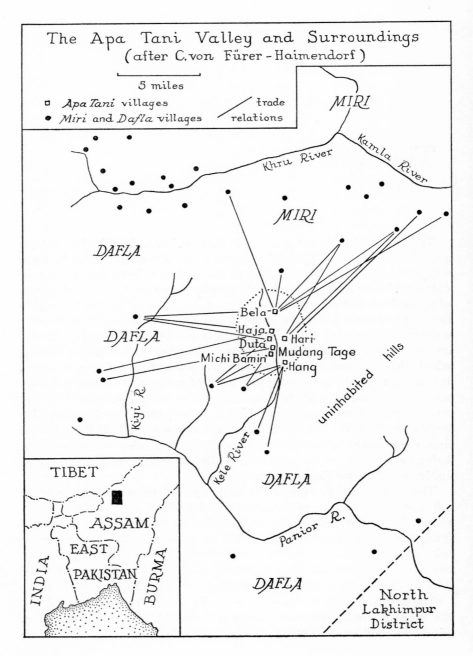

The Apa Tani Valley and Surroundings
(after C. von Fürer-Haimendorf)

5 miles

□ *Apa Tani* villages
● *Miri* and *Dafla* villages

trade relations

MIRI

Khru River

Kamla River

MIRI

DAFLA

DAFLA

Bela

Haja
Duta
Michi Bamin
Hari
Mudang Tage
Hang

uninhabited hills

Kiyi R.

Kele River

DAFLA

TIBET

ASSAM

EAST
PAKISTAN

INDIA

BURMA

Panior R.

DAFLA

North
Lakhimpur
District

Map 4

Bela, the two remaining villages on the eastern side of the valley, act together; and the other four villages, all in the western valley, make the third unit.

In physical type the Apa Tani are predominantly Mongoloid, or paleo-Mongoloid, as Fürer-Haimendorf characterizes them. He found, as he did among the Dafla and Hill Miri, some individuals with physical features different from the typical Mongoloid type: prominent noses, deep-set eyes, long rather than round faces, and a more ruddy complexion than the usual copper-brown. Among the Apa Tani the type appeared particularly in free men rather than in the slave class, in which there is more admixture with Dafla (Fürer-Haimendorf, 1962: 6–7, 10–11).

The only clues to the origin of the Apa Tani are found in their own traditions, which support a migration from the north and northeast. One tradition specifies the points at which three different streams of migrants crossed the Khru and Kamla rivers. Fürer-Haimendorf discounts a Tibetan origin, and considers affinities with the Adi of Siang and, even more, with the Naga as of greater significance (1962: 5, 6, 62–63).

Apa Tani villages are compact; bamboo houses, raised on wooden piles, closely line the lanes and streets. The 1961 census reported 2,520 houses for the seven villages; Bela, the largest, had 672 and Duta, the smallest, 160. Each house is usually occupied by a nuclear family; though polygyny is permissible it is rare. The villages are made up of quarters, each occupied by particular clans. Clans are exogamous, patrilineal, and patrilocal, although there are occasional exceptions. Each clan usually has its own assembly platform, or *lapang*, which is its social center, and a unifying force at the clan level. The clans of each quarter, however, share a single ritual center, usually a small hut, called *nago*; this sharing of the ritual center provides a certain unity to all the clans attached to it.

No organization exists at the village level with authority over the village as a whole, though a "clan council" composed of representatives of the different clans is influential in directing village activity. The clan representatives, it must be emphasized, constitute an informal body, and are primarily spokesmen for their clans rather than a village council. Their deliberations and decisions reflect public opinion rather than being judgments based on formal law. Certain families, because of their wealth and status, each traditionally provide a clan representative or two. Other men, not necessarily of prominent families, are chosen because of demonstrated ability.

Clan, rather than village, affiliation carries the greatest obligations for mutual support. Overriding clan loyalty is the realization that to survive in this restricted, densely populated area some degree of harmony and order must be maintained at all times throughout the valley. Various mechanisms contribute toward maintaining tribal solidarity and peace. Among these are ceremonies involving ritual exchange among the villages. Another mechanism is dapo pacts between villages, rather than between individuals as among the Dafla. The Apa Tani village dapo pacts were concluded so long ago that no one recalls the events which brought them about. Though fundamentally like the Dafla dapos—agreements of perpetual nonaggression—there is the important difference that the Apa Tani dapos bind villages and are recognized throughout the valley as permanent. The Apa Tani community functions without a formal judicial system or any institution embracing the tribe as a whole or, excepting the dapos, even villages as complete units.

The Apa Tani are a stable population which has remained content and prosperous on the same land for unknown generations. As farmers they are far superior to their neighbors. They cultivate intensively, growing irrigated rice on expertly engineered and carefully tended terraces, limited largely to the valley bottom. They do not terrace high up the hillsides. Rather, higher land is used for dry crops. In the dry fields two varieties of millet are grown; and in garden plots maize, beans, potatoes, chillies, tomatoes, marrow, spinach, taro, ginger, and tobacco. Apa Tani rice agriculture is so productive that in most years they not only provide handily for themselves but have a surplus available for trade. In the two qualities of stability and prosperity they are unique among the peoples of NEFA.

Despite their focus on agriculture and their success with it, the Apa Tani also need and value certain domestic animals—mithan, pigs, and chickens—for sacrifice and for flesh. Mithan are also important as an indicator of wealth and as a means of purchasing other goods, land above all. The Apa Tani, in the pattern of other NEFA peoples, make no use of the mithan for draft, in agriculture or otherwise, nor do they milk them.

The small and thickly settled valley affords little opportunity for expanding animal husbandry. Chickens, it is true, can be turned loose to scavenge in the village during the daytime, but the other animals would cause serious damage to the fields. Thus, pigs are always confined beneath the houses, and mithan are kept outside the valley.

Because of the limitations of their man-made environment, the Apa Tani turn to nearby Dafla and Hill Miri to supplement the small number of animals they themselves can raise. An interesting and mutually beneficial economic relationship has developed among these three groups with such different ways of life. The Dafla and Hill Miri, as shifting cultivators, are frequently short of grain. Yet their settlements are widely scattered; and vast forested areas, ideal for mithan browsing, are at their disposal. The system of trade that has evolved entails the barter of surplus Dafla and Hill Miri animals for surplus Apa Tani rice. Pigs are important in this trade. Sometimes common cattle and, rarely, goats also enter into it. Most important, however, are mithan.

The Mithan among the Apa Tani
Numbers and Care

The Apa Tani were estimated to have between two and three thousand mithan in 1945. Most Apa Tani mithan are owned by individuals. A few, however, are owned jointly by a village or clan, to be used for sacrifices that will benefit the entire group. Whatever their ownership, mithan are never at large in the valley and seldom in the villages. Though there is usually some clan-owned grazing land near each village, mithan are kept there, tethered with long ropes of hide, only for a short while before sale or slaughter. The main grazing grounds owned by the village or a group of clans within a village are often a day's journey or more from the valley, ordinarily in small forested river valleys where the mithan will have the dampness and shade they prefer to open sunny pasture. If a natural salt lick occurs near the grazing grounds, the Apa Tani have little fear that the animals will stray far afield. Mithan remain untended in their grazing grounds for most of their lives, feeding in the forest singly or in small groups rather than in large herds. The Apa Tani make no effort to control their breeding in any way.

Theft of mithan by the Dafla and Hill Miri whose country often adjoins the far-flung grazing grounds is common practice and a constant source of trouble. Some Apa Tani avoid this by placing their animals in the care of a Dafla or Miri, who keeps them with his own animals reasonably close to his village, since his jhum fields are usually fenced. As compensation, he is given one calf of every three or four born.

The Apa Tani also keep a few common cattle of the Assamese plains breed. Though they fill the same roles that mithan do, common cattle are regarded as less valuable. Like mithan, they are given a minimum of attention. They are not herded. They remain outdoors day and night throughout the year. In spring and summer, they graze in pasture not far from the villages, on the edge of the valley. Both rice and millet fields near the pastures are fenced to keep animals out and to prevent the cattle from finding their way to the unfenced rice terraces in the center of the valley. In winter, when the grass is gone, cattle feed on the stubble in the rice and millet fields. The manure they leave more than compensates for the damage they do to dams and terraces. Whatever the season, cattle remain in the open environment of the valley, their preferred habitat, rather than mixing with the mithan in the forest. Thus there is little hybridization between the two species. The hybrids that do turn up are considered, for ritual purposes, to be mithan.

In Economic, Social, and Political Life

In Land Acquisition

The greatest value of the mithan, supreme sacrificial animal for the Dafla, seems for the Apa Tani to be its economic role. Though in both societies only wealthy men own many mithan, the number of animals is not as important a measure of wealth for the Apa Tani as for the Dafla. Among the Apa Tani, whose economy depends on intensive agricultural utilization of land, ownership of land is the ultimate mark of both wealth and social status. Possessions other than land are valuable largely to the extent that they are useful in acquiring land. Pigs and cloth, for example, can be used to buy certain types of land, but most land transactions require cattle, particularly mithan. Indeed, in such transactions the prices are expressed in mithan.

An Apa Tani needs several kinds of land; cost, indicated in mithan, clearly shows the relative value of such land. Every man sooner or later obtains a site for his house, through inheritance or purchase. A good site fairly near the clan assembly platform in one of the main streets of the village costs about ten mithan. A place to build at least one granary, usually on the edge of the village, is worth half a mithan or one cow. Groves of cultivated bamboo to supply building and basket-making material are usually located on high ground near the village. They vary in size from a quarter of an acre to two acres. Often pines and fruit trees are planted in these groves and the entire grove is fenced and carefully tended. A large grove near a village could cost three mithan, a small grove farther up the hillside perhaps one mithan. The most valuable lands of the Apa Tani are the irrigated rice terraces, which produce the largest proportion of the food supply. Unless a man inherits a terrace or two, he has great difficulty in providing for his family. An average family of five or six persons needs from an acre and a half to two acres of good wet-rice land to meet its needs in rice. The cost of this of course depends in part on its location. One small terrace, half an acre in size, located in the main valley near a village, may cost ten mithan or more. Even smaller terraces in the main valley cost from two to five mithan. On the other hand, a half-acre terrace in a side valley, which does not hold water as well as terraces in the main valley, sells for only two or three mithan. The acreage needed for a family's rice thus could cost from twenty to fifty mithan.

Dry land, located at higher elevations, and garden plots are other desirable kinds of land. They are virtually the only kinds available to men poor in mithan. The dry land commonly is used for growing millet, though in some places higher land is irrigated and rice is grown. Apa Tani who cannot afford a terrace in the valley bottom depend on such fields for their supply of rice. It is impossible, however, to keep this land wet throughout the year, so rice yields are low and the land is much less valuable than the wet terraces in the lowest part of the valley. Plots of dry land average one or two mithan in cost, although very small ones can sometimes be bought for a pig or an Assamese silk cloth. The garden plots are located near the bamboo groves on the outskirts of the villages. They are the cheapest land, and are paid for in pigs, Tibetan swords, and cloths.

Until the late 1940's, when Apa Tani began going down to the Assamese plains to work as porters, agricultural laborers, and plantation help, it was practically impossible for a poor man to build up his landholdings. No one, rich or poor, could increase his lands without having on hand the mithan or cattle which were essential for the purchase of new land. The established way to obtain mithan was by the sale of surplus rice. For the man with only enough land to meet the needs of his family, there was little possibility of obtaining mithan. Some Apa Tani had insufficient land to feed themselves and had to work for wages (paid in goods, usually rice) for their wealthier neighbors just to subsist. Only men already holding enough land to produce more than their needs had a rice surplus. They exchanged it for mithan with which they could buy more land, raise more surplus, get more mithan, and again more land. This system tended to concentrate wealth among a few men and prevent the impoverished from ever owning land. It must not be overlooked, however, that the production of surplus rice, even given adequate land, was the result of constant effort. Negligence or indifference toward their fields could, and sometimes did, bring economic distress even to wealthy men.

The traditional situation sketched above has changed slowly since the 1940's as the Indian Government has extended its control over the hill areas. Increasingly, landless men go the plains, work for wages, buy calves (*Bos indicus*), and drive them home to the Apa Tani valley. There they can graze them in the clan-owned pastures and at last exchange the full-grown oxen for land.

In Marriage, Birth, and Death

Fürer-Haimendorf does not describe any birth or death ceremonies among the Apa Tani, and describes marriage arrangements only briefly. Contrasting this scarcity of information with the wealth of his other material on the Apa Tani, one surmises that they do not mark marriage, birth, and death with as notable ceremony as do other NEFA peoples.

The Apa Tani practice bride-price but the arrangements differ according to social class. Society, in addition to being divided into clans, consists of two classes: *mura,* slaves and their descendants; and *mite,* whom Fürer-Haimendorf calls patricians. Even though some slaves are virtually free and economically well off, they can never cross the line dividing patrician from slave. Because bride-price among patricians is not obligatory and property considerations are secondary, young people are allowed an almost completely free hand in choosing their mates. A patrician father is not concerned, as a Dafla would be, with extracting a bride-price for his daughters; he is interested primarily in seeing his sons established in their own houses and on their own land. It is true that after several years of marriage or at the approaching birth of a child, a prosperous young patrician sometimes will give his father-in-law some mithan as a bride-price for his wife. Still, there is no way for a father to collect this if the young husband is unwilling to make the gesture.

In the slave class the situation is quite different. The owner of a female slave and the owner of a male slave each has an investment at stake. When two slaves marry, they come to live in the clan quarter of the male slave's master. The master commonly pays a bride-price, the amount of which determines the fate of subsequent offspring. If he pays the female slave's full market price—one mithan, one cow, and a dao—then all of the slave couple's children belong to him. If he pays only a token bride-price, however, the male offspring belong to him and the female offspring to the owner of the female slave. In the latter case, there is a proviso that if the offspring are entirely males they will be divided between the owners of the slave couple. There are, in addition, further complications and possibilities in the marriage of people of the slave class, which we need not go into here. It is enough to note that in such marriages a bride-price—in which mithan are prominent—is more important than in patrician marriage. This is because questions of ownership are at stake in slave marriage, and mithan are recognized compensation for loss of private property.

Among patrician Apa Tani there usually is no wedding ceremony. After a couple agree to become man and wife they live for a while with the family of either bride or groom, until compatibility is assured. If during that time the pair decide to separate, they may. If a child is born after its parents separate, it goes to the father, taking his clan name, if a boy; to the mother, taking her clan name, if a girl. Should the couple decide that the marriage is satisfactory, they establish their own household. The groom's father generally gives him a house site in his clan quarter. The young man's friends and clansmen help him build his house. When it is ready to be occupied, a feast often is given for the clansmen of both partners. While a mithan or pig is generally killed at the feast, this is to provide meat, and is apparently without religious import. No religious ceremonies are connected with the feast, nor are omens taken from the slaughtered animal.

Though the Apa Tani expect an individual to marry outside of his clan, even in this they allow a certain freedom. On those rare occasions when a young man and woman of the same clan feel compelled to marry, they may do so, but they must sacrifice a mithan in atonement for their offense against custom. Such couples cannot remain in their own village, but can be accepted as man and wife in any other village where they can establish themselves.

Very wealthy or prominent families sometimes arrange the marriages of their children. In such cases greater formality is involved, and often there is an exchange of valuables—possibly including mithan—between the two families. The generally casual attitudes which have been reported toward sexual activity and procreation, along with the lack of reports on birth ceremonies, reinforce the conjecture that birth is not an occasion for great celebration involving mithan sacrifice or slaughter.

Though we have no descriptions of Apa Tani death ceremonies, certain related information is of significance to our understanding of the position of the mithan in Apa Tani life. The Apa Tani believe in two lands of the dead, Neli underground and Talimoko in the sky. Souls of people who die a natural death go to Neli, which looks just like an Apa Tani village, and existence continues there exactly as on earth. Rich men are rich. Poor men are poor. Slaves serve their former masters. All cultivate their fields and do their usual work. The cattle, including mithan, that a man sacrificed during his life on earth are waiting for him in Neli, but he has lost all claim to cattle bequeathed to his heirs on earth. Souls of people who die an unnatural death go to Talimoko. Though it is not an unhappy or un-comfortable place, existence there is not so closely modeled on the earthly situation. Souls from both lands of the dead return occasionally to the houses of men on earth. They are not welcome but neither are they feared; the Apa Tani do not worry about the influence that souls of their dead might have on the living (Fürer-Haimendorf, 1962: 145–46, 147). This attitude differs from the usual pattern in NEFA. Most NEFA peoples greatly fear the negative influence of departed souls which return to earth; and propitiation of them, if necessary including the offering of mithan, is common.

The ultimate goal of the Apa Tani is to win approval of their fellows and to gain a "favourable place within the social and economic system of this world." They make "no distinction between actions which are meri-torious within a system of supernatural values, and actions approved be-cause they are in conformity with tribal custom" (Fürer-Haimendorf, 1962: 150). Thus an Apa Tani, while on earth, works assiduously to cultivate his fields; to produce a surplus of rice, if possible; and to buy mithan and use them either in certain ceremonies which enhance his status or in buying more land, which results in the same end. If successful, he gains social position and respect, to be enjoyed now; and since he automatically occupies the same niche in the Land of the Dead as here—at least if he dies a natural death—he assures his happy existence there.

Settlement of Internal Disputes

Mithan are of great importance to the Apa Tani in matters of maintaining law and order, both among themselves and in trade relations with neighbors. Despite the need for harmony Apa Tani quarrel among themselves—usually over such questions as land transactions, trade agreements, default on debts, or situations reflecting on a man's honor or his position in the clan or village, rather than over women or bride-price.

Unless their disputes affect the peace of the entire community, individuals settle their differences themselves. The common pattern is for a quarrel to result in one of the disputants kidnapping a relative or dependent of the other disputant. This is done not in retribution but with the aim of collecting ransom, almost always mithan, for return of the person. The payment of the mithan not only frees the captured person but usually settles the issue.

Another method by which individuals settle their internal disputes is the *lisudu* (described by Fürer-Haimendorf, 1955: 73–76; 1962: 110–20), an institution unique to the Apa Tani. It is a ritual destruction of wealth, resorted to by wealthy, prestigeful men of approximately equal resources and of the same village, particularly when one feels his honor has been questioned. The injured man challenges the other to a contest in destroying wealth, of which mithan are the most important item, though other valuable property such as bronze plates and Tibetan swords is sometimes destroyed too (see pp. 175–76). The slaughtered mithan are left where they fall, and the other villagers eat the meat. The winner greatly enhances his position in the community, partly by the public humiliation of his enemy, partly by publicly demonstrating the number of mithan he can destroy without bringing economic ruin on himself, and partly by the distribution of some of his wealth—the flesh of the slaughtered animals.[1]

When men from different Apa Tani villages become embroiled in disagreement, another formalized contest, the *gambu,* is possible. This involves numbers of men from each village, and is essentially a controlled battle staged to reduce tensions between the two villages without inflam-

1. This competitive destruction of wealth, as Fürer-Haimendorf notes, has certain parallels with the potlatch of the Northwest Coast Indians of North America. See Appendix A for comparison of the lisudu with the potlatch of the Kwakiutl Indians.

ing the whole valley. There are rules and limits to the damage allowed. Animals are not involved, so the details of the gambu do not concern us here. In none of these highly formalized methods of settling problems is ceremony or ritual involved. Fürer-Haimendorf points out that after the mock battle, the gambu, which nonetheless is fought with real weapons and sometimes results in loss of life, there is no need to reaffirm the old dapo between the two villages, nor do the kinsmen of the slain find it necessary to seek revenge (1962: 119).

Fines as a means of keeping internal order seem not to be important. When misdeeds cannot be satisfactorily settled by one of the above methods by the individuals involved, and a broader disruption threatens, the clan representatives are prevailed upon to act. Their action always reflects the opinion of the group and applies only to the current situation. Sometimes they decide that the affair must be settled by the individuals and they hand the problem back. First offenders often are looked upon as a nuisance; at the repetition of an offense, a person may have to pay compensation. Habitual offenders, especially in crimes that violate property rights, usually are executed if the group agrees.

A ceremony of interest in this context is the Ropi rite (Fürer-Haimendorf, 1955: 46–48, 72, 171–72; 1962: 126, 136, 144–46). Though regularly associated with the ritual burial of enemies killed in raids or in war against outsiders, it also is performed when the Apa Tani execute a criminal from among themselves. When they kill enemies in war or in raids, they try to take a hand, the eyes, and the tongue of the slain, and bring them back to the village for burial. The trophies are kept in the ritual center until the Ropi rite is performed. At the rite the hand is burned, and the remains of it buried near the ritual center. The eyes and tongue are buried, too, without burning. By burying these organs, particularly the eyes, the Apa Tani believe they will prevent the slain person from seeing or wreaking vengeance on the ones who killed him. In addition, at the burial places, which are marked with stones, pleas are made to the victim to leave his slayers alone. Apparently animal sacrifice, too, is usually part of the ceremony. Fürer-Haimendorf mentions that at a Ropi rite held after a successful raid the animal killed is offered to a pair of gods associated with war.

Whether the purpose of the Ropi rite held after the execution of an Apa Tani criminal also is mainly to guard against the wrath of the slain person is not clear from the literature. It seems a reasonable assumption, although in the details of the execution itself a strong element of punishment is evident. At the execution of a habitual Apa Tani thief, who in this case was a patrician, the executioners "cut off the hands, 'with which he had stolen,' slashed him over the eyes, 'with which he had spied out other men's cattle,' and over the mouth 'with which he had eaten stolen goods' " (Fürer-Haimendorf, 1955: 171–72). On this occasion the entire body was burned, though one hand was taken to another village, some of whose men were involved in the affair. Nine days later the Ropi rite was performed in the village where the execution took place. A mithan, bought with public contributions, was sacrificed, and the village men danced and chanted as if they were celebrating a battle victory in which an enemy had been killed. There is no mention of burying the remains of the body.

In another case the habitual thief who was executed was a slave girl; her body, cut in pieces, was thrown into the Kele River along with her clothes and ornaments; and what Fürer-Haimendorf calls a "nominal" Ropi ceremony was held. The explanation given Fürer-Haimendorf was that a Ropi had to be held because the girl had been held captive at her master's assembly platform just as an enemy would have been. Apparently the ceremony varies under different circumstances, and possibly the social status of the person executed influences the elaborateness of the rite or the kind of animal to be sacrificed.

Settlement of Disputes with Other Groups

Kidnapping and ransoming, the usual means of settling internal disputes, are also sometimes employed by Apa Tani against Dafla. Occasionally such kidnapping is attempted not to settle disputes but as an additional way (besides the established one of producing surplus rice) of acquiring mithan, which are then used for buying land. One Apa Tani bought three terraces of wet-rice land for twenty mithan, nine of which he had collected as ransom for Dafla prisoners. Kidnapping Dafla to gain mithan to buy land holds little promise for ordinary Apa Tani however, because the risk of being taken captive one's self is so great. Usually only rich Apa Tani dare to make such raids, secure in the knowledge that if they themselves are captured, their relatives will be able to ransom them and will not permit them to become slaves.

Dafla capture of Apa Tani and theft of their cattle and mithan is common. The mithan, unguarded in the forest, are easy prey. The Apa Tani themselves are also fairly easy prey when they leave the valley to hunt, to trade, or to collect their mithan. Theft of common cattle, which remain near the villages, is notably less common.

Some of the kidnapping the Dafla do probably results from their knowledge of Apa Tani attitudes. The Apa Tani do not admire ruthlessness or violent action so much as industry, business sense, skill at negotiation, and peaceful settlement of disputes (Fürer-Haimendorf, 1962: 148). In addition, they are very sensitive about prestige and honor; and ransoming a captive, whether a kinsman or a mithan, is a question of honor as much as of concern for the fate of the prisoner. In one case the ransom paid for one mithan cow was "one mithan calf, one large pig, one brass plate, two cloths and one sword," plus fees to the Dafla mediators of "four cloths, eight pounds of salt and one brass cup," and "one axe and twelve pounds of salt" to the Apa Tani go-between (Fürer-Haimendorf, 1955: 43). This far exceeded the market value of the mithan, and indicates the prestige value of these animals. Moreover, to leave them in the hands of Dafla, the Apa Tani say, would offend the spirits.

Ransom proceedings are protracted and usually follow an established pattern. Dafla who capture an Apa Tani make no secret of their identity. The family of the prisoner obtains the services of an Apa Tani go-between, who contacts friends among the Dafla; the friends guarantee his safety, prepare the way for negotiations, and assist in conducting them. The go-between and his helpers are all specialists in such matters and are paid for their services by the kinsmen of the prisoner. They handle the entire affair, including handing over the ransom. The ransoms asked are as high as the captors think the traffic will bear. Thus the go-between's first job is to reduce the price as far as possible without a breakdown in the proceedings. The ransom finally paid is usually high, commonly involving at least one or two mithan as well as numerous additional items such as Tibetan swords, brass plates, hoes, daos, cloth, and salt. The fees of negotiators are never as high as one mithan, but are made up of combinations of less valuable articles.

The Relationship of Trade and Ransom

Much of the raiding and ransoming between Apa Tani and Dafla derives from the very trade upon which both depend. To assure the safety of traders as they take their goods to the village of a potential buyer, trade partnerships are established on a village level—between specific Apa Tani villages and specific Dafla or Hill Miri villages (Map 4). These reciprocally guarantee a trader security when visiting the partner village. An Apa Tani trader will normally visit only those Dafla or Hill Miri villages with which his village has such partnerships. A visit to another village would upset the carefully balanced economic system and bring upon him the wrath of other Apa Tani into whose territory he is intruding.

The quarrels that develop from trade normally are confined to the two individual traders, supported perhaps by some members of their clans. Even if an entire Apa Tani clan is drawn into the dispute, people in the village who are not members of that clan can continue trading. The Dafla, on their side, rarely act together as a village. Thus it is very unusual for an entire Apa Tani village to be pitted against an entire Dafla village. An avenue of contact normally remains open through which some trading and negotiation can proceed.

The main trade, as we have said, is in Dafla animals—mithan and pigs —for Apa Tani rice. A Dafla wanting rice usually comes himself to the house of an Apa Tani, often bringing a mithan with him. If satisfactory terms are arranged, the mithan is paid at once and the Dafla carries away his grain. If either party subsequently considers himself cheated, trouble will follow. Some difficulties arise from the guarantees of protection. Many quarrels between Apa Tani and Apa Tani result from real or imagined wrongs suffered by a Dafla trader while under Apa Tani protection. Trouble also springs from the Apa Tani practice of advancing rice on credit to individual Dafla. Sometimes so much rice is advanced that the Dafla, unable to pay, agrees to work out the debt and becomes a bond servant to the Apa Tani. Often a Dafla in such straits will break the agreement and escape. Then he may retaliate for the indignities to which he has been subjected, by raiding his former master and taking a mithan or even capturing a kinsman to hold for ransom. The Apa Tani may lose not only the grain he originally advanced but several mithan as well. He in his turn tries to recover his losses by kidnapping a relative of the debtor, for whose release he demands mithan and other goods in excess of the original debt. The entire trading relationship creates a peculiar situation which is always delicately poised between truce and open hostility, the boundaries continually expanding and narrowing. The trade that is vital to both sides produces situations that repeatedly threaten to bring it to a standstill.

Once in a while an Apa Tani makes individual trade arrangements with a Dafla or Miri. This is an unusual undertaking for the Apa Tani— though not for the Dafla, whose people depend in large measure on individual alliances for their security. When such an arrangement is made between an Apa Tani and a Dafla, a certain amount of ceremony, in Dafla tradition, is required, and the pact is sealed by an exchange of mithan and the pledge of the participants to assist each other as much as possible and to avenge the other's death. In general, however, trade is looked on by the Apa Tani as simply a matter of economic gain in which ritual has no part.

In their trade, the Apa Tani and the Dafla each have a table of values to express the prices of the goods they exchange. Fürer-Haimendorf only mentions the Dafla table, but he discusses the Apa Tani table in detail. It consists of standardized units, each designated with a word, and each made up of the same several items. For example one *pachu,* the smallest unit described, is the value of two eggs or one small chicken or one day's wages. One *paroe* is equal to one medium-sized chicken or one knife or seven pounds of unhusked rice. One *puliang*, the largest unit, is equal to one new, large Tibetan sword or ten baskets (of a certain size) of unhusked rice. Not only can the price of almost any article be clearly expressed, but fluctuations in price, which are common, are simple to state. An item offered for sale might be priced at two pachu today in one village and three tomorrow in a distant village. Changes in the supply and demand for rice cause considerable fluctuations in price. In years of good harvest the Dafla have little need of Apa Tani grain; in poor years, when demand increases, so does the price. Ordinarily a full-grown mithan cow would bring about eighty baskets of unhusked rice: eight puliang in the value table. When rice is scarce, the same animal might bring as little as half that (Fürer-Haimendorf, 1962: 48, 52).

It is curious that although the price of a mithan can be quoted in puliang, mithan as a unit of value are not included in the table used in ordinary trade. Mithan, as shown above, however, are regularly exchanged in land transactions and in payment of ransom—two of the Apa Tani's greatest expenditures. In these activities, which consume the greatest part of Apa Tani attention and purchasing power, a separate system of values prevails. In that system, values and prices are both expressed and paid in mithan. Details of the system are not presented in the literature so its exact functioning remains to be clarified. It is clear, however, that land and ransom prices sometimes are expressed not simply in numbers of mithan but in a unit termed a "mithan-value." Fürer-Haimendorf suggests (1962: 19) that one small bull mithan is equal to one mithan-value; he explicitly writes (108) that one full-grown mithan cow equals about five mithan-values.

In Religion

Religion, Fürer-Haimendorf acknowledges, is the aspect of Apa Tani life he had least opportunity to look into, and one which needs much more intensive study. His sketch, however, clearly shows that the sacrifice of animals—including mithan—is an important element in religious practice.

Like the Dafla, the Apa Tani believe in the existence of a variety of supernatural beings, differing in their characteristics and powers, who can affect the welfare of man. Many are paired, one male and one female being worshiped or appealed to together. The supernatural beings are reached through the mediation of priests and seers. Some deities are appealed to by individuals and some by groups such as a raiding party or an entire village or sometimes two allied villages.

One large group of related deities, called Hilo deities, was responsible for the creation of man and still relate to him in various ways. They are the object of individual appeal. One pair of Hilo deities, who live in the hills, protects man, his crops, and his "cattle," presumably including mithan. To these deities, individuals offer sacrifices of chickens, pigs, and "cattle" once a year. Another Hilo pair, who live near the Apa Tani villages, can make people wise and restrained—qualities of high value in Apa Tani society; to them, each household monthly offers animals, which may be chickens, dogs, pigs, or "cattle." Still other Hilo deities are responsible for bringing on illness, at which time individuals propitiate them.

Before going out on a raid a ceremony is conducted in which a dog, a pig, or a mithan is offered to the paired deities associated with war. They are promised additional sacrifices if the raid is successful. Still another pair of deities is able to help captives escape. They are also appealed to when a mithan is stolen; the owner sacrifices a chicken and urges them to help the mithan break loose and return to its grazing grounds.

The only times that sacrificial rites are accompanied by public festivities are at certain annual celebrations. The two greatest of these are the Morom and the Mloko. The Morom, performed by each village every year, is held shortly before cultivation starts, in January or February. It contains elements that suggest it is a fertility rite associated with agriculture. Two other aspects of the ceremony besides its fertility connotations are important. It serves to affirm Apa Tani unity. All the young men and boys of the village holding the ceremony form a procession led by a priest, and spend the day visiting all the other villages in the valley. In each they are presented with rice beer and snacks of food. Because, in the procession, the village acts as a unit, village ties are emphasized; the visit to all the villages also demonstrates the basic unity of all Apa Tani. The other aspect of the ceremony is the performance of individual rites by wealthy men to enhance their prestige. These rites terminate in the slaughter of mithan. The meat is distributed throughout the village or valley without regard to the rank or status of the recipient. All share equally. The donor of such a feast gains in social prestige for having given private wealth for the public good. There are certain parallels between the individual rites held during the Apa Tani Morom and the Feasts of Merit of the Assam-Burma border peoples, which will be discussed in connection with the Naga and Chin. The Apa Tani donor's distribution of sacrificial meat to all members of the group substantially strengthens the feeling of group solidarity. Nothing like this exists among the Dafla, for whom security rests almost exclusively upon individual alliances. When Dafla practice a ritual exchange of goods, the benefits are limited solely to the participants and their families.

The Mloko festival, held after the Morom, in March or April, probably also is basically intended to assure the fertility of the land before planting.

It also contributes to the idea of the oneness and interdependence of the Apa Tani. Each year one of the three groups of linked villages holds it: Hang one year, Bela and Hari the next, and the four western villages the third year. Though the clans of the celebrating villages make their sacrifices—chickens, dogs, and pigs—separately, with their own priests officiating, the ritual is for the welfare of the people in general. The one group of villages is host to the other two; and guests are provided with an abundance of rice beer and flesh by friends in the host village. In addition, there is a formalized giving of gifts, mainly shares of the sacrificial meat, which in this ceremony is mostly pork. This giving is regulated by tradition, with the sections of the villages performing the Mloko providing meat to specific sections of other villages with whom they have ceremonial ties. Obligations are mutual, and the receiving villages return gifts according to the same pattern when they hold the Mloko.

It seems extraordinary that a people so involved with agriculture do not mark with ceremony more activities associated with the agricultural year. Not even the rice harvest is celebrated in public ceremony. It is marked only by individuals, who, in their own homes, sacrifice a pig when they partake of the first of the late-ripening variety of rice which forms the bulk of the crop.

There are suggestions in the literature that mithan are killed and their flesh eaten on other occasions than such social and religious ones as are mentioned above. Fürer-Haimendorf reports that the Apa Tani believe that mithan are meant to be eaten (1962: 117), but it seems they are not just summarily killed and consumed when someone would like a feast. Apparently there must always be a special reason. J. P. Mills, writing of a 1945 tour of their country, describes a feast that he gave for the Apa Tani. Two mithan were killed and the meat distributed to the seven villages, but, he noted, "to the Apa Tani a mithan is far too important an animal to be casually slaughtered, and . . . the priest had first to recite the correct incantations" (Mills, 1947: 28). The recitation took half an hour. From his gestures Mills concluded that the priest was asking the blessings of the sky, the mountains, and the fields. Fürer-Haimendorf was a participant in a similar ceremony in 1944 (1955: 87–88). He was then an employee of the Government of India, and his primary job was to establish friendly relations with both the Apa Tani and the Dafla and to bring about peace between them. At that time both groups were little known, and the Dafla had a reputation as unremitting looters and murderers. Fürer-Haimendorf succeeded first in winning over the Apa Tani. They then willingly supported him in his efforts with the Dafla, since they would be the first to benefit from any curbing of Dafla depredations. Two Apa Tani villages contributed a communally owned mithan for sacrifice to confirm Apa Tani loyalty to him. A priest addressed the mithan about its impending death, telling it among other things that it was to die for a "worthy cause—the strengthening of the friendship between the Apa Tanis and Government," and that it should not object to being sacrificed, because "the gods had given the Apa Tani mithan for slaughter." When the animal finally was killed, the meat was divided and distributed to all the households of the two villages, and a share was given to Fürer-Haimendorf.

Fowl, dogs, pigs, common cattle, and mithan are all used by the Apa Tani for sacrifice. For many ceremonies, particularly those to resolve the crises of individuals, the smaller animals are sufficient. For others, a choice is possible between smaller and larger animals. For some ceremonies the pig is obligatory; for others the mithan is required.

The pig rivals the mithan as a sacrificial animal and in other ways among the Apa Tani. For eating, for example, pork is more prized than mithan flesh. Each year hundreds of pigs are acquired from the Dafla and Hill Miri in trade. Fürer-Haimendorf comments that the demand for pigs at the time of the Mloko is as great as the demand for turkeys in England at Christmas (1962: 48). The pig, however, is of minimal value in the acquisition of land, the supreme goal of the Apa Tani; it is of little if any importance in ransom payments; and in the ceremonies performed by individuals to enhance their prestige it plays no part. These are the prerogatives of the mithan.

Recent Changes in Apa Tani Life

In 1962 Fürer-Haimendorf returned to the Subansiri, which he had not visited for seventeen years. There were many changes, but the basic pattern of life remained essentially the same. Ownership of land and cattle still confer the highest prestige. The Apa Tani still skillfully cultivate their terraces and fields in the old way, rejecting attempts to introduce the plow and animal traction. They still produce a surplus of rice, although agriculture is probably not as profitable as it was formerly. This is because landowners now compete with other employers and must pay cash wages to their help. Dafla continue to be important customers for rice, but now they often pay in cash rather than in mithan.

A fundamental change in the Apa Tani–Dafla trade has also come about. The Apa Tani, who used to buy practically all their livestock from the Dafla, now sell livestock to them. Taking advantage of the motor road from North Lakhimpur to their valley, the Apa Tani have developed a lively trade in Assamese cattle. They buy the cattle cheaply in the plains and drive them fairly easily on the road up into the hills, and find a good market among the Dafla. At the same time, mithan prices have undergone a striking inflation. Mithan in 1962 cost up to 1,000 rupees, almost ten times their cost in 1944–45.

In matters of law and order, many old practices that contribute to the traditional stability of Apa Tani society and do not conflict with Government administrative policy continue as of old. The lisudu is an example, and still is employed for settling certain kinds of disputes.

8

The Adi

Until about 1960 the designation Abor was commonly used to refer loosely to the hill tribes found in the area between the Subansiri River on the west and the Dibang River on the east. The word Abor is slowly dropping out of use. Replacing it, for the tribes concentrated along the Siang River, of Siang Frontier Division, and its two main tributaries, the Siyom and the Yamne, is Adi, the name the people themselves prefer. Sachin Roy, Cultural Research Officer in NEFA in the late 1950's, distinguishes fifteen Adi groups. In this chapter attention will be focused on two: the Padam and Minyong, who together in 1961 numbered about 26,500 people, of a total Adi population of about 72,000.

The Adi conform generally in physical appearance to the Mongoloid type found elsewhere in NEFA. Although the language of the broader Adi group still awaits detailed study, Sachin Roy says that it is rich in dialects, of which he considers Padam, Minyong, Pasi, Pangi, and Gallong the most important. Another dialect, spoken in three villages of Milan Adi along the upper Yamne, differs conspicuously from the others and includes words which suggested to Dunbar a tie with Monba and Bhutia (1915: 10, 11).

By their own traditions the Adi tribes came to their present settlements from the north, perhaps from beyond the Himalayas. Several Adi groups name places in Tibet as their original home. Roy (1960: 258–63) questions a Tibetan origin, however, because many Adi culture traits show closer ties with cultures south of the Brahmaputra than with Tibetan culture. He defines a culture-shed that runs south of the Himalayas but parallel to them, from Lohit Frontier Division westward to the Bhorelli River, where it bends southward. North and west of this line, Tibetan cul-

Source: This chapter is based mainly on G. D.-S. Dunbar, 1915, and S. Roy, 1960.

ture is dominant. South of it, well into the hills across the Brahmaputra, there is a cultural pattern, to which the Adi belong, that contrasts sharply with Tibetan culture.

The terrain of the Adi homeland is essentially like the rest of NEFA, rough hills and mountains. Typically the lower and middle elevations are covered by evergreen subtropical forest and the higher elevations by alpine vegetation. The Siang River (commonly called Dihang in much of the early literature) cuts through Adi country from north to south, dividing it roughly in half. Adi settlements are located mainly along the Siang and its two major tributaries. In the middle course of the Siang, settlement is greater on the western bank. East of the river steep slopes rise to the high ranges, 10,000 to 14,000 feet in elevation; on the western bank more land is in gentle slope.

The three considerations in determining Adi village sites traditionally were access to water, availability of land for cultivation, and ease of defense. Most villages thus were located near a source of water, whether a river, stream, or spring, but well up on hill slopes or on the tips of spurs. The floors of river valleys were avoided. If a site otherwise suitable lacked a nearby source of water, the Adi constructed aqueducts of bamboo tubes, sometimes bringing water a considerable distance. When the natural defenses were not adequate, they fortified villages with barriers of boulders and tree trunks.

Adi villages, in contrast to most others in NEFA with the exception of the Apa Tani, contain many houses and have large populations. The larger Minyong villages, according to Fürer-Haimendorf (1954: 588), have from 250 to 450 houses. Dunbar found a notable difference in the size of Adi villages from south to north; in the south, near the plains of Assam, they contained only 20 to 50 houses; in the north, at higher elevations, they had 160 or more houses (1915: 33). Sachin Roy gives the population of the largest villages at over 2,000 persons (1960: 129).

Adi houses are similar to those of other NEFA peoples: raised bamboo structures with steep thatched roofs. The Adi are generally monogamous; each house usually shelters a man, his wife, and their children. Like the Naga tribes to the south of the Brahmaputra but unlike the NEFA peoples considered, the Adi have a well established system of bachelors' dormitories. These dormitories and Adi customs associated with marriage modify the pattern of house occupancy. Each village has a dormitory, the *moshup* or *bange,* usually located in the heart of the village where it can be guarded easily; boys start sleeping there rather than at home at about the age of ten. In Adi villages at upper elevations a girls' dormitory, *rasheng,* also is customary; its absence at lower elevations perhaps derives from the greater modification of traditional culture there. Where the rasheng occurs, young girls spend their nights there, and continue to do so until they settle on the young man whom they will marry. Then the girl returns home to receive her betrothed. She remains in her father's house, the young man visiting her there in the evenings and finally staying the night, until the first child has been born. At that time the husband usually builds a house, establishing a new household. If he is unable to do this, he enters into an arrangement with his parents-in-law to render them certain services (see pp. 86–88). This arrangement almost always ends with the birth of the third child, and the couple move into their own house.

Each Adi village is autonomous, strong in communal feeling, and governed by a village council, the *kebang*. Major and minor problems are directed to the council rather than being settled by individuals. In addition, the council plays a dominant role in directing village activities according to tradition, and punishes individuals who stray from the correct path.

The members of the village council are chosen by the villagers. Some of them are simply men of proven ability. Others are *gams* ("headmen"), each of whom ordinarily represents a clan. Neither the position of gam nor a place on the council is hereditary. According to Dunbar, men must campaign for the position of gam, and in doing so they incur expenses. The greatest of these is a series of feasts—consisting of mithan flesh and rice beer—that demonstrate the donor's generosity and his wealth, important requisites for a man who might one day have to entertain visitors. A year after his first feast, the candidate holds a second one. At that time someone gives a speech praising the donor. If the man wins the election, and if he can afford to do so, he gives a third feast. Dunbar notes that though such feasting counts with the villagers, it is still more important for the candidate's philosophy to coincide with the needs and interests of his group; if the gam should also obtain a seat on the village council, his constituents want to be sure that their views will be forcefully and effectively presented (Dunbar, 1915: 39; S. Roy, 1960: 116, 222–23).

In addition to deciding such community matters as the assignment of trail building and fence mending, the council hears cases of alleged wrongdoing. Usually all its decisions are accepted as final; no special village body exists to enforce them. The allotted work is done, and fines and punishments accepted without further question. What little enforcement activity is required falls to the boys and young men staying in the dormitories.

The organization of the boys in the dormitory illustrates another facet of Adi democracy. In the dormitory they divide themselves into groups, called *merums*, by choosing to sit at one or another of the fireplaces there. The merums, or fireplace associations, are entered into freely, without regard to clan or neighborhood. They result in relationships in which friendship and loyalty are important elements. One activity at the merum level is the dissemination of council decisions to the village. A boy from each merum carries word of the decisions to every other member of his merum; in this way the whole village is quickly informed of important events. Certain community work is assigned by merum, and rights to hunting grounds are held by merum.

To settle intervillage problems, Adi villages are grouped into units, each unit under the jurisdiction of an intervillage council. Should a dispute break out between two intervillage councils, there is a still higher though temporary body, the Bogum Bokang, instituted by the Indian Government to settle affairs at that level.

The Adi are shifting cultivators. They confine their cultivation to hillsides under about 6,000 feet in elevation. They employ a block system of cultivation, under which all cultivators of a village utilize contiguous fields within a block. The village at any one time may have two or three such blocks under cultivation, with the balance lying fallow, for the blocks are cultivated in rotation according to a strictly followed cycle. Clearing of a new block of land is a village undertaking, though each family works on its own land. After sowing is finished by each family, the fields are fenced, another community project. In some places, fencing is so extensive that whole hillsides are enclosed, and ladders are kept at intervals to permit entry to the area.

For the Adi, rice is the most important crop, and then Job's tears (*Coix lacryma-jobi*). Other important grains are finger millet, foxtail millet (*Setaria italica*), and maize. In addition to these field crops, several types of vegetable are grown in gardens, and fruit trees are common. The dao and digging stick are the implements used in clearing and planting. The plow was not a traditional implement of the Adi, though Sachin Roy (1960: 160) indicates that common cattle are being reared in the lower Adi Hills for plowing. Neither terracing nor irrigation is practiced.

The Adi hunt and trap both small and large animals to supplement food obtained by other means. Hunting is undertaken by individuals and by groups. Fishing is also important, and fish are looked on as a great delicacy.

The domestic animals of the Adi include mithan, pigs, chickens, dogs, and recently—especially in the lower parts of the Adi Hills—a few goats and common cattle. The mithan is by far the most important. It is the obligatory sacrifice at several religious and social ceremonies. It is the measure of a man's wealth and status. It is used as a medium of exchange, though not for bride-price. It is an important trade item. It is used to some extent for paying fines. And it is commonly needed for treaty settlements. Mithan are not normally killed simply to provide a supply of meat, but when they are killed, usually for sacrifices at various festivals and ceremonies, they are eaten with relish. Contrary to the usual pattern among the NEFA peoples, Adi priests may not eat the flesh of animals sacrificed at ceremonies over which they preside. Like Dafla priests, however, they are paid according to an established schedule of fees depending on the sacrifice offered; and for a mithan sacrifice the fee is a share of the meat. The literature is silent on what they do with this meat.

Pigs, chickens, and dogs are also sacrificial animals. After they are sacrificed, the pig and, in certain ceremonies, the chicken are eaten. The flesh of dogs, on the other hand, is not eaten. Goats and common cattle, both more numerous in areas near lowland Assam and only recently kept at all, are never used in sacrifice.

The Adi milk neither mithan nor common cattle. To the far north, however, the Ramo and Bokar—both Adi peoples—keep yaks and female dzo, the yak/common cattle hybrids, and have learned from their neighbors the Monba to milk them. The two peoples also make and use butter.

The Mithan among the Adi
Care

Adi mithan range freely most of the year in the nearby forest. There is no system of herding and no confinement of mithan. To protect their fields the Adi construct fences around them. Although the animals are owned by individuals, most mithan of a village graze together in roughly the same area. For identification, each owner cuts or punches the earlobes of his animals. The mithan know his voice, appearing when he calls them from a regular place and periodically dispenses salt to them. The salt tie is an important one, permitting the owner to collect his mithan readily when they are needed for some purpose.

When mithan are brought into the village, they are tied in a covered space at the front of their owner's house, and fodder gathered in the forest is fed to them. Generally mithan are in the village only when a man wants to sell or give away an animal or offer one for sacrifice, or for certain annual festivals in which protection of mithan is a prominent feature.

At one of these, the Luttor Solung (described on pp. 95–96), all mithan are brought in from the forest and confined at their owners' houses. Fürer-Haimendorf (1954: 597) reports that the Minyong Adi earmark their mithan at that time. Dunbar (1915: 81–82), however, found the earmarking done at another annual mithan festival which he called Asho

Agam, held in connection with community fence mending. Sachin Roy (1960: 132–33) describes a similar festival, the Ettor, also held at the time of fencing, at which "stock taking" of the mithan is done; this may include earmarking of new animals.

Mithan are subject to various diseases, and the Adi make an effort to cure animals which become afflicted. Sachin Roy describes three common ills and their treatment. For a hoof disease, which is aggravated by the bites of flies and other insects, the Adi keep the mithan standing in water. A disease of the mouth and tongue, which prevents the mithan from eating and may result in its starving to death, is treated by applying a mixture of ginger paste and salt to the sores; or the animal is hand-fed its usual feed, which is wrapped in *siie* leaves. The only symptom of the third disease is loss of weight. A paste of ginger, siie leaf, and salt is fed to the sick mithan along with its usual food; or sometimes ginger wrapped in a siie leaf is hung on its neck (S. Roy, 1960: 152).

In Economic, Social, and Political Life

Economic Uses of Mithan

The Adi, in keeping with the usual pattern in the Assam hills, do not utilize their mithan to the fullest extent possible. Besides not being milked, they are not used for packing or draft. The meat, when available after sacrifices, is enjoyed, especially when boiled with salt and chilli. The blood is not utilized as a separate item, because the usual way of killing mithan is by strangulation (see below, p. 179). The hide is used only in a limited way: sometimes for sword and dao slings; in the high country occasionally to cover shields; and very occasionally by the Gallong for hats.

The mithan serves as an indicator of a man's wealth and status. The size of a man's mithan herd is one measure of his wealth. A second measure is the number of horns and skulls of sacrificed mithan, together with those of sacrificed pigs and trophies of the chase, displayed on the front wall of the porch found on most Adi houses. In addition, the mithan themselves are assets of great value in economic affairs.

Though the literature is too scanty to generalize on the trade of the Adi or define the place of the mithan in it, a few details of interest are available. Dunbar (1915: 8) found a trade divide running from east to west across the Adi country, similar to the one discussed by Fürer-Haimendorf for Subansiri Division. North of about latitude 28° 15′ trade items come into the area from the north. South of that latitude is a strip where goods come from both north and south; and south of that, goods come from the south, including, however, Tibetan goods that have been traded down to Assam through the Mishmi country. The Bori and Bokar

Adi in the far northwest of Siang Division trade directly with Tibetans in Tibet. The Bori barter raw hides and chillies for Tibetan rock salt, woolen cloth and wool, Tibetan swords, metal bowls, and ornaments. The Bokar trade butter, as well as hides, chillies, and a plant material used in dyeing to the Tibetans. In return they get *dzo-mo* (female yak/common cattle hybrids), sheep, goats, and the usual woolen and metal goods. Bori and Bokar act as middlemen as well, bringing back additional quantities of salt and items of metal to trade to Adi south of them. Tibetans, too, cross into Siang Division, commonly through the Siang River gorge. They begin trading in the upper Siang area, coming sometimes as far south as Pasighat. In exchange for their goods they take back mithan, hides, deer horns, and rice (S. Roy, 1960: 32–33). Presumably the mithan are driven all the way back to Tibet.

Another trade route in the Adi country, not as important as the Siang route, is from the east in Mishmi country through the Aborka Pass southwest to Karko, on the middle Siang. The principal exchange is in Mishmi coats for mithan and rice. One Adi mithan will usually bring ten Mishmi coats (S. Roy, 1960: 33, 156).

Mithan serve not only as a trade item but as a pecuniary measure for the Adi. Roy divides the things they use "as money" into two categories: items of practical use, among which he includes domestic animals, skins of wild animals, and metal utensils; and items of decoration (S. Roy, 1960: 34), which presumably include beads, silver jewelry, copper bracelets, bronze bells, and metal charms. Of the domestic animals, mithan have the highest value and are used only in large transactions. Roy reported their value for 1948 as between 100 and 300 rupees, depending on the animal's rank in the Adi system of mithan grading. His information on the system came from villages of the Padam Adi. Grade I mithan, considered lucky mithan, have a forehead that is partly black and partly red or a muzzle that is always wet. Grade II mithan are somewhat undersized, but either have a good coat of hair or are completely black but with spots on both flanks and on the forehead. Grade III mithan are unlucky. They have scanty hair on the chest or are entirely white in color or are unusually thin. Of the metal utensils, the most valuable is a large Tibetan bowl cast of bell metal, called *danki*. One danki is worth one mithan (S. Roy, 1960: 34–35, 155–56).

In Marriage

The entire marriage system of the Adi is quite different from those of the other NEFA peoples. Adi boys and girls in the dormitories indulge in numerous amorous affairs until a couple decide to establish a permanent relationship. They may marry without the consent of their parents, though in practice this is unusual. Normally the boy informs his parents of his interest in a girl. If the proposed match is approved—which sometimes involves consultation with the clan elders—the boy's mother or an elderly woman approaches the girl's family with presents of rice beer, smoked squirrel, sometimes other meat, and ginger paste. The pair are considered engaged if the girl's family accepts the presents. From that time on, the boy begins spending the evening, and later, the entire night, with the girl at her parents' house. He remains, however, essentially a member of his father's household and continues working in his father's fields. The girl continues as a participating member of her family, too, helping in their fields and with the daily work in her parents' house. This basic arrangement usually continues until the first child is born, and the couple move into a house of their own (S. Roy, 1960: 203, 204, 208–9). No bride-price —such as other NEFA groups require—is set in terms of domestic animals, currency, or household property. At some time in the relationship, however, the young man enters into a formal arrangement with his wife's parents which obliges him to supply them with meat, though he still continues working in his own father's fields. The total amount of meat supplied depends upon the status of the girl's family and her own possessions, such as the number of valuable beads she owns. Sachin Roy (1960: 206) furnishes several examples of the young husband's obligations in provisions to his wife's family. He gives all of his share of fish caught in group fishing and half of what he gets on his own with a rod or with traps. He gives all of his portion of game obtained in a village hunt, but only a hind leg of animals he takes by himself. If he sacrifices a mithan, the upper part of the animal goes to his father-in-law. If the husband does not establish his own house when the first child is born, he continues to have certain obligations. These include service and supplying meat to his wife's family for as long as the girl remains in her father's house.

Adi men who marry wealthy girls, particularly those having beads to the value of fifteen mithan or more, are obliged to perform two ceremonies at some time after the marriage. Mithan figure in one, but both seem to focus on feasting, with the families of each partner participating, though the contribution of the groom's family is greater. The first ceremony must be held during a festival that takes place in February or March, when most of the community is feasting anyway; but the year in which the groom performs the ceremony is his choice and at his convenience. He accumulates a large amount of food, consisting of both cooked and uncooked rice, dried meat, smoked rats and squirrels, rice beer, flesh of at least two pigs, and a live mithan. He and his clansmen, with the food and the mithan, set out for the bride's house. The young men of her clan intercept them along the way. They hold a mock battle, but eventually the groom's party is allowed to pass. At the girl's house the women of her clan meet them with food and rice beer, which, however, is not given to them until they surrender their food and the mithan. The bride's parents also provide some pigs or a mithan, and a huge feast for both groups ensues. In the second obligatory ceremony, pigs but not mithan are offered to the bride's family (S. Roy, 1960: 206–7).

The above is the usual way Adi marriages are contracted. There are other acceptable ways of becoming married, including elopement. In all of them some compensation is made to the girl's family, but never do mithan figure in the marriage arrangements in the way they do elsewhere in NEFA.

In Birth and Death

A new baby in an Adi family causes slight distraction from the usual daily activities. No religious rites are associated with normal birth. Only if the delivery is difficult is an offering made to the spirit Nipong. This involves the sacrifice of fowl, pigs, and sometimes mithan (Dunbar, 1915: 57; S. Roy, 1960: 195–96). Usually, birth seems to be regarded as so natural and ordinary an occurrence that the occasion goes largely uncelebrated. There may be a feast for the children of the village if the parents have the means to provide it. Not even the naming of the child is celebrated. The arrival of the firstborn, however, raises the question of establishing a new household, and that is a more momentous occasion (S. Roy, 1960: 195).

The Adi look on death, at least a natural death coming at the end of the normal activities of a lifetime, as inevitable. They accept it without display of grief. Unduly early death through accident or disease is not accepted so easily, and appropriate deities and spirits are propitiated when necessary.

The Adi believe that their souls and those of their animals go to an afterworld. There the souls of humans are sorted out, each going to the realm of the spirit that was instrumental in the person's death. Existence in the afterworld is similar to life on earth. A man retains the same status and needs certain of his earthly material goods; hence many of his most cherished personal belongings are either buried with him or put on his grave (Dunbar, 1915: 76–77). Half of the display of mithan horns and relics of the hunt is removed from the front of his house and put on the grave; the remainder will go on his wife's grave (S. Roy, 1960: 66–67, 147). Sometimes imitations of such valuables as beads are substituted on the grave, and the real item is retained for the heirs (S. Roy, 1960: 211, 255). To sustain the dead person's soul, his family takes food and drink to his grave lest the hungry soul return to distress them. For about a week rice and rice beer are put daily in a small hut built on the grave; later only rice is put there. A fire is lighted on the grave and kept burning for a year for an ordinary person, and a year and twenty days for an important one (Dunbar, 1915: 75; S. Roy, 1960: 256).

At the time of a man's death, his nearest relative gives a feast for the people who dig the grave and come to the funeral. An animal belonging to the dead person is killed so that its soul will accompany his; some of its flesh is offered to his soul. The animal's soul and flesh together are believed to satisfy the soul of the man. The kind of animal sacrificed depends both on the importance of the person who has died and on the economic position of his near relatives. A mithan is offered for a man of prominence, a pig for most people, and chickens for those unable to provide more (Dunbar, 1915: 75; S. Roy, 1960: 255–56).

As the souls of men find different places in the afterworld, so do the souls of animals. Souls of mithan sacrificed at a funeral go to the soul of the dead person, but souls of animals sacrificed to propitiate specific spirits go to join the herds of those spirits. The same is true of animals, including mithan, found dead in the forest, since their death is believed to have been caused by spirits (S. Roy, 1960: 257). Dunbar (1915: 77) reported that the souls of animals eaten as food during a man's lifetime join his soul at his death. Since the Adi do, on a few occasions, kill an animal for a feast without religious ceremony, Dunbar's observation may well be correct. A man would have few mithan in the afterworld otherwise.

In Political Matters

The feasts of mithan flesh and rice beer given by candidates for headman while campaigning have already been mentioned (see p. 82). Both the intervillage councils and the highest council or Bogum Bokang, when in session, must be entertained with rice beer and the flesh of sacrificed mithan (S. Roy, 1960: 226–27). Village councils similarly are entertained with beer; and though Roy's statement is not specific, one infers that mithan flesh also is included, since mithan are sacrificed at that time (S. Roy, 1960: 225).

Fines are important in maintaining village peace and order. They frequently are measured in mithan, although pigs, beer, and food are commonly assessed for lesser infractions. The aim of charging fines is rather to compensate the victim of an antisocial action than to punish the perpetrator of the act. Several examples follow. In cases of assault and battery, the amount of the fine depends on the part of the body involved and the extent of the damage. For an impaired limb, either an arm or a leg, the maximum compensation is the current value of a mithan, but it may be less depending upon the degree of disability. For culpable homicide, the maximum fine is ten mithan to be paid to the heir (S. Roy, 1960: 231–32, 233). For cattle stealing the fine is in mithan, in proportion to the number of animals stolen (Dunbar, 1915: 59). Although divorce is fairly simple if both partners agree, adultery is a serious matter. The fines charged against the adulterous man are heavy. J. F. Needham, assistant political officer at Sadiya in 1886, gave the fines as from four to eight mithan, depending upon the circumstances. If the man is entirely at fault, the fine is six to eight mithan. If the woman is equally at fault, the man still has to pay, but only four mithan, and she is publicly humiliated (Elwin, 1959: 289). Traditionally, if the adulterer was unable to pay, he was sold into slavery (Dunbar, 1915: 58). The maximum fine for theft, according to Sachin Roy writing in 1959 (1960: 231), is the current market price of a pig in addition to restoring the stolen property or paying for it if restitution is not possible. Needham, for the much earlier date of 1886, reported that mithan constituted the fine for theft, the number depending upon the value of the property (Elwin, 1959: 289). Both Roy and Dunbar report that fines for murder are very heavy, but neither specifies amounts. The fines are paid to the family of the murdered person. In former times, before the Indian Government's efforts to limit slavery, if the murderer could not pay the fine he was sold as a slave and his price given to the victim's family.

A man who does not help in the burial of a clansman can be fined the market value of a mithan. Should he refuse to pay, a mithan or pig may be taken from him, by force if necessary (S. Roy, 1960: 232). Infringement of hunting rights carries a fine equal to the current market value of a mithan (S. Roy, 1960: 200–201, 225, 233). Dalton, in 1855, reported for a Padam village an unusual handling of a misdemeanor: if a mithan trespasses into a cultivated field, the owner of the field himself decides the amount of damage and helps himself accordingly from the granary of the guilty mithan's owner.[1]

The Adi take oaths, swearing by the earth, the sky, and the sun. One form of oath requires eating earth and pointing to the sun while proclaiming, "The earth may swallow me and the sun may burn me if I lie." In taking a solemn oath one must hold the horn of a mithan, swear by the earth and the sun, and declare, "May this animal's horn pierce me if I am false" (Dunbar, 1915: 59).

If the village council finds it cannot establish guilt beyond doubt, it

1. Elwin, 1959: 253—reprint of E. T. Dalton, "Correspondence and Journal of Capt. Dalton, . . . of his Progress in a Late Visit to a Clan of Abors on the Dihong River," *Selections* from the Records of the Bengal Government, No. 23 (Calcutta, 1855), pp. 151–69.

may resort to superhuman aid in the form of an ordeal, provided both the accused and the accuser agree to this. Needham, for an earlier period (1886), remarked that the Adi believe so completely in the reliability of ordeals that there is little chance for an irresponsible accuser to "mulct [an innocent man] out of a few mithan without the accused having a chance of proving his innocence" (Elwin, 1959: 290). Four forms of ordeal are commonly employed; mithan figure in one of them—the only such instance we have uncovered for any mithan-keeping group. When this ordeal is agreed upon, each antagonist chooses one of his mithan and the two animals are released together in the forest. The mithan belonging to the guilty man, according to Adi belief, will meet an "early and tragic fate" (S. Roy, 1960: 226).

Concluding a treaty was the traditional way to mark the end of war between two Adi villages. The treaties were simple and, Sachin Roy reports, seldom broken (1960: 120). When one side had had enough of fighting, it approached the other side with overtures for peace. The ensuing negotiations took place at the edge of a village. When agreement was reached, mithan from both sides were sacrificed, and their flesh, along with beer, was served to the people of both villages. The sacrifice of the mithan was ratification of the treaty. Dunbar (1915: 50) reports essentially the same procedure, with an added detail: each side also brought dankis (highly valued, large metal bowls of Tibetan manufacture) to the place of negotiation, and the mithan meat was cooked in them, each village using dankis provided by the other.

In Religion

Religious beliefs in general conform to those of other NEFA groups. The world of the Adi is occupied by invisible beings of great variety and number. Many are spirits whose overall influence on man and beasts is evil; they cause accidents, illness, early death, and epidemics. Other spirits are associated with nature and, while being capable of great malevolence, can also be benevolent. Among the nature spirits are Dade Bote, the lord of domestic animals, and his two associates, Eso Agam, who is in charge of mithan, and Eg Agam, whose responsibility is pigs. All of the spirits—both evil and nature spirits—are close to man and can be contacted through the mediation of priests (S. Roy, 1960: 238–40, 241, 242, 247).

Of far higher status than the spirits is another class of supernatural beings, who may be regarded as deities. Many of them have a dual character. Donyi-Polo, for example, is the sun-moon deity. Though the deities are generally benign and the source of all blessings, they are so remote from man that they are of little help in time of need. Hence the spirits are the primary objects of religious observance (S. Roy, 1960: 240, 242–43, 247).

Those spirits causing illness seem to be called upon with the greatest frequency. In 1937 Fürer-Haimendorf (1954: 588, 599–603) observed in a Minyong village an appeal to such a spirit. On the first evening the priest made certain preparations, then danced and fell into a trance during which he was able to contact the spirit and propose to it an exchange of the sick man's soul for certain food and drink. The spirit declared a mithan the necessary sacrifice, and the priest promised it. The next day, clansmen of the ill man brought one of his mithan bulls in from the forest. They killed it in the usual Adi way, by strangulation (Figure 10). The priest did not participate in any of the activity surrounding the death of the mithan. Moreover an ordinary clansman, not the priest, took omens from the liver of the dead animal. In the meantime, however, the priest put up two ceremonial structures: one in front of the sick man's house, and the other, a larger one which had small bamboo platforms for offerings to the spirit, at the side of the house. The priest smeared blood of the mithan on the ceremonial structures, put beer and cooked rice on the platforms,[2] and made a prayer which was an appeal not to the one spirit but to all spirits who might have caused the man's illness. Offering and prayer marked the end of the ritual. Then the meat of the sacrificed mithan was divided among the ill man's relatives, the people of his village, and the priest, who received an especially large share.

Some of the situations besides illness and accident that necessitate appeal and sacrifice to the spirits are the killing of an enemy in war, the carrying out of community hunts, the occupation of a new house, the loss of a person in the forest, and some of the ceremonies associated with the agricultural cycle.

In former days, when the Adi were more involved than now with war, an extended series of ritual activities was undertaken to protect the victor from the spirits of slain enemies. Traditionally, as among the Apa Tani, the right hand of the dead man was carried back to the victor's village. Minor rituals, including sacrifice of a chicken, were performed outside the village before the victorious warrior, accompanied by the welcoming villagers, went to the men's dormitory for the beginning of another ceremony called Keming. The Keming concluded with the sacrifice, performed outside the village, of mithan and pigs. Appropriately on this occasion associated with war, they were killed with sword thrusts. The

2. S. Roy (1960: 250) describes essentially the same procedure, adding only that the priest offers a share of the sacrificed meat to the spirit along with the beer and cooked rice.

blood and intestines of the dead animals were scattered around the area. A bamboo structure with a horizontal rod was erected and from it were hung the enemy's hand and the legs of the animals sacrificed. The victor then returned to the dormitory where he had to spend the next three nights, rather than at home. The old men and young girls of the village remained with him at night. During all this time he observed special regulations and performed various acts as protection against evil spirits. Finally, after fulfilling still further requirements, he could return to his own house (S. Roy, 1960: 116–19).

Hunting is sometimes an individual activity and sometimes a group effort. One special community hunt takes place on a day in February or March, the exact time being set by the village council. It is followed by a nine-day festival known as Unning. Sacrifice of mithan and a ceremony for their protection are part of the festival. During the day of the hunt village girls prepare beer and cook vegetables. The hunters exchange part of their game for the vegetables and beer, and all of the food and drink, including the day's catch, is consumed by the hunters and the girls, each in his own house. This is contrary to the usual Adi practice followed after community hunts, when the game is brought to the village and shared with the elderly and helpless who are unable to participate in hunting. On the second day of the festival the young men put up posts for sacrificing mithan. The mithan are killed on the third day, their meat distributed to the clans of the village the fourth day, the meat cooked on the fifth and sixth days and part of it given to the poor. On the seventh day mithan owners perform a ritual for protection of mithan. The eighth day is a taboo day for the entire village. On the ninth day the young men hunt again, and in the evening take all game to the dormitory, where they cook and eat it (S. Roy, 1960: 146–47).

The Minyong, and presumably other Adi too, believe that every house has its own spirit. Before a family moves into a new house a sacrifice, normally a pig, is made to the house spirit. Fürer-Haimendorf, however, commented briefly on a similar sacrifice involving a mithan. It was at the Minyong village of Rotung, when a headman rebuilt his house. The mithan was killed by strangulation in the usual way, with a priest in attendance. The offering was made both to the house spirit and to the spirit guarding the headman's cattle (Fürer-Haimendorf, 1954: 602).

An example of the appeal made when someone is missing is recounted by Dunbar (1915: 82). The Adi, he says, fear a forest spirit who dwells in the holok tree (*Terminalia myriocarpa*) and who can lure men to him by various means. When a person disappears in an unaccountable way, some villagers go into the forest to a holok tree. They beg the tree to appeal to the spirit living there to release the lost person, and promise a sacrifice if he turns up alive. To lend strength to their plea they attack the tree with sword and bow and arrow. They continue hoping for about two months that the appeal will be heard. If the person returns, a mithan or a pig is sacrificed for a thanksgiving feast.

The Adi calendar is tied to the agricultural seasons. Most stages of the agricultural year are marked with festival and sacrifice. Mithan are conspicuous in certain festivals, particularly those that combine offerings to the spirits associated with agriculture and those connected with the welfare of domestic animals. In some festivals offerings to the greater deities are also made. Clearing the forest is the first work of the agricultural year and begins roughly in March.[3] At some time before the clearing is completed, a festival, Mopun, essentially a fertility rite, is held; pigs or dogs are the usual sacrificial animals. To celebrate the completion of clearing in May another festival, called Aran or Pombi, is held. No one works in the fields for five days. A pig and a chicken, and sometimes a mithan, are the public sacrifices offered to the spirits of the fields, of the fertility of the soil, of the forest treasures, of domestic animals, and of the rain. In addition, people make offerings of meat, ginger, and rice to their individual house spirits.

After the Aran festival, planting begins. When it is finished, community fencing is done. According to Sachin Roy, the Ettor festival (one definition of "ettor" is "fence") is held annually upon completion of the fencing. At this festival offerings are made to "the *Agam*, lord of the animals," presumably the spirit connected with the welfare of mithan. A feast is held, the greatest contribution to it coming from owners of mithan. Roy reports also that at the time of this festival, "stock taking" of the mithan is done (S. Roy, 1960: 133). Dunbar (1915: 81–82) recorded more fully an annual festival held at the time of community fencing. It was called Asho Agam, and its purpose was "to give security to the cattle [mithan] and to increase the herds."[4] At the beginning of the ceremonies, which last several days, the people of a village gather at the bachelors'

3. The discussion of festivals is based on S. Roy, 1960: 130 ff., except where otherwise indicated.

4. Sachin Roy (1960: 241) names Dade Bote as "the lord of the domestic animals," and defines agam as a general term for the spirits who assist Dade Bote. Among these spirits is Eso Agam, literally "mithan agam" or "lord of the mithan." Almost certainly this is the same term as "Asho Agam," the festival described by Dunbar, which must have been dedicated to the lord of the mithan. In his discussion of the Ettor festival, Roy does not specify the particular agam to whom offerings were made, nor does he indicate what animals that agam is responsible for. Very likely he is Eso Agam, and Roy and Dunbar were dealing with the same festival, one of them identifying it by the name of the spirit propitiated, the other by the principal activity associated with it, fence repair.

dormitory. There they eat rice and drink beer which they have brought along. For the next five days the men labor to repair all of the village mithan fences. Dunbar suggested an interesting interpretation: that the strengthening of the fences is symbolic of protection against the inroads of enormous herds, which of course would be a desirable condition. During the five days the men are at work on the fences, women may not enter the fields, because of a belief that if any do, the mithan of that household will break down the fences and destroy the crops. On the sixth day of the festival the men make new mithan ropes. On the seventh day all mithan are brought in from the forest and unmarked animals are cut with the owner's mark.

After the first weeding, probably in June, there is another agricultural festival, the Lune Solung. At that time the women of the village sacrifice chickens near the household granaries. The Luttor Solung—or Sholung, as Fürer-Haimendorf called it—is held later, just before the final weeding of the crops in late summer.[5] Its main purpose is to assure protection of the mithan.

All mithan are brought to the village for the Luttor Solung. Each mithan owner collects his own animals and ties them to special posts erected in his front yard. During the ceremony, which sometimes lasts four or five days, the mithan owners sacrifice pigs and fowl in the amount they can afford, offering part of the sacrificial meat to the appropriate spirits, and feasting in their own houses. A Solung dance is held every night near the men's dormitory; a priest sings about both crops and mithan, and girls sing with him and dance.

The posts are of particular interest because of the common use of posts, usually forked, in the southern mithan country to commemorate the Feasts of Merit, an institution to be described in detail later. Fürer-Haimendorf (1954: 597–98) was unable to discover the precise significance of the Adi posts. They are short and rough-hewn, often ending in a small fork, sometimes a natural one and sometimes a carved one. No one except the owner of the mithan may enter the area while the mithan are tied to the posts. Anyone who damages one of the posts after the ceremony is fined the value of one mithan.

Harvest ceremonies are not treated in detail in the literature. The beginning of the harvest is marked with a ceremony in which the pig is the sacrificial animal. In certain Adi groups, individuals at that time also conduct ceremonies, including sacrifice of a chicken or pig, at their granaries.

5. Fürer-Haimendorf (1954: 597–98) describes for the Minyong a ceremony identical in all its main features to the Luttor Solung, except that it is held earlier, when the rice plants are about 10 inches high. He calls the ceremony simply the Sholung feast.

In the agricultural ceremonies mentioned above, the pig and chicken are the most common sacrificial animals. The mithan sometimes is sacrificed at Aran, held just before sowing, but does not seem to be sacrificed normally at the other agricultural festivities. The welfare of the mithan, however, is the main concern of the Luttor Solung and the fencing festival (the Asho Agam or Ettor), both of which are a regular part of the sequence of agricultural ceremonies.

Besides the annual agricultural ceremonies, several other rites connected with agriculture are performed when the need arises. For example, when crops have been poor for several years, a ritual requiring sacrifice of a mithan is performed. Similarly, if drought persists for several months, a mithan sacrifice may help. There is also a rite that may be held during the rainy season in an effort to bring some sun. In this a dog is the sacrifice.

One other ceremony is of interest on several counts. It was reported by Fürer-Haimendorf (1954: 593) for the Minyong, whom he visited in 1937. Certain breaches of customary law were thought to provoke the anger of various of the highest deities. Clan incest was such an act. In those days, the case would be heard in the village council and the couple condemned to social and economic, but not physical, banishment from their group. The condemnation could, however, be mitigated if the guilty man performed a ceremony dedicated to the deities concerned. The rite had the dual function of expiating the crime and restoring the good humor of the deities. The offender had to sacrifice one or more mithan and provide a feast for his co-villagers and for important men of other villages as well. This is the one clear-cut instance of invocation of deities, as opposed to spirits, reported in the literature. The practice of expiation by means of a mithan sacrifice and feast is reminiscent of the Apa Tani custom in similar circumstances (p. 71).

9

The Northern Mithan Keepers
A Summary

It may be useful here before considering the peoples of the southern range to sum up the likenesses and differences among the northern mithan-keeping peoples.

The Sherdukpen, who live in a rain shadow area of low precipitation, differ in many ways from the other peoples of NEFA. Their houses, for example, are substantial two-story buildings in which wooden planks are an important construction material, and which are raised on a stone foundation. By contrast, the houses of most other NEFA groups are made of bamboo and cane, and are raised on wooden pilings. The Sherdukpen, like other NEFA peoples, practice shifting cultivation; but unlike most others, they also cultivate permanent fields. Their important domestic animals are common cattle and ponies, not the pigs and mithan so valued in the rest of NEFA. Their principal agricultural implement is not the hoe but the plow, drawn by bullocks. Unlike other NEFA peoples, they milk their cows and consume both milk and butter. Their religion, while it contains animist elements common to NEFA, has incorporated traits of Buddhism. Animal sacrifice, perhaps because of Buddhist influence, is of little if any importance in religious or social life. This tends to reduce further the possibility of an intimate tie between the mithan and the Sherdukpen. Because of their impoverished environment, moreover, the Sherdukpen leave their settlements for several months each year, migrating as a group to the lowland borders for trade. It would appear unlikely that the mithan, which nowhere is involved in transhumant movements and seems unsuited to such an existence, could fit into Sherdukpen life. Yet it does. The Sherdukpen obtain mithan from the NEFA groups to the east, and pass them on, at a profit, to the Bhutanese, who want them for breeding purposes. There is no evidence, however, that the mithan plays an important part in Sherdukpen social or cultural life, as it does among the other NEFA peoples.

The Dafla are shifting cultivators, quite dependent on agriculture for their sustenance but skilled at animal husbandry. Frequently they have an abundance of pigs and mithan and a deficiency of grain. Out of this condition and the proximity of the Apa Tani—unusually productive sedentary farmers—has grown a trading relationship in which Dafla surplus animals are regularly exchanged for Apa Tani surplus rice.

The Dafla are an individualistic people who live in multiple-family longhouses in settlements of from three to thirty dwellings. Each long-house is occupied by several elementary families—a man and his wives, perhaps a brother or cousin and their wives, or a married son and his wives. A man's first loyalty is to his longhouse and its inhabitants, though quarrels are frequent and parts of the household break away, moving to another house or village. In this mobile society, a man expects little support from village, clan, or tribe, but builds a personal system of alliances with other individuals. His power and ultimately his prestige depend entirely on such alliances. Marriage creates one sort of alliance, formal friendship pacts another, and exchange of Tibetan bells still another. Mithan are essential for all of these and thus play an unusual role in contributing to security, and, not surprisingly, are the ultimate measure of wealth in Dafla society.

The Dafla are animists and their religion is pervasive and focuses on offering and sacrifice to numerous unseen beings whose influence is mostly evil. No offering is so effective as the mithan sacrifice.

The Apa Tani, as irrigated rice farmers, differ strikingly from the Dafla, but the mithan among them occupies an equally distinctive position. Living in seven compact villages, they have occupied a single small valley for generations, supporting themselves comfortably and producing a surplus from carefully tended permanent rice terraces. More completely dependent on agriculture than the other NEFA groups considered, they are more closely tied to their land, by an attachment which is emotional as well as practical. Most Apa Tani would never consider leaving their valley to settle elsewhere.

They have evolved several effective mechanisms to ensure the peace in the valley that is necessary to their continuing prosperity. Interestingly, a village council with authority over the entire village is not one of these mechanisms. An informal council of clan representatives, however, reflects public opinion and is influential in directing village activity. In addition, ancient peace treaties among the seven villages, along with a highly developed sense of property rights, centered on land ownership and supported by public opinion, contribute to the maintenance of overall internal order. Individuals settle their own differences unless the disruption threatens large sections of a village or the valley. Then the clan council intervenes, settling the matter more with the idea of removing a menace than of exacting compensation or of seeking justice.

There are two Apa Tani social classes, aristocrat and slave, and the line between them is impassable. Each class is divided into patrilineal, exogamous clans. The clan is the most important social unit. Though certain valley-wide public ceremonies reinforce tribal solidarity, clan loyalty is greater than tribal or village loyalty. Polygyny is permissible but is unusual, and most Apa Tani households consist of a nuclear family that occupies its own house in the husband's clan quarter of the village.

The Apa Tani, like most of the NEFA peoples, are animists, and have a continuous need for sacrificial animals. Pigs, chickens, or dogs are the usual offerings on the many occasions when an individual problem has to be solved. They are also the usual seasonal offerings to spirits and deities. The pig is obligatory for community agricultural rites, and is a strong contender for the position of premier sacrificial animal, though the mithan is offered in some religious and social ceremonies. In certain other areas of life, however, the mithan is clearly supreme: in the acquisition of land, the ultimate measure of success and wealth for the Apa Tani, mithan are the only acceptable currency; and in men's efforts to enhance their prestige through the deliberate destruction of wealth, mithan are the chief items destroyed.

Since the shortage of grazing areas in their valley severely limits both the kind and number of animals that can be kept there, the Apa Tani exchange surplus rice for the mithan and pigs of the Dafla and Hill Miri. The trade relationship, while mutually beneficial, is yet the source of much difficulty between the Apa Tani and the Dafla and Hill Miri. Economic deals sometimes lead to quarrels which commonly end in capture of people and mithan for ransom, which in turn often prompts retaliatory capturing and ransoming. Ransom, on both sides, is almost always partially in mithan. The Apa Tani consider it a point of honor to ransom captured mithan, a sentiment to which the Dafla are alert; frequently the ransom collected in such cases is greater than the value of the stolen animals.

The Adi stand out for their well developed social and political organization at the village level. Village councils are the primary governing agencies; intervillage arrangements exist for keeping peace and maintaining order; family and clan loyalties are subordinate to those of the village. Many daily activities of the Adi involve village cooperation. They hunt and fish communally as well as individually. Clearing of the land to be cultivated in a given season is a village effort, as is fencing of agricultural land. Many agricultural ceremonies, which are prominent in Adi life, are communal undertakings; and in many of them the old and helpless are special beneficiaries of the labors of their fellow villagers. Agricultural rites are essentially religious in character and require the sacrifice of animals, often pigs and chickens and sometimes mithan, as offerings to spirits and deities. The entire village participates in the ceremonies and the entire village benefits.

For the Adi, the greatest value of the mithan is as premier sacrificial animal. It is important as a measure of wealth and prestige. Men display the horns of sacrificed animals and regard the size of mithan herds as indicating a person's wealth. At the same time, the mithan is not used in ceremonies whose main purpose is to enhance an individual's social position, though it does figure in certain rites of passage. The Adi are monogamous. Their marriage arrangements are unique among the NEFA peoples considered; marriage commitments develop from liaisons originating in the youth dormitories, which are unusual in NEFA; and there is no bride-price in the usual sense, though a man has certain obligations to his wife's family. As a result, mithan are of singularly little importance in Adi marriage, and at most, mithan flesh sometimes constitutes part of the marriage feast. Mithan are sacrificed at a funeral if it is economically possible.

They are commonly part of the fine assessed for antisocial acts—with intent more to compensate the victim or his family than to punish the offender. They are fairly important trade items; but the Adi do not indulge in the common Dafla and Apa Tani practice of capture for ransom, in which mithan are an important part of the ransom.

10

Peoples of the Southern Range
Introductory

The southern range of the mithan is linked physically to the northern range. It centers on the north-south trending system of mountains and hills that extend from the head of the Assam Valley to the Bay of Bengal. The main system is a long, narrow upland (about 500 miles long and 100 miles wide) bordered to east and west by lowlands. To the east are the valleys of the Chindwin and Irrawaddy; to the west are the Assamese plains and the lowlands of Bengal. An offshoot of the main system, comprising the Garo, Khasi, and Jaintia hills, extends westward for about 150 miles and marks the southern edge of the Assam Valley. This offshoot is occupied by tribal peoples but contains no mithan today.

In the mithan's southern range, the highest crests are usually under 10,000 feet in elevation, lower than the middle and northern reaches of NEFA. The terrain, however, is commonly as precipitous and as deficient in level land as the northern range. Like the north, the south is affected by the monsoon circulation of India. The summer monsoon rains swell the rivers and often make them impassable. They also help create the forest that is the natural vegetation of much of the area.

The southern mithan range, besides being subject to influences from Buddhist Burma and Hindu India, has also experienced migrations by tribesmen from the northeast and northwest, by way of the hills at the head of the Assam Valley; and from the east, through the river valleys of the Chindwin system. Today the inhabitants of the southern range may be roughly divided into two groups: the Naga, of the north, among whom there is great variation; and the Kuki-Chin, of the south, who are equally varied. Each of these groups will be treated in detail.

11

The Naga Tribes
A General Sketch

The term "Naga" is applied inclusively to a number of tribal groups who occupy the northern portion of the mountainous country that stretches south from the head of the Assam Valley. About three-fourths of the 478,000 Naga speakers reported in the 1961 *Census of India* lived in the Indian state of Nagaland (Maps 5a and 5b), which was created in 1960. Most of the rest lived to the south, in the bordering state of Manipur, though a few were found to the west, in Assam, and to the northeast, in Tirap Frontier Division of the North-East Frontier Agency. The number of Naga living east of the international frontier in Burma is unknown.

Present-day Nagaland corresponds generally with the Naga Hills District of British days, but includes, in addition, certain territory to the east.[1] Nagaland is a long, narrow area, approximately 160 by 50 miles, lying almost wholly in the mountains, its long axis coinciding with the direction of the main ranges. The country is rough and dissected by rivers that rise

1. Assam was ceded to Great Britain in 1826, and from 1832 on the British had regular contact with the Naga. For a hundred years, however, the Government vacillated in its policy toward the tribal people in the uplands bordering the Brahmaputra Valley, unable to decide how much administration to assume. Since the Naga continued to raid the plains and to hunt heads among themselves, causing widespread unrest and anxiety, the British gradually extended control over them. In 1877 the Government established Kohima town as administrative center of the surrounding area, and Wokha, in present-day Mokokchung District, as a subcenter. In 1881 the Naga Hills District was created, but did not include the eastern region that now constitutes Tuensang District. By 1902 British administration was officially extended eastward into that area, though actually very little control was exercised there. After Indian independence, the Tuensang region was briefly included in NEFA, but in 1957 it was attached to the Naga Hills District to form a new political unit, the Naga Hills Tuensang Area. With the creation in 1960 of the state of Nagaland, whose boundaries coincided with those of the Naga Hills Tuensang Area, Tuensang became one of Nagaland's three districts.

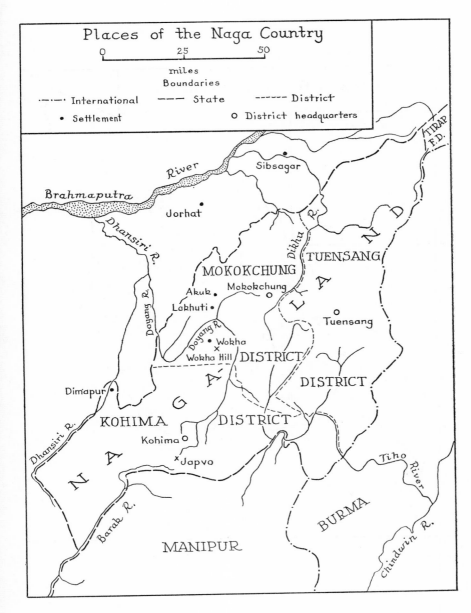

Places of the Naga Country

0   25   50

miles

Boundaries

—·—·— International   —— State   —————— District

• Settlement   ○ District headquarters

TIRAP F.D.

Sibsagar

Brahmaputra   River

Jorhat

Dhansiri R.

Doyang R.

Dikhu R.

MOKOKCHUNG

TUENSANG

Akuk •   Mokokchung ○

Lakhuti •

Tuensang ○

Doyang R.

× Wokha

Wokha Hill

DISTRICT

DISTRICT

Dimapur •

N   A   G   A

KOHIMA

DISTRICT

Dhansiri R.

Kohima ○

× Japvo

L   A   N   D

Tiho   River

BURMA

Barak R.

Chindwin R.

MANIPUR

Map 5a

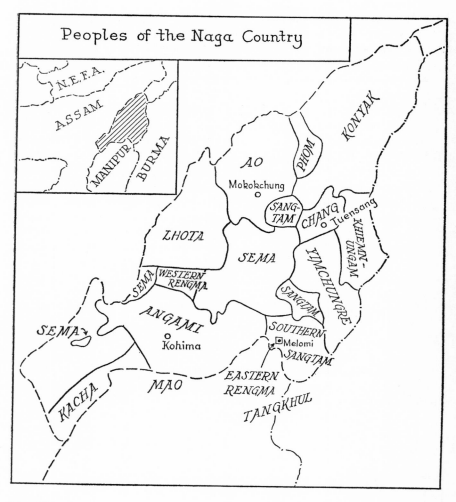

Peoples of the Naga Country

Map 5b

in the interior. Most of these drain to the north and west, where they join the Brahmaputra, though one important system, the Tizu-Tiho, joins the Chindwin, to the east. The ranges commonly reach elevations of 7,000 feet, with a few peaks rising above 8,000 feet. Japvo, the highest, is 9,890 feet above sea level. Politically, Nagaland is divided into three districts. Kohima District occupies the southern third of the state. The remaining two-thirds is divided roughly in half from north to south, with Mokok-chung District on the west, bordering the Assam Valley, and Tuensang on the east, bordering Burma. Tuensang is the most isolated and least known district and was the last area to be brought under the administration of the Government of India. As late as 1954 it was known as the "unadministered eastern tribal area," and much of it was free of government control.

Traditionally the Naga included many distinct groups who knew one another by their individual tribal names.[2] Forms of these were known and used in the plains to distinguish different Naga peoples, and a dozen such names occur commonly in the literature. The plainsmen also applied the inclusive term "Naga" to the hill people generally; but only recently, probably encouraged by the rise of Naga nationalism, did the many

2. While it is impossible from the literature alone to locate the Naga tribes precisely with reference to the present political boundaries, we offer the following approximations of population for the best-known tribes living in Nagaland itself.

Kohima District

Angami	42,800
Rengma	5,900
Southern Sangtam	2,700 ?
Sema	about 20 villages

Mokokchung District

Ao	57,700
Lhota	26,600
Sema	47,500; most in Mokokchung but a few villages in each of the other two districts

Tuensang District

Konyak	57,100
Phom	13,400
Sangtam	15,800
Yimchungre (Yachumi)	12,700
Khiemnungam (Kalyo-Kengyu)	12,400
Chang	11,300
Sema	about 12 villages

This table and the tribal locations on Map 5b are based on *Census of India,* 1961, ccxxxi–ccxxxii, and 3 maps following p. 362.

groups concerned apply the word to themselves. The principal Naga groups living in Nagaland are the Angami, Rengma, Lhota, Sema, Ao, Sangtam, Yimchungre (Yachumi), Khiemnungam (Kalyo-Kengyu), Chang, Phom, and Konyak. Some Kacha Naga live in the southwest corner of the state but most are in Manipur.

Great racial, linguistic, and cultural diversity exists among the Naga. Not surprisingly, the diversity has been emphasized in the literature more often than the few similarities, though some observers believe these similarities indicate a basic Naga unity. Much of the diversity probably springs from the several distinct migrations to which the area has been subject. Hutton writes that the Naga country has been penetrated by three great migrations coming from three directions: "from the north-east whence came the Tai races; from the north-west, whence came the Singphos, Kacharis, and Garos, among others, and from the south . . ." (1921a: vii). The cultures of the several immigrant groups were distinctive, and the degree of their influence varied in different parts of the Naga country. Isolation, partly self-imposed because of continual war and headhunting and partly resulting from the rugged, broken country of the Naga Hills, acted to perpetuate the initial diversity of the immigrant groups and tended to produce further differences, even within tribes. Before British administration, though certain channels for limited trade and social intercourse were maintained, each Naga tribe kept much to itself, regarding others, often including distant villages of its own group or clans other than its own, as enemies.

Overall, Mongoloid physical characteristics dominate among the Naga, but considerable variation occurs. Found among them are tall, short, well-built, and poorly developed types; fair skin, dark skin; straight hair and wavy or even curly hair. There is also great variety in facial characteristics, including the presence or absence of the epicanthic fold, and the occasional occurrence of what Hutton calls the "Papuan profile."

The linguistic diversity, rich everywhere, is greatest in Tuensang. The *Linguistic Survey of India* (1903–28) grouped together 29 principal Naga languages to form the Naga group, one of the five groups in the Assam-Burmese branch of the Tibeto-Burman subfamily of languages. The 1961 *Census of India* retains the same basic arrangement and lists 47 "mother tongues" tentatively grouped under 26 languages in the Naga group. Of these, however, only 17 correspond with names of mother tongues listed in the *Linguistic Survey*. The final classification of the Naga languages has not been agreed upon, and scholars continue to work on it. Writing in the 1950's, Robert Shafer (1955: 94–111) groups the Naga languages very differently. He rejects the traditional division of the Sino-Tibetan family of languages into two subfamilies (Chinese-Siamese and Tibeto-

Burman), establishing instead six "divisions" which are further divided into sections. He places all the Naga languages except those of the extreme northeast (those that are commonly designated in the literature as Konyak, Chang, and Phom) in his Burmic division, Kukish section, which also contains the Kuki-Chin languages. He puts the Naga languages of the northeast into another division, Baric, of which they constitute one section. L. G. Löffler (pers. com., Oct. 18, 1966) generally supports Shafer's position and says "there can be no doubt that linguistically the tribes of Nagaland do not belong to a common stock, since Konyak and other Eastern Naga are akin to Bodo languages [also in Shafer's Baric division] while the Western and Southern Naga are akin to the Kuki-Chin languages."

Differences among the Naga Groups

To indicate the scope of cultural diversity, some of the ways in which the Naga differ from one another are discussed briefly below. Though change has been rapid since the turn of the century, we write here in the ethnographic present.

Agriculture and Crops

Shifting cultivation is the characteristic form of agriculture of the Naga, and dry rice the principal swidden crop. The Eastern Angami, however, terrace steep slopes for the cultivation of irrigated rice. Some Naga groups, those bordering the Angami and influenced by them, also grow rice in irrigated terraces as well as practicing their traditional shifting cultivation. These include the Eastern Rengma, a few Western Rengma, and some Sema—all of Nagaland—and certain Naga of Manipur, notably the Tangkhul. Generally these groups, in contrast to the Angami, confine their terraces to gentler slopes, such as river banks and valleys. Among the Sema the effort was encouraged by the Government because of severe land shortage. Other important crops cultivated by the Naga are millets, maize, Job's tears, and taro. In some Konyak villages, contrary to the usual Naga pattern, taro is the staple crop, and millet or dry rice the subsidiary crop. The western and southern Naga groups of Nagaland (Lhota, Sema, Western Rengma, Angami) plant their grain seed; the trans-Dikhu tribes (Konyak, Chang, Phom, Sangtam, Yimchungre) and the Ao broadcast theirs.

Houses

Some groups, mostly in the south, build directly on the ground; others raise their houses on bamboo platforms. The Lhota favor a combination of the two, sometimes building on a platform but then covering the bamboo with earth. Among some groups, houses are small, simple, and rather temporary structures; among others they are large, substantial, and decorated with elaborate and costly wood carvings.

Morung (an Institution and a Building)

To avoid a multiplicity of terms, the Assamese word *morung* has become the conventional way to refer to the men's social and political institution that is found in some degree among all Naga groups. The same word also is applied to the building which is the ritual center for the activities and ceremonies of the men belonging to a morung. The morung building is the place where unmarried morung members sleep; thus it serves as a bachelors' dormitory, though it is more properly designated a men's house. Morung affiliation usually is based on clan membership; the morung group becomes a focus of a man's loyalty; the resulting cohesion and political power of the morung usually thus both originate in the clan and contribute to clan solidarity. Though the institution functions essentially in the same way in all Naga groups, there are variations in the way in which young men become associated with the morung group, in the strength of loyalty to it, and the length of time the association is continued. There are also variations in the morung buildings, which among most Naga groups are the most impressive structures in the village, being large, well built, and elaborately decorated, especially with carving on the main posts. The Angami and Sema, however, generally do not have morung buildings; the Sema use the chief's house for morung activities, and the Angami occasionally use an ordinary dwelling for certain ceremonies that require a special house for men.

Political Organization

The Konyak, of the north, are decidedly autocratic; the Sema, farther south, are less so; and the Ao, Lhota, and Angami, all west of the Sema, practice varying degrees of democracy.

Marriage

Monogamy is usual; but three groups, the Lhota, Sema, and Eastern Rengma, practice polygyny.

Tattooing and Headhunting

The southern and western Naga do not tattoo at all. Among the northern and trans-Dikhu groups, the Konyak and Chang tattoo both sexes, while the Ao and Sangtam tattoo only women. Tattooing, where it occurs, seems to be associated with qualification for marriage and reproduction; in the groups where men are tattooed, there is also a tie with headhunting. Though the British, as they extended their administration in Naga areas, made every effort to abolish headhunting, traditionally it was common to all Naga and was widely practiced. Among most, if not all, groups headhunting too had a connection with marriage and reproduction. A young man who had not taken a head had a difficult time finding a girl to accept him as a husband. Similarly, among the Konyak, a youth without tattoos, which were won only after participation in a successful headhunting raid, was not yet a "man" and was ill prepared for procreation. Though the association between headhunting and readiness for marriage is widely recognized among the Naga, the use of tattooing to mark the headhunter is of quite limited distribution.

Disposal of the Dead

Great variation occurs among the Naga in details of their disposal of the dead, though only two basic methods are employed: burial and exposure on a platform. Burial is the custom of most groups, and the variation involves such matters as location of graves, use of stone in construction of the grave and as a marker on it, erection of wooden images of the deceased on the grave, and trophies displayed on the grave. Exposure on a platform is the practice of the Ao and most of the trans-Dikhu Naga. The most striking variation among the groups practicing exposure is in the special treatment of the corpse or skull, or both. Some groups desiccate the corpse before placing it on the platform. Some separate the skull from the body and treat it with special ceremony. Some groups finally deposit the skull in a protective enclosure: a stone cist, a pottery jar, or a niche in the rock wall of a cliff. Despite these variations, many groups perform some part of the death ritual at the time of harvest or of sowing. This clearly shows belief in a connection between the dead and the continued fertility of the area.

Some Features Common to the Naga Groups

Despite the diversity among the Naga, certain generalizations apply to all groups. Some of these follow.

System of Descent

All Naga groups are patrilineal, though some writers have commented on traces of a matrilineal system of descent.

Basic Religious Beliefs

Religious beliefs are in broad terms the same. All Naga groups believe in numerous unseen beings who can affect the living. Such beings are unequal in the influence, both good and evil, that they can wield, but most must be propitiated or kept satisfied with offerings of one sort or another. All Naga also have some notion of a Land of the Dead to which souls of human beings sooner or later repair. They all share, as well, the idea of a powerful life-force which resides principally in the head. Writers on the Naga use several terms for this quality: "life-essence," "soul substance," "fertilizer," "fertilizing power," "magical quality," or "virtue"; "ghost" and "soul" occasionally are used in this sense, too. The belief in the life-force has important implications for Naga behavior, because the life-force of a person can be transmitted, in various ways, both during his life and after death, to benefit individuals and the village as a whole, especially in assuring fertility and well-being. Concern with fertility is so great, indeed, that in Hutton's view "the religion of the Naga Hills is centered very largely upon fertility cults" (1928: 399).

Extensions of the Idea of a Life-Force[3]

The belief in a manipulatable life-force, together with the Naga concern with fertility, is the foundation upon which several practices common to most Naga rest. Headhunting, certain death ceremonies, the Feasts of Merit, and the erection of memorials of stone and wood are all directly related to this belief. The life-force is particularly valued for its fertility-granting powers, which are operative during a person's lifetime and can also be utilized after his death. "Fertility," to the Naga, has very broad connotations, which include the general well-being and prosperity of the community and not only the actual fertility of the fields, domestic animals, and human inhabitants of the village.

Taking an enemy head—in which the life-force is concentrated no less than in the heads of one's own clansmen—and bringing the head back to the village, is an effective way to increase the store of "fertility" in the successful village. Each youth who participates in taking the head also benefits as an individual, for a portion of the life-force adhering to the head becomes his, thereby increasing his own supply. Acquisition of the life-force by the living, either from enemy heads or from one's own dead, is not automatic, and the Naga have devised several methods to acquire the fertility-granting power and to enhance its effectiveness. Certain ceremonies performed over enemy heads clearly are efforts to obtain and disperse the life-force. Two aspects of Naga death customs already mentioned well illustrate the same principle: the special treatment given the skull by some groups; and the special significance times of sowing and of harvest assume in relation to the dead.

3. For more detail on this subject and many supporting examples, see Hutton, 1922, 1922a, and especially 1928; for a general statement, see Heine-Geldern, 1928: 314–15.

The Feasts of Merit basically are a series of ceremonies, each more elaborate and expensive than the last, performed by prosperous individuals over a period of years. Performing the Feasts serves several ends, one of which is enhancement of the social status of the feast giver. The series varies considerably among the different Naga groups, and differs in detail from village to village within a group. Despite the variation, fertility connotations are pronounced in all the Feasts. The feast giver essentially attempts to gain fertility and well-being for himself from supernatural beings and, among the Ao, from his ancestors. He also tries to extend to the clan and village a portion of his own "fertility" or life-force, of which he has a surfeit, according to the Naga view, simply because he has accumulated the means to provide the Feast. This effort and its many fertility implications can be most clearly seen in the next-to-highest Feast of the Angami series as performed at Kohima village. The same Feast also clearly shows the role of the wooden posts which are so prominent in Naga Feasts of Merit.

In the Angami Feast (Hutton, 1922: 57–69), a new fence is put up enclosing an area at the front of the feast giver's house. Cattle that will provide meat for the last days of the Feast are slaughtered there. Among the final sacrifices, on the eighteenth day, is a black bull. After the bull has been killed, in the enclosure, the feast giver goes to a place outside the village where two posts, one straight and one forked, have been cut and shaped, and the forked one carved with a mithan head and other symbols. He blesses the posts, which, with much pageantry, are "dragged" (carried and pulled) first to his house, then through the entire village, and finally back to his house. The feast giver remains standing before his house while the posts are dragged through the village and, upon their return, he chooses a place within the enclosure for their erection. With ceremony they are set up by the presiding official. It is by means of the two posts, which the Angami say are representations of the male and female sexual organs, and which are given the names of the feast giver and his wife, that the "prosperity [of the feast giver] is communicated to the village as a whole" (Hutton, 1921: 231–32; 1922: 58). The posts remain in the same position for about a month, when the official returns to the feast giver's house, digs them up, and resets them, this time against the front of the house. There they remain, perhaps at that point becoming mainly commemorative objects, though possibly residual amounts of the magical quality adhere to them for as long as they stand.

The Naga use of a wooden post as a vehicle for transmitting a supernatural power has a parallel in the Vedic literature. Vedic sacrificial implements were personified, worshiped, and sometimes deified. The most important of the implements was the sacrificial post to which the offering was tied. In the *Rigveda* (III, 8; see also Macdonell, 1963: 154) the sacrificial post is invoked. It is consecrated and deified; and as a god is urged to go forth to the dwelling place of the gods, presumably bearing the offering and prayers of men.

The wooden or stone memorials found throughout the Naga country generally occur in association with the Feasts of Merit or with death ceremonies, both of which, in turn, are associated with fertility. Several observers have pointed out that the memorials, besides being commemorative markers, are fertility symbols, in some cases clearly phallic representations, set up for the purpose of assuring the continued fertility of the area. There can be little doubt that the memorials are important in the Naga fertility complex, or megalithic complex as it is commonly designated. One detail, however, of their role in this context needs to be emphasized. The source of the fertilizing power lies not inherently in the symbol but in the life-force concentrated in the heads of human beings (Hutton, 1928: 400). It is transferred to the symbol in various ways, the memorial thus becoming a receptacle or repository for the life-force. The power of the life-force then can be very widely distributed and its effectiveness greatly prolonged.

The Angami Feast described above and the highest one, which follows it, together provide a particularly good example of memorials as repositories of, in this case, a portion of the feast giver's life-force. In the post-dragging ceremony the posts, infused with the feast giver's "fertility," are the vehicle by which it is disseminated through the village. During the time that the posts stand in the enclosure, they probably continue to disperse remaining amounts of the feast giver's "prosperity" to passersby; perhaps they retain, to a certain extent, the same power after they are moved to the front wall of his house. The Feast which follows the post dragging bears out these conjectures. It is the highest Angami Feast (Hutton, 1921: 232–33; 1922a: 242, 244–49) and must be preceded by the post dragging. Though similar in ritual to the post-dragging ceremony, this Feast is more expensive in rice and cattle. Two stones rather than two wooden posts are the memorials. The stones are sometimes brought from a considerable distance and are dragged not throughout the village as the posts are, but directly to a conspicuous and frequented spot either inside the village or nearby, where they are set up. Stone paving and a low stone platform where passersby can sit down are part of the construction. Hutton concludes that this Feast, which few men are prosperous enough to undertake, is "no more than the translation, into the permanency of stone, of the effect previously sought by means of wooden symbols" (1922a: 242). Since the stones are not pulled through the village as the posts are, the effort on this occasion is less to extend throughout the village a portion of the feast giver's life-force than to create a permanent place for its accumulation. The stones, as repositories of the life-force, shed the valuable quality on all villagers as they pass by. The Angami believe that upon a man's death some of his life-force attaches itself to the stones he has erected during his lifetime; thus long after death the life-force of a man who has completed the Feasts of Merit continues to benefit his fellows, to "increase their fertility and the fertility of their crops" (Fürer-Haimendorf, 1939: 26). Perhaps significantly, the Angami post-dragging Feast need be performed only once, but that involving erection of stones can be repeated as often as a man has the means to do so.

Both of these Feasts, also significantly, are performed during the time the entire village is holding the ceremony to celebrate the harvest of the rice crop. The importance of sowing and harvest in death customs, where also an effort is made to utilize the life-force, immediately comes to mind. Widely through the Naga country wooden images of the dead, or sometimes stones, are set up on or near graves. Both are clearly intended as receptacles for the life-force, for death provides the final opportunity for distributing the valuable quality. Sometimes the intent of the grave objects is to provide an abode of limited duration; at other times it is to create a permanent repository. Groups in which this custom is common and its implications unmistakable are the Angami, who bury their dead, and the Konyak, who practice platform exposure and treat the skull separately. The Eastern Rengma often build a stone platform over the grave, to provide a place "from which the spirit of the dead man will watch and bless the crops and those who work in them" (Mills, 1937: 220), another way of describing the influence of the life-force.

Position of the Mithan

The Naga sacrifice pigs and chickens on many more occasions than they do mithan, but the mithan enjoys a high status among sacrificial animals. Among many Naga groups the mithan is required for sacrifice at the highest Feasts of Merit, though a few groups permit substitutes. Only among the Eastern Rengma is the mithan displaced, by the water buffalo, as the premier sacrificial animal. Indeed in one of the three Eastern Rengma villages, mithan keeping is tabooed, and in only one of the other two are mithan kept at all, in small numbers, for use at funeral feasts and as a trade item (Mills, 1937: 91). Elsewhere in Naga country there are significant differences, tribal and local, in the numbers of mithan kept, and in their relative numbers compared to buffalo and common cattle. In broad terms, among the Eastern Rengma, certain Naga groups of Manipur, and perhaps certain Konyak, the buffalo, kept under free-ranging conditions, is more numerous than the mithan or displaces it. The difference in numbers of mithan kept by various groups has led to a trade in mithan; mithan move to the Angami, Lhota, Western Rengma, and Ao, all of whom keep few of them, from the Kacha Naga, Kuki (south of the Angami), Sema, and Phom, who keep more. In general, for the Naga, the mithan is an animal of significance not by virtue of its numbers but because of its important role in sacrifice for the Feasts of Merit.

Despite the similarity in certain basic beliefs and in a few traits of material culture and in the position accorded the mithan, the rich variation found among the Naga makes it impossible to select one group as typical. Various efforts have been made, in considering the Naga, to place those that share certain traits in larger discrete groups. One common division distinguishes between eastern and western Naga, putting the Angami, Lhota, Sema, and Rengma together in the latter group. Another division distinguishes between northern and southern Naga. We have chosen this division as a point of departure in selecting one Naga group for detailed treatment. Since migration into the Naga Hills has been primarily from north and south, one would expect to find the greatest contrasts between northern and southern groups (not always true, however), and to find the middle region a meeting place of traits. Thus we have chosen the Lhota Naga—midway geographically, and to some extent culturally, between the northern and southern edges of Naga country—to consider in detail.

12

The Lhota Naga

The Lhota numbered about 26,600 in the 1961 census and were the fifth largest Naga group in Nagaland. They live in the southwestern corner of Mokokchung District, occupying the upper elevations of three roughly parallel ranges. Wokha Hill, 6,500 feet in elevation, is the highest peak and one of the prominent features of the region. On its lower slopes is Wokha village, which has been the administrative center since the British named it so in 1877. The Doyang River winds through the area and with its tributaries drains the three ranges; finally it turns northward and joins the Dhansiri, which in turn flows into the Brahmaputra. The upper slopes of the ranges are cool and pleasant, the valleys hot and malarial.

Lhota traditions of origin are contradictory, but, taken together, they indicate clearly that the present Lhota contain elements deriving from the south and southeast, from the plains, and from the north, possibly the Himalayas. Some traditions link them closely with the Sema, Rengma, and Angami or Southern Sangtam in a southern origin, south of Japvo Mountain, and a northward migration to their present territory. In others they are said to have had a common origin with the plainsmen and to have migrated from the north.

Lhota villages are usually built along ridge crests. Sites were chosen because of defensibility, proximity to a water supply, and the availability of a suitable "head-tree." Lhota head-trees, where the heads of enemies were displayed, generally are magnificent specimens of *Ficus*, and the spot where one stands is one of the most sacred places of the village. For defense, the village was commonly encircled, except where the slope was very steep, with a strong fence of bamboo and wood, made formidable by

Source: This chapter is based largely on J. P. Mills, 1922.

115

sharpened bamboo spikes affixed to it. Ordinarily villages have a main entrance at either end, and apparently several lesser side entrances for paths that lead from fields on the slopes below. Lhota villages vary in size from 12 to 350 houses. Unless the slope of the land makes the arrangement impossible, the village consists of a single street with houses set regularly on both sides.

The Lhota, unlike most Naga, are polygynous; and a Lhota house is occupied by a man and his wives—often three for a man well off—and their young children. Houses are modest compared to those of the Ao, Sema, and Angami; Mills found them cramped and uncomfortable. A Lhota, he says, would consider it a great waste of money to build a fine house as a display of wealth. Not all Lhota houses are equally modest, however; though a poor widow will occupy a simple hut, a wealthy man will have a fair-sized structure, perhaps 30 by 18 feet in size. House walls are made of interwoven bamboos; the roof is of thatch or palm leaf. Some houses are built directly on the ground and have an earthen floor. More often the house, or most of it, is raised on a bamboo platform, which, contrary to the usual Naga practice in such houses, is covered with earth. Thus the Lhota combine the two basic forms of Naga house structure.

House decoration is of much less importance to the Lhota than to other Naga groups. Carved mithan heads or other symbols of wealth and fertility do not decorate the house posts, as they often do for the Ao, Sema, and Angami. Conspicuous additions to the house, as rights gained through performance of the Feasts of Merit, are lacking. Only two items of house display, related to the Feasts of Merit, are mentioned by Mills. After performing certain ceremonies following the mithan sacrifice, a man has the right to decorate his roof with "house horns," crossed bamboos representing mithan horns. Few, however, do this, because it is regarded as a snobbish display of wealth. Instead, Lhota display is confined to the floor of the open platform at the back of the house. This floor is never covered with earth, whether or not the house floor is. If the house owner has not performed the ceremony commemorating the mithan sacrifice, he covers the platform with a layer of split bamboos laid at right angles to the whole bamboos of which the floor is made. When he has performed the ceremony, that covering is replaced by a mat made of split bamboos woven in a checker pattern.

Art motifs employing the mithan head generally appear in the Lhota village only in the men's houses or morungs (Lhota: *champo*). For the Lhota the morung, both as an institution and as a building, is important. Every village except the very smallest is divided into two or more sections (*khels*), and each khel has a morung. Lhota khels usually are simply divisions of convenience rather than divisions by clan; thus morung affiliation for the Lhota has little relation to clan membership.

Lhota boys sleep in the morung until they marry. The morung becomes the center of many of their activities; there they learn the traditions of the tribe and receive training for the conduct of their lives. Even after they marry the morung continues to be important to them. Raids, for example, are planned there. In the days when headhunting was possible, warriors returning from such raids, whether married or not, went into the morung for certain ceremonies before they entered their own houses. Enemy heads were brought first to the morung and sometimes were kept there overnight before being hung in the head-tree. Lhota, unlike some Naga, are by their own traditions absolutely forbidden to take heads of other Lhota, but villages sometimes fight one another and captives are taken for ransom; the morung is where these prisoners are held. The morung, too, is where the skull and horns of mithan sacrificed in the fourth of the Feasts of Merit are hung pending performance of the highest Feast, when they may be removed to the feast giver's house.

Certain good luck stones which are believed to affect the prosperity of the part of the village represented by the morung are kept in the morung. Other good luck stones which affect the prosperity of the whole village are kept at the foot of the head-tree; and still others are kept by individuals at home or in their granaries. In the Lhota public ceremony that marks the beginning of the agricultural year—parts of which are performed specifically to assure prosperity in agriculture, success in hunting, and increase in population—much of the ceremonial is organized by morung.

Fürer-Haimendorf has written (1950a: 139–40) that the Naga morung is the "vessel" or "focal point of the ritual virtue [life-force] of the village or village-quarter." For the Lhota as well as other Naga, this may have been more evident in the days of headhunting, when bringing an enemy head into the village was the surest way of increasing the store of life-force of the village. Though the Lhota did not store the head trophies permanently in the morung as some Naga did, the Lhota morung nonetheless was the ritual center for headhunting ceremonies, as it was for a variety of other ceremonies, all believed to contribute to continued prosperity and fertility. That the small amount of symbolic or decorative carving employed by the Lhota appears only in the morung assumes an added significance.

The Lhota morung buildings, while not comparable with the great structures of certain other Naga, are nonetheless the most impressive structures in their villages. The morung looks much like the houses, except that it is larger and has a big open verandah at the front. A wooden post, which goes up through the roof to the high front gable above, is conspicuous in the center of the verandah. Several feet behind it is a second post. Both are carved with representations of the hornbill (*Dichoceros bicornis*), considered by the Lhota as a symbol of wealth. A third large post, carved with a conventionalized mithan head, symbol of prosperity and fertility, is at the back of the morung, supporting the roof over the back platform.

Usually a morung is rebuilt only every nine years regardless of its state of disrepair. Dismantling the old morung and building the new one is an occasion surrounded with ceremony. If new posts are needed, the best wood carver in the village is given the job. If the old ones will do for another nine years they are carefully removed and used again. A priest opens the ceremonies by removing part of the roof of the old building. After the old morung has been completely taken down and the site made ready for the new structure, the priest again officiates. He ceremoniously marks the places for the posts, which are then set up. Now the new morung is built as quickly as possible, usually being finished, except for thatching, on the same day. The attendant ceremonies are fairly elaborate and include feasting and drinking as well as sacrifice and ritual. There is also a mock fight between the young men and women of the village, the young women pretending to push into the morung while the young men try to exclude them. The Lhota believe that the women who participate in the fight increase their fertility, presumably because of their contact with the morung (Mills, 1922: 24–28, 30–31, 33–34).

The Lhota, like many Naga tribes, are organized into three phratries. Each phratry, in turn, is divided into clans, some of which are further divided. In theory the phratries are exogamous, but in practice only clan exogamy has been strictly followed. Contrary to the general Naga pattern of one phratry being inferior, the Lhota phratries are of equal status. One Lhota clan, however, is regarded as inferior. With that exception, all clans have equal rights, though feelings of superiority exist here and there among them. Mills reports one clan that claims a "vague headship over the phratry . . . ," because in the old days only this clan had the right to keep mithan and to wear ivory armlets—expensive ornaments worn, in one design or another, by practically all Naga groups. Among some, the Ao for example, complicated traditions determine which clans may wear the armlets and under what conditions (Mills, 1922: 87, 88, 89, 91; 1926: 49).

Traditionally each Lhota village was independent and was ruled by a chief aided by a council of elders. The chieftainship was hereditary within the family of the village founder, though it was not always passed from father to son. Hereditary limits on eligibility for the chieftainship might seem to link the Lhota to the so-called autocratic Naga tribes. In other ways, however, democratic tradition and behavior prevail among the Lhota, and they often are grouped with the Angami and other democratic Naga tribes.

Although the Lhota are skilled fishermen and hunters, agriculture is the main source of their food and occupies most of their time. Like most Naga, they are shifting cultivators. Their most important crops are dry rice, for food, and cotton, for trade. Maize is an important secondary food crop. Millet is also grown, but is not as important to the Lhota as to certain other Naga groups. Among the other crops are sorghum, Job's tears, lentils, taro, chillies, gourds, the oilseeds sesame and *Perilla oci-moides,* tobacco, and mustard. Except for mustard, a garden crop, these cultivated plants are usually grown in fields, many of them around the edges of the rice fields or in plots within the rice fields.

The entire Lhota village cultivates one large block of land, the usual practice among the Naga, except for those who have terraced fields, and the practice of the Adi and Hill Miri across the Brahmaputra. The Lhota divide the block into smaller fields, each cultivated by a household. Within the block the individual fields are not fenced, but a rough fence is built around the entire block as protection against wild animals and cattle. In spite of this, the Lhota spend considerable time while their crops are maturing in protecting them from birds and animals.

The domestic animals are mithan, common cattle, pigs, goats, dogs, and chickens. Buffalo are absent. The Lhota occasionally buy a buffalo in the plains, to provide meat, but they are unacceptable as sacrificial animals. Pigs and chickens are kept by practically every family; they are needed constantly for ceremonies, both public and private, religious and social. The religious official next in importance to priest is called *wokchung,* "pig killer." Young pigs are kept in the front room of the Lhota house at night, but when they are older they wander freely about the village, returning home once a day to be fed. Chickens scavenge food for themselves; but for laying hens, baskets are put on shelves in the front room of the house and the chicks are hatched there. Goats, though not useful for sacrifice, are kept for their hair, which is dyed and much valued for ornamenting ceremonial costumes. At night, the goats are housed in raised huts within the village to protect them against leopards. Dogs are valued hunting animals, useful scavengers, and are needed for sacrifice at certain ceremonies. Formerly dog hair, like goat hair, was plucked from the living animal and used for decoration. Dogs are the only domestic animals to which the Lhota give names. They are fed and generally are well treated.

Mills's statement, from the 1920's, that mithan "are no longer kept in large numbers by the Lhotas," indicates that this was not always so. He gave several reasons for Lhota reluctance to keep many mithan: they do much damage to crops; they are a risky investment for the cautious Lhota because of their great susceptibility to rinderpest, which can quickly wipe out a whole herd; and their chief use is for sacrifice, for which common cattle are almost as suitable. Another reason may be a fear, which is fairly common in democratic Naga groups where wealth is relatively evenly distributed, that legal and other problems will arise from the mithan's destruction of crops. In the autocratic groups, where wealth, including land and livestock, is controlled by a few, such problems are more or less limited to those few, and they can answer complaints without economic ruin to themselves.

Besides mithan, two breeds of common cattle are frequently encountered among the Lhota: Assamese cattle and cattle of the Naga breed. The Lhota buy large numbers of Assamese cattle, but keep only a few for breeding and for food, and take most of them straight on to be sold to the Ao and Sema. The Naga breed, considered by the Lhota to be indigenous, is black or black and white in color. These animals are considerably heavier than the Assamese cattle and provide more meat (Mills, 1922: 59–63).

The Mithan

Care and Selection

The Lhota do not herd any of their cattle, but permit them complete freedom in the forest. Owners of mithan go to the forest occasionally, call to their mithan, and give them salt. Owners of common cattle go out to see them every few days; this suggests that common cattle stay closer to the village than mithan, which prefer the shade of the deep forest. Sometimes men split the ears of their mithan to mark their ownership. Some mithan owners keep very young mithan calves in the village, tied up outside their houses, until the animals' legs are strong. Hybrids of mithan bull and common cow occur; they too are turned loose in the forest but usually come back to the village for the night. Perhaps these hybrids are the cattle to which Mills refers when he speaks of Lhota villages as "swarming with pigs, dogs, and cattle" (Mills, 1922: 23, 60, 61).

The Lhota as well as other Naga groups have devised an ingenious system for spreading the risk in livestock ownership. Many Lhota will own a half or a quarter of a mithan or of other cattle. Often a man will own parts of several cattle rather than one entire animal. Ownership of pigs is also shared occasionally (Mills, 1922: 60).

Birth of domestic animals and of human beings is marked by the Lhota and other Naga by restrictions on certain human activities for a period of time. The common Naga-Assamese word *genna*, "forbidden," is used for the time the restrictions are in effect.[1] At the birth of a mithan, the owner observes a six-day genna if the calf is a male, a five-day genna if it is a female. During that time the owner must not permit a stranger to enter his house, nor may he eat the flesh of an animal killed by a tiger. The same genna is observed for all newborn cattle, and rather interestingly, for human beings, at least in terms of time—though in the case of humans the restrictions are slightly greater. The genna observed for puppies and young pigs is five days, with the same restrictions as for mithan and common cattle (Mills, 1922: 60, 61, 63, 146).

An additional small ritual is performed when a mithan calf is born: a necklace consisting of six seeds of the bean *Entada scandens* is put around the neck of a male calf and one of five seeds on a female. The necklace remains on the animal only a few hours and then is removed to be hung in the owner's house.

Mills observes that whereas purebred mithan are black with white stockings and a gray forehead, many mithan of the Naga Hills have white or brown markings. This he attributes to interbreeding with common cattle. He describes the mithan of the Naga Hills as "hopelessly contaminated" from breeding with common cattle, and notes that "any pair of mithan is liable to produce a throwback" (1922: 59–60). Color changes, however, may be in part the result of domestication, not simply hybridization, for such changes occur among various species under domestication. Furthermore, Hutton doubts that mithan and common cattle are so mixed in the Naga Hills outside the Lhota country.

When mithan are used in the mithan sacrifice of the Feasts of Merit sequence, they must meet certain standards. Among these is coloring, which must be that of the purebred animal. White marking on body, tail, or forehead disqualifies the animal. So does white on the leg, unless all four legs are white. If, as Mills indicates, Lhota mithan are hopelessly contaminated with common cattle, there must be few indeed suitable for sacrifice. This may have been a factor that discouraged the Lhota in mithan keeping. Moreover, hybrid bulls or those of common cattle are acceptable as substitutes if they are black in color. Since, as Mills writes (1922: 60, 61), hybrids of mithan bull and ordinary cow are black or dark brown and the indigenous Naga breed is black or black and white, properly colored substitutes must be relatively easily available. The Lhota also can easily obtain suitable mithan through trade.

1. *Genna* is used in various senses: 1) for a Naga ceremony; 2) for "forbidden"; and 3) for "taboo."

In Economic, Political, and Legal Matters

Since for the Lhota the mithan's main utility is as a sacrificial animal, suitable mithan bulls are saved for sacrifice, but sometimes a mithan bull with a defect making it unsuitable for sacrifice is killed just for food. The flesh of mithan cows, though, is eaten only when an animal dies of disease or old age. Mills (1922: 78) mentions that when animals of any sort are killed—presumably mithan are included—virtually the entire animal, except the hair, is eaten. He includes skin, blood, and entrails. The Naga who served in France in World War I were surprised at the wasteful European custom of discarding the offal. Lhota do not milk their mithan or common cattle, but they seem not to have the revulsion toward milk that certain other people of eastern Asia have; Mills reports that they will drink milk if it is offered to them (1922: 61).

Like most shifting cultivators, the Lhota do not use the plow, and neither mithan nor common cattle serve for draft. The shoulder blades of both these animals are sometimes made into shovels, used mainly to clean away mud and other debris from the front door of the house, which usually is at ground level.

Before British penetration into the Naga Hills and the introduction of government coins, Lhota trade probably was conducted wholly by barter. The Lhota have no tradition of an earlier form of currency. Though individuals obtained mithan for sacrifice by bartering with their neighbors to the east and south, the animals seem not to have been prominent in Lhota trade. When a mithan was traded, however, or ivory armlets or boars' tusks, an old Lhota man was employed as an intermediary. The evil, if any, from these three items especially susceptible to evil influences, was believed to fall upon the intermediary, who was paid for his risk, rather than upon the purchaser. In the 1920's the compensation was one rupee for a transaction involving a mithan, eight annas for an ivory armlet, and four annas for a set of boar's tusks (Mills, 1922: 44).

The mithan's role in Lhota political and legal matters is small, in remarkable contrast to the situation north of the Brahmaputra in NEFA. It is not generally used in fines,[2] friendship pacts, oaths, ransom, in buying slaves, in war, or in the traditional Naga ceremonies associated with the taking of a head. Its absence in Lhota war and headhunting

2. Verrier Elwin (1961: 72) does recount one incident that took place in 1909 in which mithan constituted the fine charged to Tuensang village as punishment for a headhunting raid. The fine, however, was imposed by the British, who customarily demanded mithan for headhunting violations. Hutton points out (pers. com., Sept. 8, 1966) that the British assessed fines in mithan because they were the recognized local medium of exchange; but even so, the fine was usually paid in cash at a fixed rate per mithan.

activities is extraordinary. Headhunting was a vital part of traditional Lhota life. The preparations before a raid were carefully prescribed and followed. The rituals following the taking of heads were elaborate and lengthy, and performing them conferred certain rights of dress and ornamentation on the performer, as well as earning him the respect of his fellows. Pigs, chickens, and rice beer were all part of the ceremonies and feasts involved—but mithan, despite their importance in the Feasts of Merit, were not. Thus the abolition of headhunting by the British, though it profoundly altered the Lhota way of life, did not affect the position of the mithan in society.

In Marriage, Birth, and Death

The young Lhota man selects his own bride. After his decision, the parents of the two young people arrange the bride-price, which includes a commitment from the bridegroom to work for his father-in-law for a period of time, usually about a year. After the arrangements are complete, a series of ceremonies begins that involves both families. Fowl are sacrificed at several ceremonies, and rice beer is always an important part. On two occasions a pig is sacrificed, and the meat is divided and distributed according to custom.

In both the bride-price and the ceremonies the mithan is entirely overlooked. The bride-price is figured in currency, and is divided into eleven parts. Some of the parts are paid only if the groom does not perform certain services for the bride's family. The eleventh part, the main one, is 30 rupees or about 250 baskets of rice, paid in installments, commonly over a long period of time. Often a Lhota man has two or three wives and rarely even four or five. All are of equal status.

The birth of human beings, as we have said, is marked in much the same way as the birth of certain domestic animals—with the parents of the household observing a five-day genna for a girl and a six-day genna for a boy, followed by ceremony. During the time of genna they may not speak to strangers, nor may strangers enter the house. The family does not feast—on mithan flesh or anything else—to celebrate the birth. Indeed, one of the prohibitions is that freshly killed meat may not be brought into the dwelling (Mills, 1922: 146).

Though the mithan is absent in marriage and birth ritual, it plays a slight role in death ceremonies. The Lhota bury their dead, as soon after death as possible, in the village street in front of the dead person's house. They perform certain rituals and sacrifices before the corpse is buried, and more elaborate ones afterward, in which a mithan is sacrificed for a man who has taken heads. Immediately after burial two bamboo posts are erected on the grave, one at the head and one at the foot, and a bamboo pole is suspended between them. The dead man's prized possessions are hung on the pole, along with a basket containing a gourd of rice beer, six pieces of meat, and some rice. On a woman's grave only a basket, containing five, rather than six, pieces of meat, is hung on the pole. A fire is lighted on the grave. For a man, all members of his household observe a six-day genna, during which they may not speak to strangers or kill any living organism. For a woman the genna is five days. The personal possessions are removed from the grave afterward, and it is decorated with various symbolic items, including some that indicate the number of times a man has performed the head-taking ceremony and his achievements as a hunter. His mithan skulls, which show his progress and generosity in the Feasts of Merit, are also displayed on the grave. It is customary for the wives of a dead man to be taken as wives by his brother, who does not have to pay a bride-price or perform a marriage ceremony for them. Should a widow prefer to remain unmarried, she keeps one of her husband's mithan skulls instead of putting it on the grave. This act is regarded as a vow of perpetual widowhood. At the end of the genna, the clansmen of the dead person offer sacrifices—a mithan and a pig for a man who has taken heads, but only a pig for a man who has not, or for a woman. The fire on the grave is kept burning and food offerings are made until the time of the annual public ceremony known as Tuku, marking the end of the agricultural year—which may be many months after the death. The final death rites are then performed for all the dead of the village, who are believed to depart for the Land of the Dead at that time. On the last day of the Tuku objects are removed from all graves in the village, the fires are extinguished, the bamboo structures taken down, and the graves again become just a part of the village street.

In addition to the offerings made at the grave, similar offerings are made on the village path that leads to the Land of the Dead, which is believed to be under Wokha Hill. Immediately after a man has died, two relatives go out of the village on this path, carrying with them a gourd of rice beer and a stick marked to show the heads he has taken and which of the Feasts of Merit he has given. The stick is set up in the ground and the gourd hung on it; they are intended to support and refresh the dead person. At the end of the genna a bamboo structure is built beside the path, and symbols recording the man's achievements, similar to those put on the grave, are attached to it. If he has not performed any of the Feasts of Merit, only a single bamboo pole is put up. When the final rites on the last day of the Tuku ceremony are performed at the grave, a miniature altar is built at the bamboo memorial on the path, and the last offerings of meat, rice, fruit, together with various imitation ornaments and weapons, are placed on it. Sometimes an additional small bamboo platform is put up then, with a notched stick for the departing spirit to use as a ladder; offerings are placed on this platform too. The obligations of the living to the dead are then concluded (Mills, 1922: 129–30, 154–55, 157–60).

Certain death ceremonies of the Naga tribes commonly are tied to the time of sowing or of harvest, periods which seem particularly susceptible to the influence of fertility-bestowing rites. The Lhota custom of performing the final death ceremonies for all the dead of the village in conjunction with the public ceremony that concludes the agricultural year represents such a tie. Although Mills does not say so, the Lhota delay may be an attempt to utilize the life-force of the dead for a limited time. Hutton and Fürer-Haimendorf both have written about how the Angami and Konyak extend and make use of the life-force of the dead, chiefly by means of wooden grave images, stones placed on the grave, or stone containers to hold the skulls of the dead; each of these objects is intended as a habitation for the lingering life-force. It is quite possible that the bamboo grave structures of the Lhota have the same purpose, in this case to provide a temporary abode for the life-force of the dead. That these grave structures are taken down in a final ceremony at the time the dead are believed to depart for the Land of the Dead seems to support such a conjecture.

All Naga peoples have a horror of certain forms of "accidental" death. For the Lhota, to die by drowning, fire, falling from a tree or falling on one's own spear, by attack from a wild animal, or in childbirth comes in this category. Such a death requires special purificatory rites. In most such situations, the body is buried close to the place of death; Mills gives a detailed account of the precautions taken by the family of a drowned person and by anyone associated with him at the time of the disaster. In addition to various rituals, the family abandons the house and all the property of the victim. His crops stand unattended in the field. His money is thrown out and remains untouched on the ground where it falls. His animals, presumably including his mithan, present a special problem, for to kill them would defile the dao. They are therefore simply abandoned, but if they become a bother to the village they are put to death by being driven over a cliff. One of the rituals performed by the southern Lhota for such forms of death requires sacrifice of a chicken. As this is a very risky job, Lhota living near the Sema will hire a Sema to carry out the sacrifice. He is paid the livestock of the dead man, which he usually kills before taking away. He cannot be paid in beads or money, for these contaminated items could readily circulate back to the Lhota (Mills, 1922: 160–62).

Precautions of this sort after "accidental" death are taken by many Naga groups. Rarely may the body be disposed of in the normal place.

Hutton looks on this as an attempt to protect the life-force of the living from the evil influences surrounding such a death (1965: 32). The life-force of a person who has died "unnaturally" seems to have been contaminated, and its effect on the living, their prosperity and fertility, would be detrimental rather than beneficial.

In Feasts of Merit

For all Naga peoples the Feasts of Merit are of great importance. This institution, significant among the Kuki-Chin peoples also, will be touched upon again in Chapter 14 on the Central Chin and discussed in detail in Part III.

The Lhota series (described by Mills, 1922: 136–44)[3] usually consists of four Feasts, the fourth of which is the mithan sacrifice. After that the Lhota, unlike most Naga, embark on stone-dragging ceremonies, which in a sense commemorate in stone the mithan sacrifice. Like all the Feasts, the Lhota Feasts of Merit require sacrifice of numerous animals—chickens, pigs, common cattle, and mithan—and public feasting and drinking. They increase in scope and lavishness; in earlier days a man who had done the entire series gave one last Feast that provided even for the birds and beasts. Food was scattered on the ground for the village chickens and pigs, and carried to the feast giver's fields for the birds. Generosity on this scale is impossible today, and while all Lhota men aspire to performing the entire series of Feasts, few reach their goal.

The first Feast is relatively simple, and a man often is able to give it before he marries. He sacrifices a bull of common cattle, of any color, dividing the meat among his guests, who consist of those members of his clan residing in his village who have also performed the first Feast. The host also supplies generous amounts of rice beer. Traditionally, the feast giver sent small amounts of meat to fellow clansmen in nearby villages.

The second Feast is more involved and expensive, and is usually not undertaken by an unmarried man. The ceremony takes two days. On the first day the feast giver sacrifices a large pig and, again, a bull—of any color—of common cattle. The guests are largely husbands of the women of the feast giver's clan, though a few blood relatives and senior men of the village are invited, too. The second day two small pigs and some cocks are sacrificed. Guests on that day are, as in the first Feast, village men of the feast giver's clan who themselves have given the second Feast.

The third Feast is virtually a repetition of the second; in Mills's day it was beginning to be either combined with the fourth Feast or elim-

---

3. Mills uses the expression "social *gennas*," in his book on the Lhota, to refer to the Feasts of Merit.

inated entirely. After the third Feast and all subsequent ones, an additional small ceremony requiring the sacrifice of two pigs and two chickens is held near the granary of the sacrificer.

The fourth Feast, most important of the series, requires a mithan for sacrifice. An unblemished mithan bull is the traditional animal. If a black hybrid or a black bull of common cattle is substituted, it is spoken of as a mithan. Many preparations are made for the mithan sacrifice. Large amounts of rice beer are made ready, and the whole village is notified of the impending festivities. On the day of the sacrifice, the sacrificial animal, its horns decorated with leaves, is tied at the front of the feast giver's house. His wife gives it water and salt. After a prayer by the religious official known as wokchung, it is thrown to the ground and killed, with a spear thrust to the heart, by an old man who immediately runs off while the observers throw lumps of earth at him. The feast giver then ritually cuts the animal as if he were dividing the meat. He is inside his house, however, when the meat actually is divided. He must not, under any circumstances, take any of this meat, nor may his household, lest they go mad. Quite often he may avoid mithan flesh entirely for a year for fear of eating flesh from his own mithan.

The body of the sacrificed mithan is not divided haphazardly, but according to tradition. The clan of the feast giver receives the chest, the clan of his wife the hindquarters. Husbands of the women of his clan receive the forelegs. The meat of the head goes to certain of those same husbands—those who made the public announcement of the Feast. The old intermediary who helped buy the mithan receives the tongue. The old man who killed the animal receives the lower part of the stomach. The feast giver has a right to the skull and horns, but they must hang in the bachelors' dormitory until the man drags a stone. Then he can display them in his house.

Among most Naga groups, Y-shaped wooden posts are set up in connection with the Feasts of Merit. For a few, including the Lhota and Angami, whether or not Y-shaped posts are used in the Feasts of Merit, the erection of monoliths is a part of the sequence. In these two groups a "stone-dragging ceremony," culminating in the setting up of a large stone or pair of stones, follows the mithan sacrifice, if the person has the means to undertake the ceremony. Among the Western Rengma, monoliths are erected in a similar ceremony, which can be performed only after completing all of the Feasts; despite this requirement, the Rengma monoliths are not tied so directly to the Feasts of Merit, but occur in a broader context (Mills, 1937: 195–97).

A Lhota must have performed the first four Feasts before he can proceed to the stone-dragging ceremony. The first time he performs the ceremony one stone is set up. In any subsequent ceremonies two stones are dragged and erected. The Lhota place a limit on the number of times the ceremony can be performed. The limit is different in different villages, but is high enough so that Mills knew of only one man who had achieved the limit. In that case twenty-five stones had been set up, representing thirteen performances of the ceremony (1922: 136–37). The stones are massive, some as much as seven or eight feet long and three or more feet wide. The northern Lhota carry the stone, lifting it by means of a specially constructed bamboo frame; the southern Lhota actually drag it on a sledge made of branches. Mills describes in detail a stone-dragging ceremony for one Lhota village, adding that details vary from village to village. The stone dragger and his family make elaborate preparations for this ceremony; among them is selecting the stone, which may be as far as two miles away from the man's house. Many rituals precede actual removal of the stone from the ground. After removal, the stone, with more ritual and prayers, is taken to the dragger's house, and laid flat in front of it. He provides a bull of common cattle, which is killed, and the village spends the evening in feasting, singing, and drinking rice beer. The stone dragger, his household, and his clan members do not take any of the meat. On the next day the stone is placed upright in its final resting place amid more ritual and festivity, and ever after reveals to all passersby that the man of that house has performed the mithan sacrifice.

Once in a while the Lhota put up large forked posts, ten to twelve feet in height, rather than stones, to commemorate the mithan sacrifice. This is done usually when suitable stones are not available, although a division of one Lhota clan is forbidden to erect stones at all, and always puts up forked posts (Mills, 1922: 136–44).

A Lhota who performs the Feasts of Merit greatly enhances his social status. By the special cloths that each Feast entitles him to wear and by the monoliths or forked posts around his house, he is at once recognized as a man of wealth and thus as a man of some importance. When he has completed the series and dragged a stone, he also becomes eligible, provided he meets other qualifications, for the position of *puthi*, village priest, and for various lesser religious posts.

The Lhota Feasts, like all Naga Feasts of Merit, are performed not solely for the benefit of the feast giver and his family but as part of the Naga fertility complex. The feast giver is attempting to extend to his village a portion of his prosperity and success. The Lhota series of Feasts is neither reported nor analyzed as closely as those of certain other Naga peoples, but fertility connotations can nevertheless be discerned. Throughout the series, for example, there are many small rituals intended to assure fertility. One is the minor ceremony performed at the granary of the feast

Figure 1
The mithan.

Figure 2
Two mithan in a Sema Naga village (photo by H.-E. Kauffmann).

Figure 3
A pied mithan (photo by H.-E. Kauffmann).

Figure 4
Dark- and light-colored Dafla mithan (photo by C. von Fürer-Haimendorf).

Figure 5
The gaur.

Figure 6
The banteng.

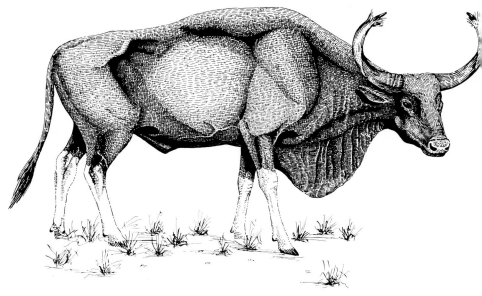

Figure 7
The kouprey.

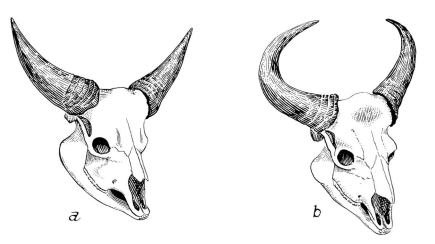

Figure 8
Skulls of mithan and gaur (after W. T. Blanford, 1888–91): *a.* mithan; *b.* gaur.

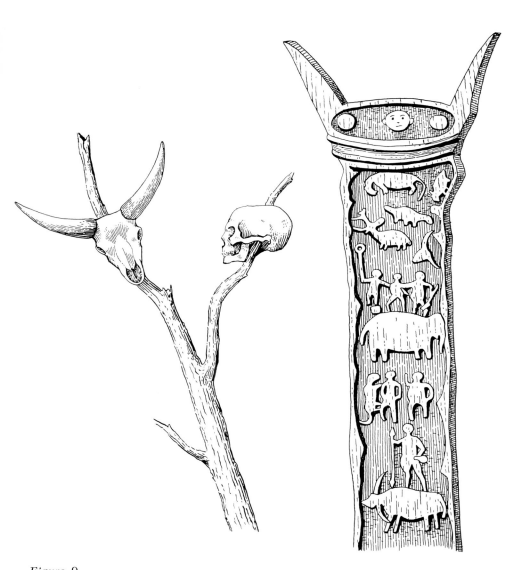

Figure 9

Northern Chin memorials to a dead man (after Carey and Tuck, 1896). Among the carvings on the wooden plank (*right*) are tallies of the dead man's accomplishments in killing enemies, in taking slaves, in hunting, and in sacrificing animals at feasts. On the forked pole (*left*) are the skulls of a human and a mithan, both presumably killed to accompany the man to the afterworld.

Figure 10

Mithan being killed among the Minyong Adi by strangulation (after C. von Fürer-Haimendorf, 1963).

Figure 11

An ancient Ao Naga ceremonial *dao* exhibited at mithan sacrifices. The V-shaped marks indicate mithan sacrificed previously (after J. P. Mills, 1926).

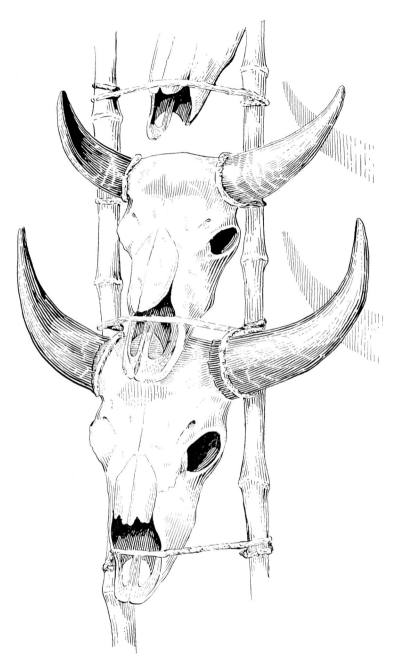

Figure 12
Detail of bamboo frame holding skulls of mithan and other cattle in a Khumi
village, Chittagong Hill Tracts (after sketch by D. E. Sopher).

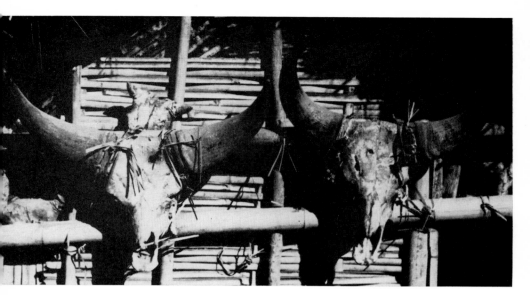

Figure 13

Mithan skulls displayed on the house wall of a Sema Naga man who has given Feasts of Merit (photo by H.-E. Kauffmann).

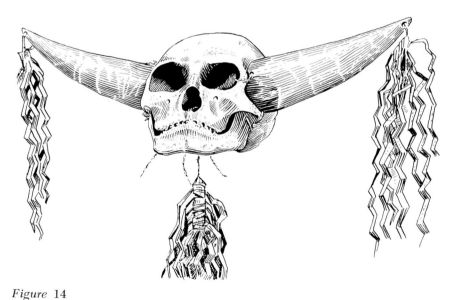

Figure 14

A Konyak Naga war trophy: a human skull decorated with mithan horns and grass tassels. Apparently the horns, symbolic of wealth and fertility, add to the magical power of the head (after J. H. Hutton, 1921).

Figure 15

Warrior of the Kalyo-Kengyu Naga with a headdress of mithan horns, boar
tusks, tiger claws, and hornbill feathers, all associated with the successful
headhunter (after C. von Fürer-Haimendorf, 1939).

Figure 16

Sema Naga house post carved with mithan heads and horns (after J. H. Hutton, 1921a). The other conventionalized design on the post is known as "enemies' teeth" and represents an article of dress worn by the successful headhunter.

Figure 17

Heads of mithan carved in wood on Naga house (after C. R. Stoner, 1953–54).

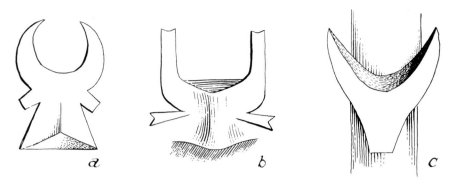

Figure 18

Conventionalized mithan heads carved in wood:
a. and b. among the Angami Naga (after J. H. Hutton, 1921);
c. among the Lhota Naga (after J. P. Mills, 1922).

Figure 19

Angami Naga house with house horns (after J. H. Hutton, 1921).

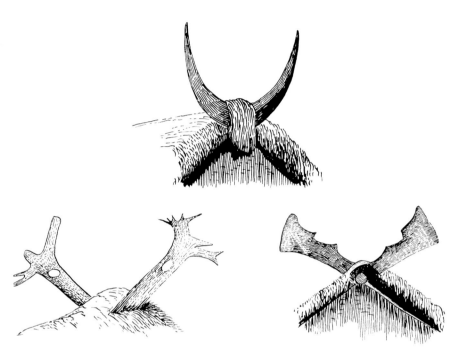

Figure 20
Types of Angami Naga house horns (after J. H. Hutton, 1921).

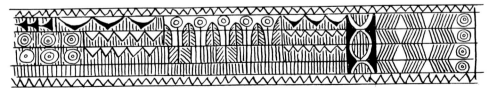

Figure 21
Lhota Naga textile design with mithan motif (from J. P. Mills, 1922).

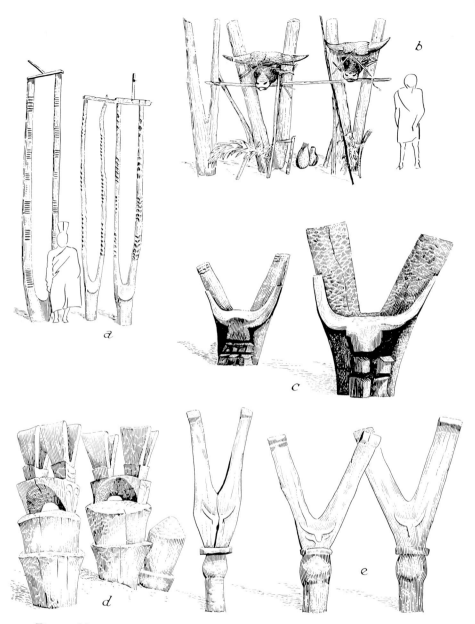

Figure 22

Forked sacrificial posts:
a. Falam Chin (after H. N. C. Stevenson, 1943); *b.* Northern Sangtam Naga (after C. R. Stonor, 1950); *c.* Sema Naga (after J. H. Hutton, 1921a); *d.* Ao Naga (after J. P. Mills, 1926); *e.* Lushai (after J. Shakespear, 1912).

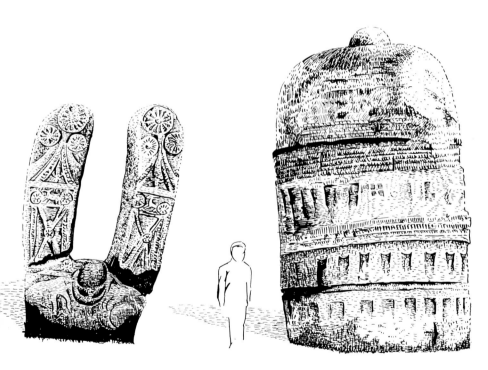

Figure 23
Forked stone and phallic stone of Dimapur (after J. H. Hutton, 1922).

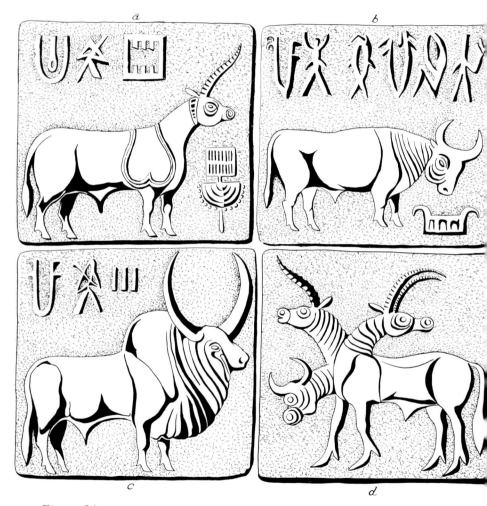

Figure 24

Bulls on Indus Valley seals (after J. Marshall, 1931, and J.-M. Casal, 1964): *a.* "aurochs"; *b.* "short-horned bull" (gaur?); *c.* zebu bull; *d.* three-headed animal from Amri.

Figure 25

Bull from hunting shrine at Level V at Çatal Hüyük, Anatolia (*c.* 5850 B.C.) (courtesy of J. Mellaart).

a. General scene. Note the naked woman with exaggerated sexual features (mother-goddess?) beneath the bull, and the man on the bull's back.

b. Detail of scene. Note the leopard-skin garments and hats (the leopard was associated with the mother-goddess), and that the scene suggests festivity, perhaps baiting rather than hunting.

Figure 26

Reconstruction of a shrine at Level VII at Çatal Hüyük (*c.* 6150 B.C.) (after Alan Sorrell). Note the clear evidences of a cult centering on concern with life and death: human skulls, disposed of separately; vultures pecking at headless human corpses; women's breasts; and aurochs, ram, and boar heads of clay but incorporating the skull and horn cores of actual animals.

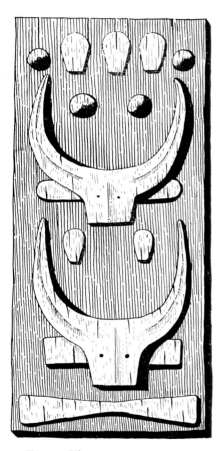

Figure 27

Angami Naga village gates (after H.-E. Kauffmann and J. H. Hutton). The motifs are associated, in one way or another, with prosperity and fertility: bovine heads, enemy heads, women's breasts, rows of "truncated breasts," concentric circles (probably representing moon or sun), warrior and spear heads.

Figure 28

Shrine in Level VI, Çatal Hüyük (*c.* 5950 B.C.), showing bench and pillars
with horn cores of the aurochs (after J. Mellaart, 1965).

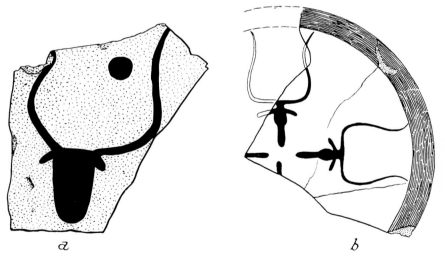

a   *b*

Figure 29

Bull head or bucranium designs from Arpachiyah in Iraq (*c.* 5000 B.C.) (after
Mallowan and Rose, 1935):
a. bull head with disk between horns; *b*. naturalistic bull head on circular plate.

giver at the third Feast and any subsequent ones. Another is the prayer said over the sacrificial mithan, which asks among other things that "the village may flourish and grow big." In the stone-dragging ceremony, one of the rituals performed over the stone before it is brought into the village involves a chicken and that universal fertility symbol, an egg; both are carried by the performer while the stone is being pulled. The wokchung prays for prosperity for all the village as well as for the performer and his wife, then kills the chicken and places it with the egg before the stone. The descriptions of the Lhota do not specifically identify the monoliths as repositories of the life-force of the individual concerned. Since, however, Hutton and Fürer-Haimendorf have repeatedly pointed out the role of the Angami monoliths as repositories of the life-force and their significance in the Naga fertility complex, it seems a reasonable assumption that this holds for the Lhota too.

In Religion

At the time Mills wrote his book on the Lhota, one of his early works, he was not as fully aware as he and others later became of the deep concern with fertility that seems to underlie much of Naga life. The Lhota hunt heads, they perform the Feasts of Merit and certain of their death ceremonies in a religious spirit and in the firm belief that these activities will bring prosperity to the individuals concerned and contribute to the well-being of the clan and village generally.

Although the Lhota believe in the existence of various supernatural beings and make propitiatory offerings to them, they apparently are not burdened, as are the Dafla for one, by constant fear of a host of wrathful spirits. On the contrary, Mills (1922: 113) notes that the Lhota carry out "cheerfully" what they consider to be their religious duties. Lhota religion in practice revolves around the correct performance of numerous ceremonies: community ceremonies for the general welfare of the village, community ceremonies tied to the agricultural cycle, individual rites performed at regular intervals, and individual rites performed in specific circumstances such as illness. These ceremonies and rites, like the Feasts of Merit, are directed to individual and community well-being and their continuation. To omit any of the usual ceremonies would be dangerous, though not disastrous.

Notions about the Land of the Dead and the souls of men are definite in certain respects but vague and contradictory in others. The same may be said about most Naga groups. The Lhota are certain about the existence of the Land of the Dead; they can point out the entrance. It is a cave that lies at the end of a narrow stratum of white rock on the eastern face of Wokha Hill. Just below it, at the end of another conspicuous rock stratum, is another entrance, for animals, for they also go to the Land of the Dead. The Lhota believe that existence there is very much like existence on earth. There is a vague feeling, however, that a good life on earth earns a good life in the Land of the Dead; that those who did good deeds while living may expect to find a rich and happy existence awaiting them, and those who did evil will be poor and miserable. One's stay in that Land is not eternal, but the Lhota are not altogether clear on how long it lasts or what the next existence will be. They are equally vague on the matter of souls: how many souls a person has, just when a human soul goes to the Land of the Dead, or if indeed it is the soul that goes there. Mills sums up the situation: "the fact is that the Lhota does not analyse the details of such an unpleasant certainty as death" (1922: 118–21).

Mithan are not mentioned in any purely religious ceremonies Mills describes. Pigs, dogs, and fowl are the animals sacrificed. Though Mills reports that the Lhota believe souls of animals also go to the Land of the Dead, he is not specific about whether these are the souls of domestic or wild animals or both. Since, however, a Lhota family is reunited in the Land of the Dead, and life there is much the same as it was on earth, it seems reasonable to assume that a man will also be reunited with his mithan. Certain other Naga, notably the Ao, Sema, and Western Rengma, believe that their mithan or those they sacrificed will be awaiting them in the Land of the Dead.

Mills's single mention of mithan in purely religious matters concerns a stone on the path between two northern Lhota villages, Lakhuti and Akuk. This stone, named Deolung, is not worshiped, but respect is paid to it by all passersby, who place a leaf on a stone in front of it. Near Deolung is another stone, named Matishi. Matishi is looked on as both Deolung's friend and guard, and as his mithan. Sometimes a lowing sound is heard coming from Matishi, which is believed to prophesy impending disaster (Mills, 1922: 116–17).

For the Lhota, the role of the mithan is quite different and more restricted than it is for most of the peoples of NEFA. Yet the animal has prestige and importance, deriving largely from its role in the Feasts of Merit. This association of mithan with that series of Feasts, by the Lhota and many other Naga groups, is noteworthy, for the Feasts of Merit are one of the most conspicuous and important features of the Naga fertility complex, and bovine sacrifice is always part of the higher, more important ceremonies.

13

The Chin Tribes
A General Sketch

Location and Identification

The term "Chin" is an English word taken from the Burmese *Khyang*, and originally was applied to the Chin peoples of Burma, including both hill and plains groups. The tribal Chin groups of India and Pakistan, who are hill people, were sometimes called Kuki and sometimes referred to by their individual ethnic names, such as Lakher or Lushai. Today the languages of the Chin and Kuki peoples are grouped under "Kuki-Chin" together with the related speech of the Meithei of the Indian state of Manipur.

"Chin" as used in a general sense hereafter will not embrace all Kuki-Chin speakers, but only the hill tribes of Chin and Kuki mentioned above. These hill tribes occupy a large area, centered on the hills and mountains that extend southward from Nagaland, in the borderlands of India, Burma, and East Pakistan (Map 6). The core of their country is the Chin Hills of Burma, the contiguous Lushai, or Mizo, Hills of India, and Manipur. Such Chin tribes, however, are also found north of the core area, mainly in the Naga Hills and Cachar District of Assam; west, in the Chittagong Hills of East Pakistan; and south, in the Arakan Hills of Burma. "Chin" as we use it will not include the Meithei of Manipur or the Plains Chin of Burma proper and of Arakan. Though these two peoples speak Kuki-Chin languages, they differ significantly in culture from the Chin tribes of the hills. The Meithei are Hindus and have long had a traditional state; and the Plains Chin have been extensively acculturated to the Burman way of life.

"Kuki" has been applied by writers to various of the Chin tribal peoples of India and Pakistan (i.e., Kuki of Chittagong, Thadou Kuki), and

Source: This sketch is based mainly on B. S. Carey and H. N. Tuck, 1896; J. Shakespear, 1912; W. Shaw, 1929; N. E. Parry, 1932; H. N. C. Stevenson, 1943; T. Das, 1945; F. K. Lehman, 1963; and D. E. Sopher, 1964.

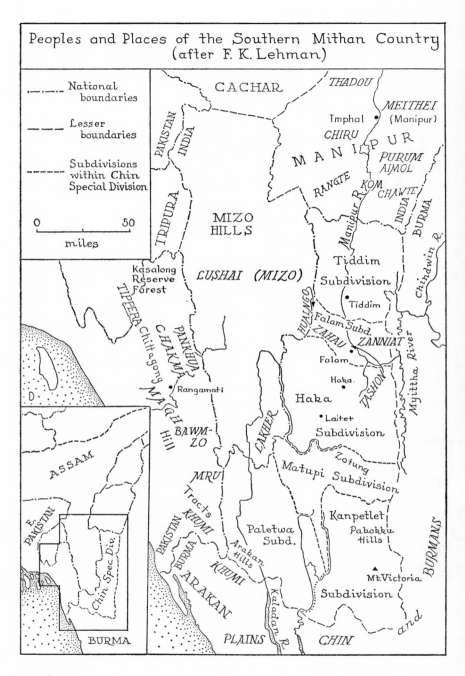

Peoples and Places of the Southern Mithan Country
(after F. K. Lehman)

Map 6

we often follow the writers' usage in designating specific groups within those countries. When we use "Kuki" in a general sense, however, we will not use it for all the tribal Chin groups of India and Pakistan, but will restrict it to the tribal Chin of Manipur and areas north of it. In this usage, it includes the "Old Kuki" and the "New Kuki" groups, but not the Meithei or the Lushai, Lakher, and other Kuki-Chin speakers south of Manipur. The term "Old Kuki" embraces several groups (among them the Purum, Chiru, Chawte, Aimol) who migrated northward and probably first entered Manipur in the sixteenth century. The New Kuki are a single tribe, the Thadou, who also entered Manipur from the south, but later, in the middle of the eighteenth century. The Chin of the Chin Hills of Burma are divided, following F. K. Lehman (1963: 14–17), into Northern and Southern Chin; within the Northern group, Lehman distinguishes between "true Northern Chin" and Central Chin. The "true Northern Chin" are the groups of Tiddim Subdivision; the Central Chin are those of Falam and Haka subdivisions, together with the adjacent Zotung country; and the Southern Chin are those of the rest of Matupi Subdivision, and of Paletwa and Kanpetlet subdivisions.

Language and Numbers, Physical Type, and Origins

The Chin peoples speak many languages and dialects which are mutually unintelligible, and most have not been satisfactorily studied. Traditionally the Chin languages have been arranged in groups within the Assam-Burmese branch of the Tibeto-Burman subfamily of languages. The languages of the Naga, northern relatives of the Chin, have usually been placed in a separate Naga group within the Assam-Burmese branch. Shafer, in his classification of the Sino-Tibetan languages (1955: 94–111), however, puts most of the Naga and Chin languages together in the Kukish section of his Burmic division.

In the 1961 *Census of India*, Kuki-Chin speakers numbered one million. The "Chin" of Burma (including Plains Chin) probably number over 400,000, and those of Pakistan less than 10,000. This gives a total of over 1.4 million Kuki-Chin speakers, of whom perhaps 600,000 belong to the hill Chin tribes.

In physical type the Chin are Mongoloid. Some scholars believe that the ancestors of the Naga and Chin belonged to a relatively uniform linguistic unit not too long ago; that they migrated southward to their present territory from the north, possibly in the first centuries A.D. In later times, perhaps in the sixteenth century, the Chin seem to have undergone a rapid population increase, and certain of them pushed northward again. Whatever may have been the actual sequence of history, the Chin represent a way of life, a hill society, that is distinct from the high civilization of the Burmans. At the same time, they have long been in contact with Burmans to the east and Indians to the west.

Settlement Pattern and House Type

In the Chin country in pre-British times, raids and ambushes were commonplace, and the Chin generally lived in compact, fortified villages located in sites such as steep slopes or ridge crests that were readily defended. Such sites are still common today, though fortifications have been abandoned. Villages are usually several miles apart, and in earlier times trips to other villages or to distant fields could be hazardous. Water may be brought by flumes to a village some distance downslope from the crest; otherwise, the village women carry water from a spring or stream as it is needed.

Within the village, houses, along with the household gardens, are in some places enclosed by a hedge or fence, to keep mithan and other domestic animals away. The houses, each generally occupied by a nuclear family, are long, thatch-roofed rectangular structures, commonly constructed of wood and bamboo. In most places they are raised off the ground on stilts. At the front of the house is a verandah, covered with an extension of the house roof. On the verandah are displayed the skulls of domestic animals sacrificed and wild animals killed in the chase. In some cases a house also has a raised open platform at the front, and a courtyard; some have an open platform at the back. Beneath raised houses there is usually a place where mithan and other domestic animals can spend the night in safety. Besides the ordinary houses, there are various more imposing structures within the settlement, such as the village men's houses and houses of the headman and other wealthy individuals. These are conspicuous because of their greater size and elaborate wood carvings and other decorations. Conspicuous also are the forked posts put up near the houses of persons who have performed the Feasts of Merit. Characteristic features of the Chin cultural landscape, too, are the memorials to the dead, and the cemeteries. The memorials (Figure 9), of both wood and stone, are usually outside the village. Outside, too, in former times were wooden posts on which were displayed the heads of enemies killed in raids. For some groups, the cemeteries are also outside the village.

Agriculture and Animal Husbandry

Traditionally the Chin were shifting cultivators, using as implements the dao, ax, and hoe. Plow cultivation, usually associated with wet rice, was known mainly among the Meithei and some adjacent Kuki tribes to

whom it had spread, and among the Plains Chin of Burma. In modern
times, however, the plow and wet rice cultivation have spread to certain
other hill tribes, as, for example, in the Chittagong Hills, where they have
been adopted primarily in valley sites. Dry rice is the staple of those
Kuki of Manipur who have not taken over plow and wet rice, and of
the Lushai, Lakher, and southern Chin of Burma. Among a few sections
of the Thadou taro is the staple; and among the northern Chin of Burma
maize, though there are indications that for them millets were the staples
in the last century.

Commonly, though not universally, the Chin shifting farmers practice
a block system of cultivation. The village authorities select a single large
block of land for cultivation, and the block is divided into smaller plots
cultivated by individual families. Though what Lehman (1963: 66) calls
"pseudo-terracing" is found, involving felling trees or piling of rocks on
slopes especially subject to soil slippage, the careful terracing of the
Angami and certain other Naga groups is not traditional. The most common form of sowing is digging a hole and planting the seed, though
broadcasting is also known. Harvesting of cereals is often done simply
by plucking the heads or the entire plants by hand, though cutting the
heads with sickle or knife is also found.

The traditional domesticated animals of the Chin are the pig, chicken,
dog, mithan, and goat, commonly kept as free-ranging household animals.

Men's House

The men's house (sometimes called bachelors' dormitory, youth house,
or youth dormitory), whether as institution or as building, is less common among the Chin peoples than among the Naga. It is most often
found among the Chin groups of the west and north: the Lushai, certain
Kuki groups of Manipur and the Lushai Hills, and the Hualngo of Burma.
It is absent among the Meithei; and seems not to have occurred among
the Lakher, most of the Burma Chin, or scattered groups elsewhere. Some
of the Kuki peoples who do not have men's house structures have traditions that they existed in former times; among a few such Kuki groups
young unmarried men sleep together in the houses or on the verandah of
particular important persons of the village. Where the men's house occurs among the Chin peoples, it seems less important in social and political life than among the Naga. Hutton (in Parry, 1932: x) insisted that
this was true of the Lushai, the Chin group among whom the institution
was perhaps most prominent. There is nothing to suggest that the Chin
men's house was or is involved with a fertility cult, as among the Naga.

With the introduction of Christianity to the hills, certain Chin peoples, notably the Lushai, abandoned the institution of the men's house after conversion and under missionary urging. The missionaries viewed the men's house as an evil place where men drank.

Political Organization

For most Chin groups the basic political unit is the village. Among many (Lushai, Lakher, Thadou, many Burma Chin) the village is ruled by an "autocratic" hereditary headman assisted by a council and various officials, including a priest who supervises ritual activities. Certain other groups (Old Kuki, and the Zanniat and Tashon Chin of Burma) have been designated "democratic" because their villages are not ruled by hereditary headmen but by elected headmen or councils of elders. Among some Chin wider political groupings have developed, most of them under chiefs. Though such associations have risen and fallen through time, the political structure at the village level has persisted. The traditional state exists in Chin country only among the Meithei, who depart notably from the Chin not only in political organization but also in other aspects of culture and economy.

Certain of the Southern Chin of Burma are exceptional in having "no distinct political offices," and no headmen or chiefs (Lehman, 1963: 88–89); their villages are usually divided into several wards, each occupied by a different maximal lineage of a single clan. These lineages are the largest political units, and are responsible for assigning building sites and fields to their members. There is no overall village political organization; indeed it sometimes happens that one ward is at war with other wards of the same village.

Marriage and Systems of Descent

Among the Chin peoples, monogamy is the common practice; though polygyny is generally permitted, it is rare and confined to headmen, chiefs, and other wealthy men. Descent is patrilineal. For the Lakher, there are traits that may be survivals from an earlier time when the matrilineate prevailed.

Religious Beliefs

The Chin—except for certain groups who have abandoned their traditional religion—believe in various kinds of supernatural beings. Among these are numerous spirits, various deities, and, for most Chin, a vaguely defined supreme creator sky-god. One group disclaims knowledge of the high god. Most Chin consider both the spirits and the supreme god important in daily life, and sacrifice to them regularly. The Lushai, in contrast, regard the supreme god as remote, and reserve their sacrifices for other supernatural beings, who influence more directly the life and condition of man. The Chin employ seers, individuals who have special abilities to divine which of the supernatural beings has caused illness or other trouble, and to determine what sacrifice, whether mithan or some other animal, must be made to eliminate the difficulty. Belief in witchcraft and in the evil eye is common.

Traditionally all the Chin believed in a Land of the Dead (Village of the Dead) to which the souls of human beings journey after death. The way there is guarded by a being or beings who usually harass the souls of the dead. Some Chin (Lushai, Thadou, certain Old Kuki groups, and the Rangte) believe, however, that the souls of men who have performed certain great acts are freed of harassment. Among such acts are the killing of specified wild animals, the slaying of enemies, and performance of the highest of the Feasts of Merit. Some Chin groups also believe in a second place where a man's soul may go, and some believe in a third. The Chiru and Lakher, for example, say that the souls of people who die an accidental or unnatural death go to a separate place; and the Lushai and Lakher, along with the Central Chin of Burma, speak of a separate Plain of Heaven, where the souls of illustrious individuals go. A man becomes eligible for the Plain of Heaven through such acts as slaying enemies, killing certain wild animals, and, for those groups who practice the Feasts of Merit, completing that sequence. Thus, whether the Plain of Heaven or the usual Land of the Dead is believed to be the ultimate destination of souls, a man's activity during his lifetime determines his fate in the afterlife, unless he dies an untoward death. The souls of the wild animals that he has killed in hunts, the enemies he has slain, and the domestic animals he has sacrificed belong to him and are for his use there. To make certain that the souls of wild animals and enemies killed actually go to the afterworld to await their slayer, the Chin commonly perform special ceremonies after such killings.

Disposal of the Dead

The diversity in ways of dealing with the dead seems even greater for the Chin than for the Naga. In some instances, people dispose of the corpse quite simply, by burial or cremation. In others, the body is treated in various ways, such as exposing it to the elements or smoking and drying it over a fire, before final disposition. In such cases the body or bones may eventually be buried, or the dried bones and skull may be kept in a container at home, or the head may be removed from the corpse and dealt with separately. In those few cases where the head is removed (among Thadou and certain Lushai), it is kept in a basket at home, or buried in a pot; if the deceased was an important person, the Thadou place it in an inaccessible hole or niche in the rock face of a cliff. The Thadou explain separate disposal of the head as an effort to keep it from falling into the hands of enemies. There are also variations in the place of disposal. In some Chin villages the dead are kept within the settlement; in others, outside. All of the Chin, like the Naga, handle the corpses of individuals who die "accidentally" in special ways and bury them apart from the other dead, outside the village.

Like the Naga, virtually all the Chin erect memorials to the dead, of varying types and in a variety of locations, sometimes at the grave, sometimes elsewhere. Most common among the memorials are 1) posts, usually straight, which are carved in decorative designs and with tallies to indicate a man's accomplishments, as in hunting, in sacrificing animals, and, formerly, in killing enemies or capturing slaves (Figure 9); in a few areas, posts are carved to represent crudely the human form; 2) vertical stones, which in some cases are carved, too; and 3) flat stones, raised above the ground to form platforms for people to sit upon. It is common, too, to find items at the grave or memorial intended to provide for the deceased in the afterworld. Among these are the skulls of animals and, in former times, of humans as well. At the funeral rites the deceased's family commonly sacrifices animals to accompany him to the afterworld and assure his status there. Sometimes a ritual hunt is carried out to obtain animals for this purpose. There are also records from the past of the sacrifice of slaves and the hunting of enemy heads specifically to provide for the dead person in the afterworld.

Lehman (1963: 186–94), writing of the modern Burma Chin, views their burial practices as part of a "memorial complex" intended to perpetuate the memory of the dead. He nevertheless feels that memorialization is believed to contribute indirectly to prosperity and fertility. That various of the Chin groups once did believe the dead to have an influence on the fertility of the living is clearly stated in a few accounts and is implied in others. Most definite among the statements is that describing the sacrifice the Lakher performed "to the spirits of their ancestors to induce them to help to make the crops good, the domestic animals healthy and fertile, and to give good hunting" (Parry, 1932: 445–46). Somewhat less definite is the Lushai custom of carrying effigies of the dead around the village in connection with one Feast of Merit, evidently, says Shakespear (1912: 89), in the belief that the ancestral spirits can have an influence on the living, for good or bad. Among the suggestive fragments is the widespread Chin practice of separate disposal of the bodies of those who die "accidentally," a practice which springs from a desire to avoid contamination and to preserve village well-being. Of further interest are the accounts that show the disposal of the dead tied to planting or harvest time. Though such a tie has not been widely reported for the Chin, it is mentioned in a few early reports. Shaw (1929: 54) notes a 1790 account which indicates that the Kuki of Tripura linked disposal of the dead with the harvest, and that they offered the first fruits of their fields at the graves after burial. There is also a report of 1799 that the Kuki or Luncta of the Chittagong Hills kept the bodies of the dead on platforms until a spring celebration, when the accumulated bodies were burned together (Shaw, 1929: 54). These practices parallel the ones of those Naga peoples who try to utilize the life-force of the dead to assure fertility. Another 1790 observation is that some Tripura Kuki stored the bones of the dead in a bowl and used them in taking omens. Implied in this practice is the continued usefulness of the dead to the living by imparting information— much of it related in one way or another to the well-being and fertility of individual and village alike.

Head Taking

The Chin villages, before British intervention put a stop to it, were quite active in raiding one another, as well as raiding villages of other ethnic groups. The primary motivation of most raids seems to have been economic, especially the seizing of loot and captives who could serve as slaves. The heads of enemies slain on raids were taken back to the raiders' village, where various ceremonies were carried out, including one to make certain that the soul of the enemy went to the afterworld as the slave of the slayer, and did not remain to trouble him or his village. There was a widespread fear of the enemy's soul. Some groups did not bring the head into the village but kept it outside, usually displayed on a forked branch or on a post or, for certain Lakher, on a head-tree. The heads revealed to everyone the accomplishments of the raiders. At the same time, for most Chin the taking of heads was an incident of the raid and not its primary motivation. Nevertheless, there are reports for certain Chin groups (Thadou, Lakher, certain Central Chin of Burma) of men going out, after the death of a chief, specifically to hunt heads. Though the Lakher said that the heads were taken to prevent bad dreams, for other groups the headhunting was intended to provide the chief's soul with attendants in the afterlife.

Various writers have observed that generally the Chin motives for taking heads were quite different from those of the Naga. The Naga commonly went out specifically to hunt heads; the Chin often took the heads of those slain on raids, but only occasionally did certain Chin groups go raiding for heads alone. For those groups, the need for heads was to provide for the dead rather than the living. Chin head takers had no desire to capture the life-essence of the slain, in order to assure fertility and well-being to the village. Hutton (in Shaw, 1929: 78) views the Naga, who took heads *primarily* for that reason, as true headhunters. The Chin ("Kuki") he considers slave hunters, who probably adopted from the true headhunters their practice of taking heads but did not adopt their beliefs.

With the elimination of raids on enemy settlements and the decline of hunting among the Central Chin of Burma, performance of the Feasts of Merit came to assume increasing importance in guaranteeing a man's life after death. Indeed, Stevenson wrote (1943: 22) that Chin beliefs about the hereafter were a powerful stimulus to individual agricultural effort. This was because, in his time, it was only through performance of the Feasts that a man could raise his status in this life and thereby assure his position in the hereafter; and he could assemble the items necessary for holding the Feasts—including mithan—only through diligence in farming.

Feasts of Merit

Traditionally the Feasts of Merit were as characteristic of the Chin as of the Naga. The institution occurs or once occurred among all or virtually all Chin groups, with the possible exception of some of the Lakher. The Chin feast giver tries to obtain the good will of supernatural beings so that he may prosper. He gains status in society. Commonly he also enjoys rights of display, economic and political benefits, and special treatment at death. The Thadou, for example, perform a ceremony at death for men who have completed the Sha-ai, first of the Feast sequence, and for women who have performed the Chang-ai, a special feast carried out by women. The death ceremony includes slaughter of a mithan, a recital by the priest of the good acts of the dead person, and a blessing offered to the spirit on its trip to the afterworld. The Thadou dry and smoke the body of a man who has performed the Chon-ai, highest of the Feasts, and parade the desiccated corpse around the village seven times, apparently over an extended period of time, before disposing of it (Shaw, 1929: 55–56, 74–76). The feast giver among almost all Chin groups is thought to receive special consideration in the afterlife.

In the Chin Feast of Merit sacrifices, the mithan is the most prestigeful animal, more universally even than among the Naga. The sacrificial post, commonly Y-shaped, is widely used, and is left standing after the ceremonies as a memorial. Some Chin mark stages in the Feasts of Merit with other forms of memorials: monoliths (Thadou, Aimol), piles of stones (a few Old Kuki groups of Manipur), and flat stone platforms (Purum, Aimol, and Chawte—all Old Kuki groups of Manipur). Generally, however, stone memorials among the Chin seem to be associated with the dead, and their occurrence in the Feasts of Merit is of limited distribution.

There are notable parallels and differences between Naga and Chin in the ideas behind the Feasts of Merit. Prominent in the thinking of both groups are the gains in prosperity and well-being; social status; economic and political benefits; special treatment at death; and, for many peoples, advantages in the afterlife. Important among the Naga is the view that the feast giver is sharing his life-force directly with clan and village; though the ceremonies of a few Chin groups hint that they too see the feast giver as dispersing his life-force directly to others, the idea is not clearly documented for any Chin group. The forked posts and monoliths erected by the Naga in connection with the Feasts are receptacles for the life-force of the feast giver, as well as memorials; the Chin seem to view such posts and stones instead as memorials. These differences appear relatively minor when viewed against the numerous similarities.

The Mithan in Chin Life

The mithan is not kept by the Plains Chin of Burma and apparently not by the Manipuri, but it is widespread among the hill Chin tribes. Ownership of this valuable and prestigeful animal is concentrated in the hands of the wealthy. It is not used for plowing or other traction, and it is milked only in rare instances today. Its primary uses are in exchange, as in paying bride-price, and in sacrifice, notably at the Feasts of Merit. Most groups keep mithan under systems of free-ranging, though certain Burma Chin herd them.

Common cattle and water buffalo have long been known both in the lowlands bordering Chin country and in Manipur. A few earlier were brought to the hill tribes by raiders and traders, but most seem soon to have been slaughtered. Among the few Chin groups who in modern times have taken up plowing, common cattle and buffalo rather than mithan serve this end. The position of the mithan has been somewhat undermined by conversion to Christianity and other changes which have encouraged abandonment of many traditional beliefs and customs. In some groups the Feasts of Merit are not performed at all; in others, increasing substitution of other bovines for mithan as sacrificial animals has occurred.

14

The Central Chin of Burma

This chapter focuses on the Central Chin tribes of Burma, especially those of Falam Subdivision studied by Stevenson in 1934–36 and those of Haka Subdivision with whom Lehman spent about nine months in 1957–58.[1] The Haka and Falam Chin numbered almost 82,000 in 1953. Not only are they the best studied of the Burma Chin peoples, but their area is centrally located and of great importance in Chin history, because Chin elsewhere, such as the Lakher, Lushai, Thadou Kuki, and others, claim it as their ancestral home.

The Chin Hills comprise the rough, largely forested hill and mountain region in western Burma which is a continuation of the ranges stretching south from the Himalayas through Nagaland and Manipur. The Chin Hills are about 250 miles from north to south and average about 60 miles from east to west. They are bounded to the north by Manipur, to the east by lowlands and Burma proper, and to the west by the Lushai or Mizo Hills of India. To the south, through their extensions, the Arakan and Pakokku Hills, they gradually descend to the lowlands bordering the Bay of Bengal. Generally, crest lines in the Chin Hills are about 7,000 feet in elevation, the highest single peak being Mt. Victoria, just over 10,000 feet. The northern sections of the hills are cut through by the Manipur River. This river enters the region from the north and turns eastward in the Falam area to join the Myittha, which empties into the Chindwin, the great western tributary of the Irrawaddy. The southern Chin Hills

Source: This chapter is drawn largely from B. S. Carey and H. N. Tuck, 1896; H. N. C. Stevenson, 1943; and F. K. Lehman, 1963.

1. In this chapter "Chin," used alone, means Central Chin of Burma, except in a rare case where it has a more general or more restricted application which will be obvious from the context. "Falam" usually refers not to the settlement of that name but to Falam Subdivision; "Falam Chin" refers to the peoples of that subdivision as a whole.

and their extensions are drained partly by Irrawaddy tributaries, and partly by rivers such as the Kaladan which flow directly into the Bay of Bengal.

In 1949 the Chin Hills were joined with areas to the south to form the Chin Special Division, a semiautonomous unit of Burma. This division consists of six subdivisions: from north to south, Tiddim, Falam, Haka, Matupi, Paletwa, and Kanpetlet. Because of the poorly developed transport network, most Chin villages have not been in close contact with the outside world. Some sections where outside influence is strong have been quite altered; but others, especially in the south, are little modified.

In viewing their landscape, the Chin distinguish between *khua*—the inhabited area embracing a village, its houses, and gardens—and *ram*, the uncultivated forest and grassland owned by a village. The cultivated fields represent a transitional stage between the two. The Chin consider their villages as outliers of human culture in the midst of ram. Whereas khua is warm, human, and, in balance, protective, ram is unfriendly. When in ram the Chin "treads softly, uses special vocabulary so as not to offend the spirits of the game, and uses euphemisms and circumlocutions for referring to the larger game animals by name." Though women work in the fields and even live there in huts at certain times, their domain is largely confined to khua. They are, in a sense, intruders when they enter ram, whereas men are at home in both khua and ram (Lehman, 1963: 172–73).

The houses of the Chin are rectangular, one-story structures with thatch roofs, and usually are occupied by a nuclear family. In the Haka area at the end of the last century, houses were 30 feet or so wide and from 50 to 200 feet long, depending on the wealth of the owner (Carey and Tuck, 1896, 1: 177). Usually houses are built of rough-hewn planks, and are entirely or mostly raised on piles. Along the western margins of the region, however, bamboo is the principal construction material; and in the northern sections of Falam houses are built directly on the ground (Lehman, 1963: 43). The house commonly is built with its length extending across a hillside. The up-slope side rests on the ground or is just a few feet above it, and contains the main fireplace. The down-slope side may be as much as 15 to 20 feet above the ground, if the hill is steep. At the front is a flat yard cut out of the hillside, and in the yard is a platform used for various family activities. The roof of the house extends over a front verandah which has walls on three sides. Decorating the walls or piled on the ground are the skulls of wild animals killed in hunting as well as those of domestic animals, such as mithan, which have been slaughtered at feasts. In headhunting times human heads were not kept with those trophies but were mounted on posts outside the village.

Beneath the house is a pen for mithan and pigs. At the back or at the sides and back of the house are the family gardens, generally enclosed by a fence or hedge.

Late in the last century Chin villages averaged about sixty houses and three hundred people; Falam, the largest settlement, had five hundred houses. Villages were usually several miles apart. People traditionally preferred village sites that were easily defended, such as high slopes or ridges; where possible, villages were located also with an eye to having water nearby or to being able to bring it to the village by bamboo flumes or split logs from higher up-slope. Other factors considered in choosing village sites were proximity to the village fields, protection from strong winds, and a position to catch the early morning sun (Carey and Tuck, 1896, 1: 175; Stevenson, 1943: 22–23; Lehman, 1963: 72). Some villages were stockaded and otherwise fortified, because there was much fighting among Chin villages. Each village has a place of sacrifice (*mual* or *bual*), commonly not far from a large banyan tree and in the heart of the settlement. For the Chin, the village is the basic political and economic unit. Though there are tribal chiefs, traditionally the power of a chief was weak beyond his home village, and the village headman was the more powerful and prestigeful person locally (Stevenson, 1943: 17–18; Lehman, 1963: 147–54).

The Chin are primarily shifting cultivators, though permanent cultivation of irrigated rice is spreading. So far it has been adopted, as a supplement to shifting cultivation, mainly by a small number of rich villagers who can afford the expense of preparing paddy fields and of purchasing draft animals and other necessary equipment. The rest of the group continues the traditional shifting cultivation, with the hoe as the principal implement of field cultivation, though the dibble stick is used for much planting, and the ax and dao for clearing. Traditionally, animals were not used in any way for agricultural labor.

Chin cultivation is divided between shifting fields, where the bulk of staple crops such as maize, millets, hill rice, pulses, and others are grown, and household gardens, where crops such as plantains and oranges, gourds, cucumbers, and tobacco are cultivated. Fields are usually within several miles of the village at elevations of 4,000 to 7,000 feet (Lehman, 1963: 10, 69). The only crops that are identified with mithan in any way are onions and leeks, which Stevenson (1943: 30) maintains are ordinarily grown in a tub of earth dug from beneath the house and enriched by the droppings of pigs and mithan.

The largest agricultural unit is the village, whose cultivable lands are divided into large blocks, *lopil*, by headman and village council. These large fields are cultivated in succession, thus permitting a rotation embracing all of the village agricultural lands. In Falam Subdivision (Stevenson, 1943: 30–31, 56–58) a village usually has about four such large fields at various stages of cultivation and fallow. The fallow field next due for cultivation is designated the *siapil*, or mithan field, and is used for grazing the mithan, one suspects because the Falam Chin recognize the value of droppings as fertilizer. The lopil is divided into smaller plots, known as *lo*, each cultivated by one household. The household plots are individually owned, can be sold, and can figure in formal gift exchanges. The lopil of Falam are bounded by natural features such as streams or ridges but are not usually fenced.[2] Household plots are bounded by rows of small stones or by hedges. For neither unit of land is there any serious obstacle to entry by wild or domestic animals.

In pre-British days raiding was an important activity of the Chin, to obtain slaves and loot and, to a lesser extent, to obtain human heads. Of all villagers, the cultivator was in greatest danger; Carey and Tuck (1896, 1: 211) estimated that nine of every ten persons who lost their heads were killed at or near their fields. For this reason, distant fields were worked under the watch of armed guards.

Though agriculture is the basis of Chin sustenance, hunting, fishing, and gathering provide useful additions. Success in hunting and performance of Feasts of Celebration (see pp. 153–54 below) provide an important way for a man to advance in social and economic position. They are also necessary for him to enter Pial Rang, "the Plain of Heaven," higher of the two afterworlds of the Chin. "To a man: war; the hunt; and the feast—to a woman: work in the house and the fields" runs a Chin proverb (Stevenson, 1943: 62). Among the hunted animals which figure in the Feasts of Celebration is the gaur, which today is very scarce in the Chin Hills proper but at the end of the last century was "always to be found" in specified parts of the Chin country (Carey and Tuck, 1896, 1: 218; Stevenson, 1943: 48; Lehman, 1963: 10).

Late in the nineteenth century the domestic animals of the Chin included mithan, horse, pig, goat, chicken, dog, and cat; occasionally common cattle and water buffalo were found in the villages. Some Chin groups in earlier times, it is true, captured many buffalo on raids in Burma, but they invariably slaughtered and ate them (Carey and Tuck, 1896, 1: 179–81). By the 1930's buffalo and common cattle had been brought into Chin country in small numbers from the lowland, but at least in Falam they were not fully assimilated into Chin culture; they were sometimes used differently from indigenous livestock and were not fully subject to tradi-

---

2. Among the Zanniat tribe, commonly a fence is constructed between the *siapil* and the *lopil* (Stevenson, 1943: 57).

tional rules governing acceptability for sacrifice (Stevenson, 1943: 47–50, 58–61). The situation has changed notably since then, for in the 1953 census (*Union of Burma, First Stage Census, 1953,* 1957: 76) "cattle" (presumably common cattle) outnumbered mithan in Haka and Falam subdivisions by 7,423 to 5,659. Pigs and chickens are useful village scavengers. Other indigenous Chin livestock have been useful mainly for sacrifice or for slaughter and eating.

The Mithan among the Chin

Importance and Economic Uses

The mithan is by far the most prestigious domestic animal of the Chin. No matter what other animals a man may own, his wealth is judged by the number of his mithan. The mithan has the highest value among Chin pecuniary measures. It is the required animal for various of the more important sacrifices. Mithan must be sacrificed by a man to attain the highest social status. The birth of a mithan is celebrated as is the birth of a child, with sacrifice and a day of ritual abstention from work. The theft and slaughter of a mithan are among the most serious of crimes; traditionally, the guilty person was banished and his property seized. The mithan is also conspicuous in Chin metaphors involving beauty and strength.

Mithan are not packed, ridden, or used for draft. They were not milked traditionally—milk was regarded as unclean. Their primary use is for sacrifice and slaughter, and their main consumable product is their flesh. Carey and Tuck (1896, 1: 181) report that before a mithan is slaughtered it is tied and given nothing to eat or drink for three days, in the belief that this will make the flesh tender. This suggests that in sacrificing mithan the Chin are concerned with more than social and religious factors. The hides of mithan in Falam are usually cut up with the flesh and consumed as crackling, but hides of mithan that are slaughtered at funeral ceremonies or die accidentally are dried in the sun and used as sleeping mats (Stevenson, 1943: 50). The use of mithan horns as powder flasks was reported at the end of the last century (Carey and Tuck, 1896, 1: 226), but has probably disappeared with the introduction of modern arms.

Care

The Chin of Falam, as Stevenson noted (1943: 24, 54–56), grow their staple crops mostly in field plots rather than in household gardens. Moreover, neither the cultivated fields nor the mithan field, the siapil, are always fenced. This makes it necessary to herd the mithan, which are watched by boys during the daytime and kept in the village at night. Mithan found wandering without herd boys are seized, and the owner is charged for their care until he claims them. Should the animals not be claimed they are used by the village for communal needs. Pigs, chickens, and goats, by contrast, wander about the village clearing untended.

This system of herding mithan and driving them into the village at night, as practiced by the Chin of Falam in the 1930's, apparently is not of recent origin. Carey and Tuck (1896, 1: 180–81) reported that Chin mithan were "herded near the villages and brought home and penned in the compounds at night." At the same time, they noticed at Haka and other villages a large semiwild herd of mithan, including hybrids with common cattle, which although permitted to roam freely was watched, and, if it moved too far from the village, was driven back. Whereas ordinary mithan could be tied up and slaughtered, those of the semiwild herd were shot, because they could not be caught. In permitting certain mithan to range freely, the Chin of Carey's and Tuck's day resembled many mithan-keeping peoples, but in herding animals and bringing them to the village every evening their practice resembles the usual one of the peoples of the high civilizations bordering their country. One wonders what may have led the Chin to develop their system of mithan care. May fear of headhunters have encouraged them initially to keep mithan close to the villages? This would enable an owner to have regular contact with his animals safely and without risking the danger of the dark, distant forest. Given the Chin desire to keep their mithan nearby, failure to fence the fields offers a ready-made situation for herding to take hold.

The Problem of Damage to Crops

Despite the Falam Chin custom of herding mithan, the animals do some damage to crops. The angry cultivator then seeks justice. Usually claims are settled without violence, though in certain villages the offended farmer has been known simply to spear and hack at the guilty mithan. Normally the farmer, on discovering that his fields have been invaded, tracks the animals, determines their owner's identity, and then pays a visit to the headman of the owner's village. If the evidence is convincing and the fields are unfenced, the headman immediately fines the guilty owner in beer. Where communal fences have been constructed, more severe fines are imposed. A main determinant of the amount of the fine is the time the animals have spent in the field. The Zahau Chin of Falam reckon this time in one of two units. The first, *leh lang*, is a day or part of a day; the second, *zan riah hnawh*, is a day and night. Only rarely do offenses fall into the second category, for mithan normally are confined at home during the night. Should more than one owner's animals be involved, all guilty owners are fined. If so many animals are involved that they cannot be traced to individual owners, all mithan owners of the offending village are fined. The offended party can seize property of an owner or owners who refuse to pay, and hold it until he receives the beer that is his due. When an owner settles the claim immediately, the fine is drunk at his headman's house, and both owner and headman share in consuming it. Should the owner demur but the fine eventually be paid, it is drunk in the house of the offended party's headman, the owner receives but a small share, and his headman gets none. Thus there is pressure on both the mithan owner and his headman to settle the claim with dispatch. Almost nowhere is the fine equal to the damage done, though there are rare cases where a man's crops have been completely destroyed and compensation in grain has been exacted (Stevenson, 1943: 56–58).

In Religion and Society
Religious Beliefs and Sacrifice

As with other mithan-keeping peoples, the world of the Chin is inhabited by supernatural beings. Many are spirits, including souls of the dead, but a few, according to Lehman (1963: 177), "may be called gods." The spirits, who have human attributes, are divided into categories. Some are tied to places, such as the house, village sacrificial area, or particular landscape features. Others have no specific residences or personalities. All can influence the affairs of man for good or evil. Certain important spirits are offered sacrifices regularly; to others offerings are made only when misfortune strikes. At such a time the spirit is approached through the mediation of a seer and is placated with offerings of food and liquor and by the sacrifice of animals, including mithan (Stevenson, 1943: 151, 156; Lehman, 1963: 174–77).

The Chin also believe in an afterlife in which a man's soul assumes the position he enjoyed on earth. The Falam Chin believe that at death the soul goes to the Mithi Khua, a Land of the Dead which is beneath the earth. Mithi Khua is divided into various villages, and the guardian spirit assigns each soul to its proper village according to the way he lost his life. Some souls, however, merit a place in Pial Rang, the Plain of Heaven, which is in the sky. Entry into Pial Rang is attained only through major effort by a man in his earthly life, as he performs the Feasts of Merit and Feasts of Celebration (Stevenson, 1943: 21–22).

In accordance with their religious beliefs, the Chin sacrifice various domestic animals at a variety of personal, household, and community ceremonies. Chickens and pigs are the usual victims at the majority of personal and household sacrifices, whereas for community affairs the pig and mithan are prominent. One such communal sacrifice, in Falam, is held at the opening of a new siapil, or mithan grazing ground. If the guardian spirit of the field is powerful, a mithan is sacrificed; if not, a pig suffices. The spirit is asked to keep the animals well and to deter them from falling down precipices, a common fate of Chin mithan (Stevenson, 1943: 56). Another community sacrifice, which requires mithan, is reported by Carey and Tuck (1896, 1: 206–7) for the village of Laitet, south of Haka. A spring with miraculous qualities there had been enlarged to form a shallow well. In the well lives a powerful spirit named Shiarpanlai. Whenever there has been a murder in a nearby village, the water of the well turns the color of blood; a sacrifice must then be made at the well to propitiate the spirit. Small sacrifices are also made frequently, and once every three years a mature female mithan is sacrificed. Should the spirit be neglected, tradition holds, women and domestic animals would become barren and crops would be blighted.

At times of illness lesser animals are sacrificed first in the hope that they will satisfy the offending spirit. If they do not, a mithan may be required. Carey and Tuck say that at the illness of a Chin chief as many as ten mithan may be sacrificed (1896, 1: 197).

The mithan has a place, too, in certain Falam Chin mortuary feasts. Usually a death is followed by a mourning feast, at which animals are killed. For poor men a pig suffices for the feast, but for wealthy men mithan are traditional. For very wealthy men, another mortuary ceremony is held by the family and heirs. This is a ritual hunt intended to increase the number of souls of wild animals that will accompany the deceased to the afterworld and, above all, to provide the required number of animals for him to gain entry to the Plain of Heaven. In honor of the hunt, the heirs also kill domestic animals; traditionally the mithan was the largest of these (Stevenson, 1943: 131–33).

The Chin are concerned that they not be forgotten after death, and erecting memorials to the dead—at the grave and elsewhere—is conspicuous in Chin ceremonial life. These memorials are usually put up by the family after a person dies, but occasionally living people set up their own memorials and carry out the appropriate ceremonies. The Chin death memorials take several forms, and are reminiscent of those of the Naga. One Chin death memorial is an upright stone. Another is a wooden post, in some cases carved to resemble the human figure. At Falam the feast held in connection with erection of the memorial post traditionally involves killing a pig for a poor man and a mithan for a wealthy man. Some Chin, like some Naga, construct miniature houses at the grave, for the spirits of the dead. The Naga who follow this custom do so in the firm expectation that the houses will be visited by the spirit of the dead person; though some Chin say that possibly this will happen, the belief is not widely held.

The most important Chin death memorials are fair-sized structures made of earth and rubble built up to a height of about three feet, and faced and covered over with flat stones. These memorials, like those of the Naga, are built along paths and are intended also as resting places for passersby; the weary traveler supposedly remembers the dead person as he rests upon his memorial. Lehman (1963: 193) states emphatically that these Chin memorials are not (like those of the Naga) visited by spirits of ancestors, nor do they contribute directly to the fertility or prosperity of the area, though "indirectly they do." Chin death practices parallel Naga practices in another way, too. The Chin place at the memorial certain personal possessions of the dead person, along with tallies, in various forms, of his achievements. The Naga also set out such possessions and tallies, at the grave itself. The sorts of things recorded in the tallies are similar for both groups: an indication of a man's wealth in ornaments and beads, the number of mithan sacrificed, and the number of animals killed in the chase. Headhunting did not occupy the same position among the Chin as among the Naga, and the tally of heads taken was not prominent in the Chin memorials. Amorous feats, which in some Naga groups are scrupulously tallied, seem not so significant for the Chin, though Lehman mentions (1963: 192 n.) that a Chin method exists for recording slain enemies and seductions.

Feasts of Merit

Stevenson (1943: 137) argues that the Feasts of Merit are the cornerstone of Chin economic organization, that most Chin surplus goods are used in the Feasts, and that the individual obtains the bulk of his "psychological and spiritual satisfactions" through them. Our account here of the place of the Feasts in Chin social, economic, and religious life, and of the role mithan play in them, is based on Stevenson's description of the Feasts for the Zahau Chin (1943: 119, 137–47).

Every Chin householder, writes Stevenson, is affected by four circles: the village-community circle; the kinship and bond-friend circle (a man has two bond-friends to help him and to be helped at crucial junctures of life); the circle of those who have performed Feasts of Merit and are thus members of a "Feasters' Club"; and the circle of those who have performed Feasts of Celebration and constitute a "Hunters' Club." His position in the first two circles is based on both the place of his dwelling and his inherited family—and acquired marital—associations. His position in the second two circles, however, is gained through his own efforts and success in cultivation, herding, and hunting.

The Feasts of Merit, with their established sequence of ceremonies held over several years, necessitate a series of sacrifices, the most important of which require mithan. Performance of the Feasts gives the feast giver certain rights of display, and gains him status within the Feasters' Club and in the village as a whole. It also gives him real economic advantages, of various kinds, and sometimes political position as well. Performance of the highest Feast earns a man a seat on the village council, and this in turn brings him further economic benefits. In addition, the feast giver adds to his standing in the afterworld, where his status is equal to that he has achieved on earth. At the same time, the Feasts benefit society in many ways. The village is entertained. Beer and flesh are widely distributed and add to the diet of numerous persons. Flesh is divided according to tradition. Much goes to members of the Feasters' Club, who divide it among themselves according to rank in feast giving. The Feasters' Club also receives a specified amount of the best quality beer. Other shares of the meat go to the headman, blacksmith, bond-friends, and kin.

Feasts of Merit can be held only with the cooperation of kin and bond-friends. They contribute some beer and lesser animals, and in some cases other items necessary for the Feast. They also help at the Feast. The feast giver is obligated to provide shares of meat to them, and on occasion other things as well. There is reciprocity, too, on the part of members of the Feasters' Club. Accepting the largesse of the feaster obligates them, when they in turn hold Feasts, to provide him with a share. Thus each Feast not only raises the giver in status but establishes a new series of obligations.[3] The sacrifices carried out at the Feasts of Merit, rather than being a waste of resources, are an ingenious joint effort which results in broad sharing according to one's contribution in time and goods. The Feasts, altogether, serve as an important stimulant to further economic activity.

Stevenson, in a somewhat confusing statement (1943: 119–20), points out an interesting side issue connected with the Feasts of Merit. This is the "permit payments" the village council imposes on the feast giver for permission to perform the Feast. These payments, usually in beer or currency, are graded, with payments higher for more important Feasts.

The person wealthy enough to give Feasts of Merit is singled out in another way for taxation. The village council, to meet its needs for various social and ceremonial occasions, has the right to collect articles from every household in turn, including those of the headman and members of the council. For purposes of the collection, householders are put into one of three categories: 1) those who are exempt temporarily or permanently: for example, persons unable to carry out agricultural labor;

---

3. For a detailed discussion of the benefits and obligations incurred by feast givers among the Zahau Chin, see Stevenson, 1943: 137 ff.

2) those who, though they can afford grain, have not found it possible to give Feasts of Merit; and 3) those who have the means to hold such Feasts. Members of the first group make no contribution. Members of the second and third groups are assessed beer, fowl, pigs, and grain as their turn arrives. The grain so collected is used by the council to buy pigs and mithan for communal use. Though Stevenson does not indicate that the third group is assessed at a higher rate than the second, one assumes that this is what happens. If so, the feast givers not only are subject to a payment at the time of the Feast but are permanently subject to differential taxation by the council.

Mithan and pigs are the animals sacrificed at Feasts of Merit among the Zahau Chin. In the first of the four larger Feasts pigs alone are sacrificed; at the last three, mithan are sacrificed as well. The second of the four, Sia Thum Thah ("three mithan kill") requires the sacrifice of one young female pig and three mithan, including a bull, a cow, and a young animal. The third, Sia Hra Thah ("ten mithan kill"), does not, as the name implies, require the sacrifice of ten mithan, but rather of one sow and four mithan, including a bull, a cow, and two young. The highest Feast, Khuangtsawi, requires sacrifice of seven pigs and three mithan, including two bulls and one cow. In this series, then, mithan are reserved for the higher Feasts, and the higher the Feast the larger the number of mithan or the larger the number of mature mithan that is required.

Stevenson and early writers do not treat adequately the religious implications of the Feasts of Merit of the Chin. We are forced, therefore, to rely on one source, the monograph in which Lehman reports field observations of 1957–58 (1963: 172, 177 ff.). He bases his account almost entirely on data from the Haka area, but states that, except in minor ways, religious concepts similar to those of Haka are found throughout "the Chin area."

The Chin feast giver, as observed by Lehman, tries to gain the goodwill of various supernatural beings and thereby prosperity and well-being. The Chin believe that mithan ritually sacrificed go straight to the Land of the Dead; they are considered, in a sense, as obligatory gifts sent on ahead of the feast giver, which both please and impress the inhabitants, but which the feast giver expects to have again. He has thus established connections in the Land of the Dead which will assure his status and guarantee his wealth when he arrives.

Besides arranging for his status in the afterlife, the sacrificer is also attempting to provide for the status of his descendants who will remain in this world after his death. Lehman is not explicit as to how this is done. As he puts it (181), the feast giver establishes "to a certain extent, the status potentialities of his descendants, but those descendants themselves must validate this status." The Chin deny believing that the dead act to assure the prosperity of their living descendants; nevertheless some connection with the ancestral past, established chiefly through the Feasts of Merit, apparently helps in assuring prosperity.

Feasts of Celebration

Membership in the Feasters' Club is one major avenue of social advancement among the Chin. A second is membership in the Hunters' Club. This is gained by performing Feasts of Celebration, usually held at the slaying of wild animals, and formerly of human enemies. The Chin of Falam, says Stevenson (1943: 25–26, 62–63, 134–36), divide wild animals into various categories. Feasts of Celebration for most small creatures, such as birds, require only beer. Feasts for the lesser game animals, such as barking deer, customarily involve in addition killing a pig which is at least half grown. Feasts for the highest categories, "large game animals" and tigers, require the slaughter of at least a mature pig or, if one can afford it, of a mithan, as well as an abundance of beer. The "large game animal" category, *sa hrang*, traditionally included elephant, bear, wild boar, banteng, and gaur. Though today only wild boar and bear are found in the Chin Hills proper, the others can be hunted in the foothills or in forest reserves in the plains.

When a Falam hunter kills an animal of the large game category he sings a song of triumph, joined in by others, to notify people, especially those of his village, of his kill. In addition, before he can eat again he must perform a special ritual to protect himself from evil results of the killing. He must also hold a Feast of Celebration, a certain number of which are necessary for a man to enter the Plain of Heaven. At the feast for big game animals and at the feast for tigers, beer is divided into five types; the best one of these, the *sia hau zu,* or "mithan kill beer," is distributed only to those who have already slaughtered a mithan at a big game celebration feast; the second category of beer is for those who have slaughtered a pig at such a feast. In drinking these categories of beer, moreover, a system of priorities is observed, with the greatest hunter and giver of Feasts of Celebration taking precedence over everyone else. The greatest hunter also has certain other benefits. Among them, he receives the choicest food at the feast, and his hunting skill and generosity are praised extravagantly by other men as well as by himself. In such affairs, he is given precedence over all others, including village headman and chief, if they happen to be there. The lesser hunters present engage in boasting competitions, too, but the position of prominence remains with the great hunter. Because others seek to emulate him, various economic activities are started, additional hunts planned, and impetus is given both to cultivating grain for beer and to increasing the numbers of mithan.

The flesh of the mithan or pigs slaughtered and of the dead game animal is divided according to tradition. That of the game animal, for example, goes to satisfy various obligations incurred by the hunter: to headman, blacksmith, loaner of guns, beaters, and others. This division, in turn, places reciprocal obligations on the recipients. And the village as a whole benefits from the meat and beer provided at the feast.

Lehman's account of the Feasts of Celebration (1963: 182–84), based almost entirely on observations among the Haka Chin, differs in certain respects from that of Stevenson for those of Falam. Lehman mentions, for example, that the killer of one of the larger wild animals is permitted to perform the Sasawm Tuk, or "wild animal–increase celebration," which is intended to make certain that game animals continue to let themselves be taken "and not disappear from the forest." The giver of a Sasawm Tuk is required to make minor sacrifices, and he benefits in demonstrating that he enjoys a special position regarding ram, the forest realm. The Sasawm Tuk resembles certain ceremonies found elsewhere in mithan country which are dedicated to an increase in the numbers of mithan. For instance the Unning of the Adi also involves a hunt and the sacrifice of mithan; but its ritual is intended for the protection of mithan rather than wild animals.

The holder of a Feast of Celebration can display the skulls of the hunted animals on his verandah walls, along with those of mithan sacrificed at the feast. The display gives the owner status in his village, the mithan skulls showing his wealth, and the skulls of wild animals his prowess as a hunter.

In Bride-Price, Ransom, Tribute, Fine, and Oath

The mithan does not enter into the Chin wedding ceremony, but it figures in bride-price. The Falam Chin value an unmarried girl for her childlessness, beauty, character and personality, health, strength, diligence, and the social standing of her parents. The Falam bride-price is divided into two parts, the main price and the lesser prices. The main price for the daughter of a poor man is about one small mithan, and that for an attractive and hard-working daughter of a chief is seven mature mithan (Stevenson, 1943: 121–23). Carey and Tuck reported that the suitor of a Haka chief's daughter had to pay perhaps ten mithan, fifty pigs, ten guns, ten gongs, several slaves, and much grain as well as supply many pots of beer for the wedding feast (1896, 1: 190).

As with other peoples considered, the Chin have used mithan in payment of ransom and tribute. In addition, they are used in payment of fines for various offenses. In Zahau eyes, the most serious offenses are the stealing and slaughter of mithan, and the stealing of guns and gongs. For these offenses the present-day fine is up to two large cow mithan. For lesser ones the fines range from a young mithan down to a small amount of grain. Combinations of pigs, beer, grain, and salt, and sometimes beer alone constitute other fines. These payments in kind are also given cash values. In Stevenson's time the cash value was determined by the deputy commissioner of the Chin Hills. The distribution of fines varies from one Chin tribe to another. In some, the entire fine goes to the offended person. In others, he gets the bulk of the fine, such as the mithan and pigs, whereas the village elders keep the beer, grain, and salt for communal uses (Stevenson, 1943: 152–53, 165).

Carey and Tuck (1896, 1: 194–95) assert that the Chin take oaths when making agreements of all sorts, and that the most common form "is for both parties to kill an animal and paint each other with its blood." They describe an oath of friendship to be taken by two villages. The seers of the villages pour liquor over a mithan, and call to the spirits to make note of the agreement. The two chiefs together kill the mithan with spears or guns. As the animal collapses, its throat is cut and its blood is drained into bowls. Then the animal's tail is severed and dipped into the blood. With the bloody tail, the chiefs and elders of the two villages paint each other's faces as the seer speaks the oath: "May the party who breaks this agreement die even as this animal has died, and may he be buried outside the village and his spirit never rest; may his family also die and may every bad fortune attend his village." The British adopted a somewhat altered form of oath taking on occasions when a Chin group submitted to their rule. The representative of the Government and the Chin leader shot the animal and cut off the tail, which the leader held while making his oath. The painting with blood was dispensed with, and the wording of the oath was somewhat different. The chief swore "never to cut the telegraph wire or shoot the troops and always to pay tribute regularly." He appealed to the spirit to kill the government representative if he attacked the Chin without sufficient provocation, and to bring calamity on himself and his village if they violated the oath. For all the fine words, it appears the oath was often broken.

Changes in the Position of the Mithan in Modern Times
Contact with Burmans

The amazing thing about the relations between Chin and Burmans[4] is how little Burman social, political, and religious ideas have penetrated the hills. The Burmans have found little to attract them economically in the Chin Hills, and they never ruled them in pre-British times. True, they

---

4. Burman, as used here, refers to the dominant ethnic group of Burma who occupy the lowland east of the Chin.

raided the hill Chin and were raided in turn; they enlisted support from various Chin, starting in the eighteenth century, in campaigns against Manipur, and on other occasions; and they made halting efforts to convert the Chin to Buddhism, without eminent success. It is also true that the Chin, recognizing the greater variety and amount of Burman trade goods, made every effort to obtain them. They recognized the power and extent of Burman government, feared it, and made claims of affiliation, albeit exaggerated. Overall, however, Chin traditional life seems to have been little influenced by Burman ways, and the position of mithan in it remained unchallenged. Carey and Tuck record Chin raids in the last century which netted many buffalo, but neither buffalo nor common cattle became numerous at that time or well integrated in Chin culture. The modification of traditional Chin ways dates from the time of British intervention, though the British themselves tried to limit Burman influence on the hill people. They did, however, permit Christian missionaries to enter the hills; they brought Indian troops to support their administration; and they soon had Western-oriented teachers to introduce their ways to the Chin. Teachers and missionaries were among the major agents of acculturation who have acted to modify traditional Chin culture and incidentally the position of the mithan. This position has been further threatened by the migration into Chin country of Indian dairymen or *gowalas*.

The Missionary

According to Lehman, "the basic ideology of traditional Chin religion continues to flourish almost everywhere" in the Chin Hills (1963: 220). Many villages are entirely pagan or contain only a few Christians. However, Christian missionaries, particularly of the American Baptist Mission, have made inroads, and today more than half of all Haka and Falam Chin profess Christianity. Christianity, moreover, has had an indirect impact that cannot be measured in the number of conversions to the missionaries' denominations. There is, for example, the indigenous cult started just after the turn of the century by a man named Pau Chin Hau, which is known as *Lai pian* ("Chin congregation"). Laipianism represents a modification of the Christian missionaries' teachings and the elimination of those elements most repugnant to the Chin. The cult has remained largely a Tiddim-Falam phenomenon. In 1960 membership was estimated at 40,000 (pers. com., T. Stern, Dec. 9, 1966).

Like Christianity, Laipianism claims only one god, and is opposed to belief in spirits and sacrifice to them. Some members of the cult, however, persist in sacrificing to the spirits, and are not excommunicated. In overlooking such departures the cult is more tolerant and better adapted to Chin ways than is Christianity. Moreover, Laipianism does not prohibit performance of the Feasts of Merit, as Christianity does. The net effect, however, of Laipianism and Christianity seems to have been to reduce the number of sacrifices, in which mithan were the most prestigeful animals. Even among Chin who are not converts to these religions, there is a questioning of traditional religious ideas which suggests that the position of the mithan may be altered still more[5] (Bennison, 1935: 166–67; Stevenson, 1943: 45–46, 50, 161–62, 180).

The Gowala

With the British occupation of Burma the gowala, or Indian dairyman, moved into the Chin Hills (Stevenson, 1943: 59–61, 132). The gowalas were Hindus, who, though they cultivated small gardens, were primarily interested in the milk and clarified butter (*ghi*) that their common cattle provided. They represented a form of economic organization previously unknown in the Chin Hills, one which could function there only because of the demand for milk created by the British Indian occupation forces. Characteristically, the gowalas established small settlements and grazed their cattle in the surrounding country. To provide better grazing they regularly burned forest, altering the habitat to the detriment of the mithan. In addition, their animals caused such damage to Chin fields that a flood of lawsuits resulted. The gowalas were not willing, as were Chin mithan owners, to settle claims quickly and equitably. They contested every claim and even made the impossible demand that each guilty animal be identified. It is true that the tribal chief received yearly rent from the gowalas, but the individual Chin farmer apparently was overlooked.

Curiously, the entry of Indian dairymen seems not to have encouraged dairying and milk consumption among the Chin. Only in a few Christian villages, observed Stevenson (1943: 49) in the 1930's, were goats and cows milked. The average Chin still regarded milk as unclean. And there is no indication in the literature that mithan were milked in imitation of common cattle. The gowalas, however, had an impact on the position of the pig. They sold their surplus common cattle to poorer Chin for sacrifice, instead of pigs, at death ceremonies not requiring appeal to the spirits (Stevenson, 1943: 60). Wealthy Chin would not consider substituting common cattle for mithan at such feasts, but poorer men were tempted by the low price of Indian cattle, about a fourth the cost of pig per pound.

5. In many Chin villages a reduction in water supply has followed the decline of belief in spirits. Once people no longer fear the spirits of their springs they cut down trees surrounding them for firewood. In the village of Lotsawm a well almost completely dried up, and some people were forced to move (Stevenson, 1943: 45).

15

The Southern Mithan Keepers
A Summary

The Naga and Chin peoples resemble each other in a significant number of ways. Both, with the exception of a few Naga groups, are placed by Robert Shafer in the Kukish section of the Burmic Division of the Sino-Tibetan languages. Most groups of Chin and Naga live in compact villages which in former times were fortified. Both practice plowless shifting cultivation, and have the same basic assemblage of domestic plants and village animals. Both keep mithan and generally permit them to range free, though certain groups have either given up mithan keeping or put their mithan in the hands of herdsmen during the daytime. Neither Naga nor Chin, with rare exceptions, milk their mithan or use them for plowing or other traction; the primary uses are in sacrifice and in exchange.

Traditionally both Naga and Chin believe in a great number of supernatural beings whose goodwill is necessary for a man, his family, his fields and herds to prosper. Religious rites center on sacrifice and offerings to these beings, and are based on men's wishes for fertility, prosperity, and well-being. For both Naga and Chin, with a few exceptions, the mithan is the most prestigeful sacrificial animal, used at the more important ceremonial occasions. Both groups perform the Feasts of Merit for the purpose of enhancing status; but also involved, in varying degrees of intensity, are concerns with assuring prosperity in this life and confirming status in the afterlife. Both peoples share the idea that status in the afterworld is related to status on earth. More common for the Chin, perhaps, is the belief that mithan sacrificed in this life will go to the Land of the Dead to be part of the sacrificer's herd there. Both groups erect sacrificial posts, commonly forked, in connection with mithan sacrifice at the Feasts of Merit; both set up various memorials for the dead which are similar in form.

Here the similarities end. Though the assemblage of traits is much the

158

same, Naga and Chin seem to differ significantly in their motivations. The Naga's well defined fertility cult embraces the Feasts of Merit; sacrifice of animals, notably mithan; the erection of posts, stones, and other memorials; and formerly headhunting. In the Feasts the Naga is trying to transmit some of his life-force or fertility to his clan and village; posts and monoliths connected with the Feasts, as well as grave images and death memorials, are receptacles for that life-force, which may long continue to be dispersed from them. Naga headhunting involved wishes to obtain for the taker and his village the fertility of the slain. Thus the Naga are concerned to a considerable extent with the living, and with assuring their continued prosperity.

The Chin, by contrast, seem to focus more on benefits for the dead, on securing a desirable place in the afterworld and in not being forgotten by the living. Completion of the Feasts of Merit helps a Chin establish connections in the Land of the Dead and confirm his status there. For some groups it also helps him gain entry to the Plain of Heaven. In Chin death memorials the primary intent apparently is that the deceased shall not be forgotten. Though the Chin formerly took heads of enemies they killed in raids, usually the purpose of the raids was more to acquire slaves and loot than heads; the heads were taken merely as trophies of war, not to enhance village fertility. An exception was the raiding sometimes undertaken after a death to supply the deceased with slaves for his use in the Land of the Dead.

The possibility remains that at an earlier time Naga and Chin Feasts of Merit and memorialization of the dead were similar not only in outward appearance but in motivation as well. The Chin memorials may once have been intended to have a direct influence in spreading prosperity and fertility to the living. If so, the modern Chin have lost and forgotten the original intent.

Part III
The Mithan in Society
and Economy
A General View

16

Ownership, Care, and Selection of Mithan

A survey of the general information we have collected on mithan keeping shows that mithan are usually owned by individual men. Only for the Apa Tani are there reports of group ownership of mithan, by an entire village or clan; sacrifice of such mithan is in the interests of the whole group.

Among the Naga there is the custom, applied to mithan, other cattle, and even pigs, of men sharing ownership of an animal. A man may choose to hold shares in a number of animals, rather than own entire animals, to limit risk of loss, as through rinderpest and other diseases (Hutton, 1921a: 74; Mills, 1922: 60). Sema Naga joint owners belong to different villages, a practice which further limits risk. Two Lakher men frequently combine their resources in purchasing a cow mithan when neither can afford the animal on his own. When she has borne two calves, one of the owners takes possession of the calves and the other keeps the mother (Parry, 1932: 271).

The means by which a man can acquire mithan have certainly not been fully explored through field work. In some cases it is presumably a simple exchange of mithan for currency. More generally mithan are obtained by barter, or as compensation for services, as fines or in settlement of disputes, as marriage payments or in friendship pacts. A Dafla, as we have indicated, is given a share of the mithan born of mature animals he is herding for their Apa Tani owners.

The Zahau Chin of Falam have an extraordinarily complicated method of acquiring mithan and certain other livestock (Stevenson, 1943: 50–53). For them, an animal born under one's own roof is preferred, and there exist three systems of mithan purchase to assure this. Under the first system (*sia su lei* or "mithan vagina buy"), the purchaser usually assumes care of the mithan cow from the time she is five months pregnant until the calf has been weaned. With the birth of the calf, the purchaser pays the owner for it (15 rupees in predepression times plus 1 rupee for each month of pregnancy at the time the contract was initiated). The second system requires the purchaser to take over the care of a mithan for several seasons. He is permitted to keep the third calf born, by paying an additional purchase price (5 rupees). The third system, followed by poor men, resembles the second but does not involve any payment of currency. Instead the third calf of a young cow or the fourth of a mature one is given in compensation for care of the mithan cow up to the time that calf is born.

In addition, the Zahau Chin have a system of "borrowing" mithan when a man needs one quickly for sacrifice. Here repayment is made in mithan; the amount is determined by the growth, possible birth of calves (if the borrowed animal was a female), and other factors that would have operated between the time of borrowing and time of repayment. Similar systems are found among certain other Chin groups, and may also occur elsewhere, though the literature is silent on the point. Although "borrowing" of common cattle, water buffalo, and ponies occurs among the Zahau Chin, the systems of purchase do not apply to these recently introduced animals.

For at least two Naga groups, the Ao and Lhota Naga, the purchase of mithan exposes the buyer to special dangers (Mills, 1922: 44; 1926: 105). To avoid these dangers, he takes along an old man to act as paid intermediary. The old man not only has expert knowledge of the characteristics of mithan which disqualify them as sacrificial animals, but bears the risk of misfortune if a mistake is made and an unsuitable mithan is sacrificed.

Most mithan-keeping peoples permit their mithan to range free, to browse without herdsmen, in the forest during the daytime. With certain groups, especially in the south (Lushai, Lakher, most Chittagong hill peoples), the mithan voluntarily return to the village in the evening.[1] Each animal is given salt by its owner and stays the night, usually confined in a compound or cattle shed, or under the house, or is tied nearby. The mithan are not provided with feed, except for the rare animal which is confined and denied access to the forest.

Other groups, more commonly in the north (NEFA peoples, many Naga tribes, but also Thadou Kuki and Mru), permit their mithan to stay in the forest for days, weeks, or months at a time.[2] The owner maintains

1. The mithan of the Lakher are troubled by flies in the forest during the heat of April and May; at that season they return to the village in midday to shelter under the houses (Parry, 1932: 165).

2. This is part of a free-ranging pattern of bovine keeping, never thoroughly

contact with his mithan through occasionally providing them with salt. He may have a call which his mithan recognize. Hutton (pers. com., Jan. 25, 1966) describes going with Innamiren, an Ao head-interpreter, into a wooded valley with a large bag of salt for Innamiren's mithan: "He stood there in the open bottom and cried in stentorian tones, 'Ho! Ho!' Black heads began to appear here and there on the surrounding slopes and in half-an-hour's time we were being gently jostled by these enormous beasts all expecting a handful of salt." An owner may bring his animals to the village on rare occasions to determine how many new calves have been born, or to show them to prospective buyers, or because the animals are ill or are needed for sacrifice or ceremony.

Salt not only establishes a tie between the mithan and its owner but probably contributes to the reluctance of a mithan to leave the village of its birth. When, among the Lakher, mithan are sold or given as part of the bride-price to someone from a different village, the animals are apt to cause trouble and return to their old homes. Should a mithan refuse to go to the new village, the Lakher place eggs in its hoofprints, in the belief that "the village spirit," which is held responsible, will be appeased and permit the animal to go (Parry, 1932: 165).

Such groups as the Lakher, Sema Naga, and Angami Naga keep track of their mithan by putting around their necks bells made either of hollowed wood or of bamboo (Parry, 1932: 164–65; Hutton, 1921a: 57–58; 1921: 80). The Sema and the Lhota Naga tie a string of the bean *Entada scandens* around the neck of a newborn calf; the necklace is worn for just a few hours and then is removed and hung up in the mithan owner's house; the belief apparently is that by keeping something that has been close to the animal a man maintains a degree of control over it. There is also an association between *Entada scandens* beans and fertility, and it seems that the use of necklaces of these beans is tied to hopes for the animal's fertility (Mills, 1922: 60; Hutton, 1921a: 73; pers. com., Hutton, Sept. 29, 1966).

To aid identification some peoples slit, cut, punch, or brand their animals on the earlobes. Dunbar (1932: 220) sketched forty such marks which were cut into the ears of Adi mithan; each sept of a clan, he claimed, has its own mark. Even with such marks, some mithan keepers lose many animals by theft; the Apa Tani, we have seen, have that constant problem with the Dafla and Hill Miri and are often called on to ransom stolen animals.

---

investigated, that is found in scattered parts of Southeast Asia and adjacent India. See Appendix B, "Free-Ranging of Bovines in Southern Asia," for further information.

Some groups have departed from the traditional free-ranging patterns of mithan keeping. In the Falam area, as we have seen, the Chin agricultural lands include household gardens as well as fields. Minor crops are cultivated in the gardens, and people are less concerned about damage inflicted on them by the pigs, dogs, chickens, and goats which scavenge freely within the village. The fields, however, contain the staple crops—which are of vital importance—and are not always protected by fences. Thus the mithan must be herded to prevent crop damage. Though one field, the siapil or mithan field, is set aside for them within the fixed rotational sequence, mithan generally feed in the scrub jungle, which makes herding difficult. Adding to the difficulty is the animal's habit of feeding singly or in small groups and of moving several miles a day while doing so. As a result, more herd boys are needed for mithan than for common cattle. Among the Zahau Chin of Falam, villagers who own mithan form a group and take turns in providing boys for one or more days at a time for mithan herding. In certain other Falam Chin tribes, the individual mithan owner makes arrangements for his own animals. Under both systems, the herd boys drive the mithan home each evening and pen them under the houses or, rarely, under the village men's house ("youth's house"). In the morning, after the villagers have left for their fields, the mithan are freed and driven to the jungle. Stevenson notes that the problems in mithan keeping contribute incentives for giving feasts; too large a herd of mithan would be a serious burden for a man (1943: 53–56).

The Apa Tani, as we have mentioned, have particular difficulty in keeping mithan in their small, intensively cultivated valley. One solution is to keep the animals in scattered forest areas outside the valley; another is to place them with Dafla and Hill Miri acquaintances, shifting cultivators who have vast forested areas at hand.

It is clear that mithan are ideal in many ways under the traditional system of shifting cultivation that is so widely practiced in the forest.[3] They require no open grassland, and no forest need be cleared for their pasture. They can obtain all of their own feed and need only salt to tie them to the village. They need no herdsmen to guard them from animal predators, for they protect themselves quite successfully against most of these. The chief difficulty with mithan is the damage they can inflict on cultivated plants. To minimize the danger, some groups fence their fields or confine their mithan until the crops are harvested. The Falam Chin, because they do not fence all their fields, are burdened by the need of providing herd boys to watch their mithan; and the Apa Tani must pay neighboring shifting cultivators to care for many of their mithan.

3. See J. E. Spencer, 1966, for detailed treatment of shifting cultivation in Southeast Asia.

The evidence suggests that greater numbers of mithan are found in areas of shifting cultivation. When the density of fields increases around a village, as under sedentary cultivation or increased need for shifting fields, the mithan can become such a burden that a decline in mithan keeping results. Care and even feed must be provided, yet the owner fails to reap the benefits he might derive from using his mithan for milking, plowing, or transport. A careful study of the changing ecology of the mithan is greatly needed. There are involved not only the amount of available forest for browsing and the methods of animal care, mentioned above, but also the introduction of Hindu, Moslem, Christian, and Buddhist beliefs, and the undermining of traditional religions in which mithan sacrifice was important.

Although animal keepers in many parts of the world have deliberately bred their animals for special qualities,[4] there is little convincing evidence that in mithan country proper, peoples have purposely bred their mithan. Fürer-Haimendorf (1962: 38–39) reports that "neither Apa Tanis, Daflas, nor [Hill] Miris control the breeding of mithan, and as the animals are largely left to themselves and the bulls never castrated any selective mating would indeed be impossible." Hutton (pers. com., Jan. 25, 1966) has "never seen or heard of any trace of deliberate efforts of Nagas or Kukis to breed their mithun for particular qualities." He adds that "almost all mithun are kept in a semi-feral condition under which selected mating could not be practised." H.-E. Kauffmann, too, has never—in his travels or in his readings on mithan country—seen or heard of any deliberate breeding of domestic animals for desired qualities, with the exception of pig castration (pers. com., Oct. 10, 1966).[5] According to a native informant the Bawm-Zo of the Chittagong Hills do not deliberately breed their mithan (pers. com., H. J. Spielmann, Feb. 7, 1966). In sum, indifference to breeding mithan seems to prevail throughout the mithan country proper, though in Bhutan mithan and mithan hybrids are deliberately bred.[6]

---

4. For some interesting examples of this, see Epstein, 1955.

5. The Naga and Thadou Kuki, H.-E. Kauffmann (1938: 288–89, 292) and Hutton (1965: 29) report, keep no mature boars at all, but castrate all males within a few months after birth, to obtain the fattest animals possible. Reproduction of the species, they insist, depends entirely on the activities of the young males before castration and on occasional mating of domestic sows with wild boars. Though many young males cannot reproduce before castration, others can, with the cooperation of the adult females. The inbreeding that occurs has no apparent ill effect. It must, however, retard change in the domestic species, which even today differs little from the wild swine of the forest.

6. Stonor (in Zeuner, 1963: 255; also Stonor, 1964: 1697), however, has suggested that "along the Burma frontier it is the tribal custom to breed for colour as near to the wild gaur as possible"; he also writes, apparently in general terms, of "rigorous

Factors that operate to change the mithan species are thus chiefly of two types: unplanned interbreeding with other species of bovines, and unconscious selection by man of animals within the mithan species itself. The breeding of male gaur and female mithan would tend to retain in the domestic animals the qualities of the wild relative, and genetic divergence would be retarded. Hybridization with common cattle, now quite widespread, especially in the southern range of the mithan and in Bhutan, would speed up divergence of mithan from gaur.

The selective process within the species operates in more subtle ways, as in the choice of animals for slaughter or sacrifice. Among the Chin of Falam Subdivision and the Lakher, for example, if a mithan attacks and kills a man, atonement for the death must include slaughter of the guilty animal at the mourning feast (Stevenson, 1943: 58; Parry, 1932: 273–74). Over a long period of time a custom such as this would favor the development of tameness in mithan.

The role of sacrifice in selection involves three questions: the characteristics sought in the sacrificial animal, the opportunity allowed such animals for reproduction, and the fate of unsuitable animals. Among the characteristics that commonly contribute to the value of a sacrificial animal are body shape and size, general condition, color, length of horns, and the occurrence of marks or features which are viewed as ominous or auspicious. Black—like the gaur—is required by some groups in sacrificial mithan. The ominous or auspicious features are many and vary from group to group. The following factors detract from the suitability of mithan for sacrifice among the Chin of Falam (Stevenson, 1943: 48): a body with white or gray blotches, except for the normal white stockings and the gray of the forehead and frontal bone; an eye blind, discolored, or faulty in some other way; a horn, hoof, or tooth which is broken; a head marked by whorls of hair; an ear which, apart from the earmark, has been partly torn away; a tail cut off; and incurable sores. There are also temporary hindrances to sacrifice: broken bones and sores that have not yet healed.[7]

---

selection" for horns "over countless generations" by tribal breeders. We have uncovered nothing to support his claim that such selection occurs today or did in the past. Even the questionable report of Carey and Tuck (see p. 31) about the nineteenth-century Chin involved not "rigorous selection," but merely the driving of common cows and later their hybrid offspring to places frequented by gaur, to encourage crossing and the development of the mithan species.

7. Sachin Roy (1958: 148) lists the features affecting the suitability of a mithan for sacrificial purposes among the Adi. Mills has done so for the Rengma (1937: 186) and Lhota Naga (1922: 137–38); and Hutton for the Ao (1921: 79).

The criteria of selection for sacrifice of bovines and other animals in the Old World deserve careful investigation. There are, for example, remarkable parallels

What becomes of the blemished animals? Are they slaughtered early for food—which would favor reproduction of unblemished types? Stonor (1964: 1697) indicates that the Naga weed out wrongly colored calves. Fürer-Haimendorf writes that in NEFA blemished male animals "are presumably slaughtered for food in preference to animals which could also serve as sacrificial animals" and that their chances of survival are "less than those of unblemished animals which increase in value over the years" (pers. com., Oct. 16, 1966). This suggests that it is the unblemished animals that have greater opportunity to breed and to reproduce their type.

The evidence now at hand suggests that if the present selective processes prevailed in the past—before common cattle contaminated the breed—long periods of time would have been needed to bring about the significant differences that exist between the mithan and its wild ancestor.

---

between requirements for the sacrificial mithan in the Assam hills today and those for a sacrificial bull in one ancient Babylonian document. The Babylonian sacrifice (Albright and Dumont, 1934: 119–20) required selection of a "perfect black bull with intact horns and hoofs," chosen after inspection by a specialist. A bull was disqualified if it had "been beaten with a staff . . . or lashed with a whip" or if it had seven white tufts of hair "like stars" (or "like the Pleiades"). Such tufts of hair, also known as "Pleiades," were noted by the Vedic Indians, too, for animals used in the horse sacrifice; on those horses, however, the markings were auspicious. Even today, Hutton observes (in Mills, 1926: 105 n.), such markings are still important in parts of India "in choosing a horse," and apparently in choosing an elephant, too. They are considered by the Dusun of Borneo, too, of great significance on buffaloes.

17

The Primary Role of the Mithan
as Sacrificial Animal

Its Position Relative to Other Sacrificial Animals

Generally among mithan-keeping peoples chickens, pigs, and dogs have less prestige as sacrificial animals than do cattle. Most hill groups regard the mithan, among the various species of cattle, as preferable for the higher sacrifices—although the water buffalo seems a serious contender for preference in a few places. The Adi, among whom common cattle are recent and found only at lower elevations, never use them for sacrifice (S. Roy, 1958: 160). Various other groups do accept them for sacrifice, but most of these use them primarily in lesser ceremonies. The Lhota may substitute a black bull for the sacrificial mithan, though people refer to the substitute as "mithan" (Mills, 1922: 137). Some groups, the Apa Tani and Lhota among them, accept common cattle/mithan hybrids as substitutes for purebred mithan in sacrifice.

Occasions and Contexts of Sacrifice and Slaughter

Mithan are sacrificed on a variety of occasions: at marriage and death ceremonies; at times of illness or misfortune; in rites to maintain fertility and well-being; to mark important events, such as friendship pacts or treaties to end war; and, throughout the southern range of the mithan, in the Feasts of Merit.

Feasts of Merit

The Feasts of Merit are not found north of the Brahmaputra, but are a characteristic feature of the ceremonial life of both the Naga and Chin. It is said for the Naga that it would be unthinkable not to proceed as far as possible in this series of lavish ceremonies which commonly extends over several years, despite the great expenditure of effort and wealth required. Most obviously the Feasts are a means for a person to enhance his social status, but the underlying fertility motivations are equally, if not more, important. The feast giver, in performing the Feasts, publicly celebrates his success in having achieved prosperity, which he shares with his fellows on an ever-grander scale, and for which he is given recognition. He also is attempting to add to his own fertility, well-being, and prosperity—and among some groups to extend his powers of increase to his clansmen and co-villagers.

All the Feasts are highly ritualistic, and are conducted under the direction of a religious official or an individual who, though not a priestly person, has other qualifications. The Feasts include sacrifice of animals, public feasting and drinking, and, for some groups, distribution of gifts, most of this at the expense of the feast giver.[1] Sacrifices are usually made to various supernatural beings, and prayers are offered them asking for continued or greater prosperity, fertility, and well-being. In the first Feasts, pigs and common cattle, along with numerous chickens, generally are the sacrificial animals. Usually the series culminates in the mithan sacrifice. Among some groups, such as the Eastern Rengma, however, the buffalo is used for the highest sacrifice; and for the Konyak the buffalo is as important as the mithan in sacrifice. Already in the 1920's, bulls of common cattle were frequently being used in the "mithan sacrifice"; and as mithan keeping declines among the Naga and Chin, such substitution has become more widespread. In all of the Feasts, the requirements for the sacrificial animals are carefully laid down. Where mithan are used, the sacrificial mithan must be an unblemished animal, and usually a bull.

Performance of the Feasts of Merit involves the feast giver in a complex of reciprocal benefits and obligations, both economic and social. In addition, he gains the right to certain outward, conspicuous symbols of status. Among these are decorative additions to his dress; additions to his house, which for some groups are substantial; and the wooden posts or monoliths that are erected in the course of the ceremonies and remain standing, thus becoming, among other things, marks of his progress in the Feasts. The rights of display increase as the performer progresses through the series. Besides the benefits that accrue directly to the feast giver and his family and ritual associates, certain benefits extend more

1. For details on the performance of the Feasts of Merit among specific groups see Parry, 1932: 372–78 (Lakher); Shakespear, 1912: 87–90 (Lushai); Stevenson, 1943: 137–47 (Zahau Chin); Lehman, 1963: 177–82 (Burma Chin generally); Hutton, 1921: 230–33, 345–47; 1922: 60–69 (Angami Naga); Mills, 1937: 62–63, 181–95 (Rengma Naga); Stonor, 1950: 1–12 (Northern Sangtam Naga); Hutton, 1921a: 227–28 (Sema Naga); Mills, 1922: 136–44 (Lhota Naga); Mills, 1926: 257–62, 370–96, and Majumdar, 1924: 72–77 (Ao Naga).

generally. There is feasting and gaiety for many villagers, including the poorest. There is also a reinforcement of clan solidarity and pride, for clansmen not only share in the food, drink, and gifts distributed by one of their fellows but also participate in the ritual that celebrates his success.

Instances of the concern with fertility in the Feasts of Merit are numerous, though this is better documented for the Naga than for the Chin. The prayers which are offered at various stages in the ceremonies provide one of the clearest examples. In the words of an old Rengma man praying to two spirits before killing the boar offered by a fellow clansman:

> We are offering you a boar so big that when he roots on the mountain-side a spring bursts forth. May rice grow on rocks and trees in the fields. May rice pests be mad and forget to eat the rice. May the rats be mad. May the birds be mad. May each rice-plant grow like a basket spreading from its narrow base. May rice grow tall as *nsongphung* reeds. May every ear hold a thousand thousand grains. May each grain be as big as a sago-palm berry or a can-berry. May one mouthful of food fill the stomach . . . . May children be as ants, and as herds of elephants, and as herds of buffaloes, and as flocks of hornbills, and as spiders' eggs, and as crabs' eggs. May there be no illness. I have no brothers. I am going to eat this pig, but you are to partake of it first [Mills, 1937: 182].

Among many groups certain Feast ceremonies are held at times of planting or harvest, and some are performed at the granary. Omens are sometimes taken, following the sacrifice, to see what the future holds for the feast giver, another indication of his concern with continued well-being. A few groups try to obtain the goodwill of ancestors and thus their assistance in the quest for well-being. The Ao Naga are one such group; the Lushai apparently are another. The Lushai carry effigies of dead relatives around the village during one of their Feasts, to please the ancestral spirits and presumably to gain their favor (Shakespear, 1912: 88–89). The Lakher—at their highest Feast—stage a wrestling match between two youths, one a Lakher and the other a Lushai; the victory of the Lakher youth is prearranged (Parry, 1912: 377) and may well reflect hopes for continued strength and competitive success of the village men generally.

The wooden posts and monoliths erected in connection with the Feasts of Merit are the vehicles by means of which the Naga feast giver attempts to transmit part of his life-force, to which his prosperity is due, directly to the clan and village. In some cases the post is carried through the village, thus literally distributing the valuable quality to all quarters. More often, the post or monolith is set up in its appointed place directly. In either case, these repositories for the life-force of the feast giver will communicate that desirable quality to passersby, sometimes long after his death.

The Chin apparently do not share the Naga view that the post or stone is a repository for the feast giver's life-force; for them it seems to be rather a memorial. Nor is there clear evidence that the Chin think that the feast giver distributes his life-force straight to others—though a few groups may hold the view. There are, for example, the suggestive practices, in connection with the Feasts of Merit of the Rangte and Lakher, both Chin peoples (Shakespear, 1912: 147; Parry, 1932: 377–78). The guests at the Rangte Feasts "hold hands and form a circle round the house of the giver of the feast, who has to anoint the head of each of them with pig's fat." Is this done in order to obtain a share of his life-force? The Lakher terminate their highest Feast by a "saturnalia of free love" at the home of the feast giver, in which the young men may enjoy any of the women on hand, regardless of their marital status, with no restriction except that the women may protect themselves if they wish. Is such an affair especially appropriate at this time and place because the feast giver has transmitted to all a share of his life-force and fertility?

Certain Naga groups (Sema, Ao, Western Rengma) also believe that sacrificed mithan will join their owners in the Land of the Dead. For these groups, performance of the Feasts of Merit thus establishes a tie between the feast giver and the Land of the Dead, with the idea of securing for him a desirable position there. This concept is also common among the Chin, and storing up wealth and gaining status in the afterlife is a primary motivation of most Chin groups in performing the Feasts.

The Feasts of Merit have striking parallels to similar institutions found elsewhere. Hutton has likened them to certain Vedic sacrificial series, by which men gained status through performing a sequence of ceremonies in which sacrifice of bulls and cows was prominent (*Census of India,* 1931: 397). The Feasts have also been compared to the potlatch of the Northwest Coast Indians of North America because of the competitive hospitality offered, and the efforts to establish status by public consumption of property. Certain Chin, for example, at a special ritual meal in connection with the Feasts, attempt to force guests to consume excessive quantities of food and drink; and the guests are urged on by helpers armed with sticks (Lehman, 1963: 178–79). Among the Lakher, the performer's wife mounts a platform and throws gongs, brass basins, and money down to the guests—but this distribution is sham, and the gifts are returned after the ceremony. The Lushai chief who scatters such valuables at such a feast intends the recipients to keep them (Parry, 1932: 376–77).

Concepts of the Ao Naga[2]

The Ao Feasts of Merit clearly show the concern with fertility that is typical of the Naga Feasts, but they contain embellishments either not usual or not reported for other Naga. The Ao call the life-force *aren,* which has been translated as "mana" or "innate prosperity." Aren is a natural endowment of rich men. It also is an attribute of the dead, who, in the Ao view, can disperse their own aren among the living if they choose to do so, if they are pleased with the living. It can be acquired from the great men of earlier times for the benefit of the clan and village through the performance of the Feasts of Merit; it can also be acquired from a well endowed dead person by performing another special ceremony, not part of the Feasts sequence. The life-force is not described in quite this light for any other Naga tribe. All of the Naga, it is true, see an association between the dead and continued fertility, through utilization of the life-force; but only the Ao seem to look on the dead as capable of retaining control over their own aren and of influencing the fate of the living by giving or withholding it.

The Ao also believe that in performing the Feasts of Merit they gain prosperity, honor, and status for themselves not only in this life but after death as well. Presumably this comes in part through the belief that life in the Land of the Dead will be very much like life on earth, with the rich, rich and the poor, poor, and the mithan sacrificed on this earth constituting their herds there.

In addition to establishing a beneficial link with the dead by performing the Feasts of Merit, the Ao also inadvertently become involved with another group of supernatural beings every time they sacrifice a mithan. The association is undesirable but unavoidable. It centers on the unique Ao concept of the "celestial mithan." The Ao believe that each human being has three souls (*tanela*) and one fate (*tiya*); his fate, which lives in the sky, in turn has three souls of its own. The entire group, then, consists of eight: the human and his three souls, and his fate and its three souls. The fates of all earthly humans are commonly spoken of as "sky folk." One of the human's three souls is a "celestial mithan," which is in the sky and under the care of his fate. The fate, on its part, has one soul in the form of a mithan on earth. Should a man's celestial mithan die or be sacrificed, the Ao believe the man would lose his life. Similarly, the death of any mithan on earth involves the death of a fate; the sky folk, to save the life of one of their group, will try to prevent the mithan sacrifice.

2. Based on Mills, 1926: 223–26, 231, 257–62, 288, 370–96.

Thus the Ao take various actions, before a mithan sacrifice, to confuse the sky folk, and afterward take further measures to avoid their inevitable wrath.

The Lisudu and Morom

The lisudu,[3] that Apa Tani institution for settling disputes by competition in destruction (see p. 70), bears certain similarities to the Feasts of Merit, but differs in its motivation and in involving mithan slaughter rather than sacrifice. The lisudu is a means of settling a serious quarrel between two wealthy men of one village. It ensues when a man of high prestige feels his honor has been attacked by another man of approximately equal standing—an intolerable insult to the honor-sensitive Apa Tani. The injured man challenges the offender to a lisudu, a contest of destroying mithan and sometimes other forms of wealth. In theory the man who continues the contest longest wins the loser's land and other possessions. In practice, however, the council of clan representatives intervenes and negotiates a solution without either party's suffering such abject humiliation.

Recounting one lisudu will illustrate how the institution functions. A Dafla man, long the guest of another Dafla who resided in the Apa Tani village of Hang, was seized by a prominent villager, Belo Lampung, and his clansmen for a past robbery. The Dafla host was the freed slave of a rich, influential Apa Tani, Ponyo Tamar. As is customary in such cases, Ponyo Tamar offered to ransom his slave's guest. The captor, Belo Lampung, rejected the ransom offer; he and his clansmen instead beheaded and dismembered the captive and threw the pieces into a river. Offended by the act, Tamar killed two of Lampung's cattle within sight of the latter's house. Perhaps out of fear, Lampung did not retaliate. Still furious at the insult to his house and prestige, Tamar challenged Lampung to a lisudu. He slaughtered three mithan cows in front of his rival's house and destroyed a bell, bronze plate, and sword. Lampung responded by slaughtering four mithan in front of the challenger's house. In his turn Tamar slaughtered ten mithan the following day, and Lampung responded by killing twenty. The fourth day Tamar killed thirty. Undaunted, Lampung gathered sixty mithan and slaughtered them the next day. Tamar appealed to his kinsmen for the loan of mithan, assembled eighty animals, and prepared to kill them. Lampung could not have

3. The discussion of the lisudu is based on Fürer-Haimendorf, 1955: 73–76; 1962: 110–20.

matched this, and his cause was doomed. Here the members of the clan council (except those of the disputants' clans) intervened, for continued destruction of mithan would have been injurious to the village. They urged that Tamar slaughter just sixty beasts, to equal but not outdo his rival. Tamar agreed, but insisted that Lampung admit his error and compensate him for killing his slave's guest. This was agreed upon, and Ponyo Tamar received one female mithan as a fine, thus ending the affair to his satisfaction. As can be seen in the details of this lisudu, Tamar's interest lay entirely in reaffirming his prestige, which had been challenged by the insulting acts of Lampung. Tamar had suffered no material loss at the hands of Lampung, but as one of the influential men of Hang, the attack on his honor had to be vindicated.

The lisudu's competitive destruction of wealth, as Fürer-Haimendorf notes, has certain parallels with the potlatch of the Northwest Coast Indians of North America (see Appendix A). The destruction is not simply waste. The slaughter of mithan provides a welcome abundance of meat which is eaten by other, usually more humble, villagers. If the supply is sufficient, people from nearby villages also participate in the feast. Thus, the slaughter results in the distribution of meat to people who otherwise might not have it. It also reduces the wealth of the competitors, and tends to level economic differences within the village. The competition, moreover, is not permitted by other villagers to go so far that it threatens the livelihood of the entire village or large sections of it.

No institution similar to the lisudu is mentioned for any other mithan-keeping group, though the paucity of literature on NEFA leaves the possibility that it occurs among other peoples there. Fürer-Haimendorf indicates its absence among the Dafla neighbors of the Apa Tani; and it is definitely absent among the Naga and Chin.

Closer in motivation to the Feasts of Merit is the effort by certain Apa Tani men to enhance their prestige at the annual village-wide agricultural celebration, the Morom. During this celebration men wealthy enough to do so hold individual ceremonies which culminate in the slaughter of mithan. The meat is distributed without restriction and in equal shares throughout the village or the valley, depending upon the magnitude of the donor's performance. As in the Feasts of Merit, the performer gains great prestige, and others benefit from the distribution of the meat. The Apa Tani donor however gains no outward marks of distinction such as the Naga and Chin rights of display. Nor is there any indication in the literature that the Apa Tani, in the lisudu or in the Morom, are particularly concerned either with establishing their prestige in the Land of the Dead or with extending their prosperity and fertility to the village—two elements prominent in the Feasts of Merit.

Marriage Feasts and Death Ceremonies

While the killing of mithan for marriage feasts frequently occurs, there is no indication of ritual significance. The accounts generally indicate merely that the family of the bride slaughters mithan for a great wedding feast.

Most mithan-keeping peoples traditionally believe that when a man dies, his soul goes to the Land of the Dead. There he takes up a new existence, many groups hold, surrounded by the things he has known in this life.[4] Some believe that mithan he has sacrificed during his lifetime— or certain of them—await him and form part of his wealth. The Rengma Naga fear that if during his lifetime a man sacrificed too many mithan at short intervals his herd in the Land of the Dead would become numerous and troublesome, and the dead might call him to death. Hence the Rengma—unlike certain other groups—sacrifice only male mithan; a female would breed and increase the herd in the Land of the Dead (Mills, 1937: 187). Fortunately for feasters, animals slaughtered solely for meat have no afterlife, and the Rengma place no limit on how many can be killed. Many groups sacrifice a mithan or other animal on a man's grave, some apparently with the expectation that it will join him in the afterworld.

Some NEFA peoples fear that departed souls or ancestral ghosts may return to harass the living. Thus in some funeral rites sacrificial animals are offered directly to the soul of the dead person almost as a payment to induce the soul to keep away from the family, the house, and the village. Some groups believe that certain souls or ghosts return anyway, and must repeatedly be propitiated by sacrifice. Often a fowl or pig will suffice, but sometimes a mithan is necessary.

Times of Illness or Misfortune

In times of illness or misfortune the spirits which abound in the traditional world of the mithan-keeping groups must be propitiated. Among the Chin of Burma (Carey and Tuck, 1896, 1: 197–98), each of the many spirits that infest house, fields, and countryside can cause sickness, control rains, induce crop damage, or cause other misfortune. Each spirit makes its own demands. It helps not at all to sacrifice a pig to a mithan-demanding spirit, or a chicken to a pig-demanding one. If a sick man's illness persists, one animal after another may be sacrificed, starting with a young chicken or small dog and sometimes working up—as for a Chin chief—to ten mithan.

4. There is considerable variation in specifics of belief from group to group. For a general discussion, see Fürer-Haimendorf, 1953.

The Idu Mishmi do not deal directly with the evil spirit that causes illness. Instead, a priest is called in and performs the Amrasa ceremony, in which he invokes his tutelary spirit to drive the evil spirit away. Sacrifices made to the tutelary spirit may include chickens, pigs, rice beer, and on occasion mithan. Sometimes this spirit holds out and demands greater sacrifices: " 'Look! I have come a long way, and I am tired. This household has a number of *mithuns* [mithan]. Can they not offer me a *mithun* for the service I will do them?' " The priest then praises the spirit, cajoles it, and reaches a bargain in which the spirit's services are obtained in return for the sacrifices. The tutelary spirit is then expected to ward off the evil spirit, and the man to recover (Baruah, 1960: 78–81).

When a man is seriously ill and loses consciousness, the Api Tani believe that his soul has wandered to the Land of the Dead and is being detained along with the souls of the departed by one of the spirits who live there. The sacrifice of a mithan is a sort of ransom of the soul, which then returns to the man's body and permits him to regain consciousness (Fürer-Haimendorf, 1953: 42; 1962: 137–38, 146–47).

Some Other Occasions

Among the other occasions on which mithan have been sacrificed are the ending of a clan feud, and the conclusion of a peace treaty between tribes or villages. When two Lakher villages have fixed the terms of a peace settlement, the payment is made and a mithan or pig is sacrificed. The blood of the animal is smeared on the foreheads of village representatives, who then swear an oath: "If we start hostilities afresh first, may the blood flow from our foreheads in the same way as the blood of the animal sacrificed has flowed today" (Parry, 1932: 218).

Cementing a pact of personal friendship is another of the occasions on which mithan may be sacrificed. Fürer-Haimendorf (1955: 218, 222) described such a sacrifice at the sealing of a Hill Miri dapo pact—the most binding of their personal alliances—in which he was a partner. The god Potor-Met was involved, and a violator of this dapo would have brought upon himself the god's anger and eventually his own death. At the ceremony, two holes were dug, and in one a thorny tree called *tage*, which takes root easily, was planted. The sacrificial animal was tied to the tree while a priest prayed. A man from the family of the Miri entering the pact beheaded the mithan, allowing its blood to flow into the second hole. Fürer-Haimendorf then was asked to set up a stone in the hole, for his Miri partner. Nearby two other stones were set at right angles, an upright one for Fürer-Haimendorf, and a flat one for his wife. All this strongly suggests a fertility rite.

Other occasions of mithan sacrifice are agricultural festivals of one sort or another, and celebration of a man's killing a big game animal or important enemies. An Adi, at the time of a British expedition against his people, boasted that for every coolie he killed he would slaughter a goat, "for every sepoy a pig, and for every white sahib a mithan" (Millington, 1912: 132).

Methods of Sacrifice

In summing up here the traditional methods of sacrificing mithan we shall write, as we often have in this book, in the present tense. It should be understood however that government orders have in many cases changed these methods.

Mithan are sacrificed in three ways: by strangulation; by chopping, stabbing, cutting, or spearing; or by beating the animal on the head. Strangulation is found only among the Adi groups. Fürer-Haimendorf has noted isolated cases of ritual strangulation of animals elsewhere in India, as with the pig among the Baiga in Middle India, and with the horse in ancient India; but he doubts a direct connection between these cases and the Adi method of strangling mithan (1954: 602–3). Instead, he looks to Tibet as the place from which Adi sacrifice by strangulation may derive. Matthias Hermanns (1949: 208) not only mentions the practice for the A-mdo nomads of eastern Tibet but views slaughter or sacrifice by suffocation as characteristic of the earliest cattle-, reindeer-, and horse-herding cultures; suffocation was resorted to presumably because the seat of the soul and of life was thought to be in the breath and not the blood. It may have been practiced to keep the breath, the most significant element, within the animal sacrificed. Perhaps the Adi accepted part of Tibetan sacrificial practice—death by strangulation—in the same way that they accepted selected items of Tibetan material culture coming to them through trade.

Strangulation is generally accomplished by the Adi with the aid of a wood or bamboo rack.[5] This rack is made of two ladder-like frames which are tied at the upper end while the lower ends are spread out to form an inverted "V" (Figure 10). The sacrificial mithan has a rope tied around its neck. Men pull the rope across the rack and raise the beast until it chokes to death.[6] It is then skinned, and its flesh is divided among those entitled to a share.

5. An exception is indicated by H. H. F. Williams for the Karko Adi. Two ropes were passed around the neck of the mithan, and the fighting men pulled on the four ends to strangle the animal. He saw three mithan killed in this way (Fürer-Haimendorf, 1954: 602 n.).

6. A series of photographs of a mithan being strangled by the Minyong appears in Fürer-Haimendorf, 1954: Plate 2. For descriptions of the practice, see Dunbar, 1915: 43; Fürer-Haimendorf, 1954: 600–601; Sen Gupta, 1955: 76; and S. Roy, 1958: 147–48.

Though the brutality of sacrifice by strangulation offends Hindus and Westerners alike, sacrifice by other means can be equally brutal. The Gallong sometimes tie a mithan's legs and strike it in the neck with an ax. Before the animal is dead a bamboo device is forced into the throat to collect blood. Then the creature is struck again until it dies. Occasionally a mithan breaks loose and runs amuck, but it is caught again and killed with the same ax by the person who started slaughtering it; otherwise misfortune would strike his family (Sen Gupta, 1955: 76). T. T. Cooper (1873: 234) observed an equally harsh mithan killing among the Mishmi. The animal was first held by a slave in the center of a circle of men armed with knives.

> Then, amidst a solemn silence the chief or head of the house steps forward with his large Tibetan knife, and calmly surveying the animal for a few minutes, with a sudden tiger-like spring, delivers a frightful cut at its loins, apparently paralysing it. The chief then retires, and all the men rush in and with horrible yells hack and hew at the wretched beast until it falls with piteous groans, and long before life is extinct lumps of the quivering flesh are cut off and thrown to the women and children, who scramble for the warm bloody pieces, and with almost frantic shouts of delight carry them to the house, where they are boiled for the feast.

Cooper was told that prisoners were killed in a similar way. In the Arakan Hills the mithan is tied to a post and killed by spearing (Tickell, 1854: 110–11; St. John, 1873: 238). One account describes the "villagers wrought up to frenzy and drink, [the mithan] being dragged into the village, tied down to a stake, and then slowly dispatched by numberless stabs with spears, the whole crowd dancing round and round and deliberately sticking it in every part of the body." Spearing is also reported for the Mru, Khumi, and Pankhua of the Chittagong Hills (pers. coms., D. Sopher, 1965, and L. G. Löffler, Oct. 18, 1966). Löffler reports still another method of slaughter for Mru and Khumi, involving cutting the throat of the animal with a dao. This method, which is very rare and accompanied only with minimal rites, he suspects may be an old Burmese custom introduced to these hill peoples.

Several methods of mithan sacrifice are described for the Naga. The Ao custom of hacking the animal to death with daos has been suppressed (Risley, 1903: 212; Molz, 1909: 64; Smith, 1925: 188–89). A method mentioned for the Sema, Lhota, and Northern Sangtam causes the animal little pain. The sacrificer, usually an old man, first hits the tied and thrown animal two or three formal blows on the head with a stick, then plunges a spear into its heart; or he makes a slight cut behind the animal's shoulder, then drives a wooden stave into its vital organs and twists it about. The animal dies almost instantly (Hutton, 1921a: 229; Mills, 1922: 140;

Stonor, 1950: 5). The method described for the Chongli clan of the Ao Naga (Mills, 1926: 379–80) involves deliberate torture. It begins with the baiting of the mithan by a warrior who crashes his shield against the mithan and hits it with a stick. Then the animal is smeared with a lather to make it slippery and difficult to grasp. Later young men march around it in procession and then attack it. They throw it to the ground, hold it so that it cannot rise, and some of them jump and dance on it until it is exhausted. Then it is released and permitted to get up. After a little while it is again thrown to the ground and danced on, the entire process being repeated three times. The third day, after more ceremony, the mithan is finally dispatched by an old man who spears it behind the right shoulder. This thrust does not kill the beast, and the young men then cut the knee tendons, hamstringing the animal, and drag it alive to the sacrificer's house. There a puppy is dashed against its forehead. The mithan, whether dead or not, is then cut open and disembowelled, and left thus until morning. This "mithan sacrifice" takes five days, with the mithan actually being killed in the third day. The Mongsen clan of the Ao also torture the sacrificial mithan (Mills, 1926: 390–91) but in a somewhat different way. The Ao sometimes use a special ceremonial knife on which each mithan sacrifice is indicated with a mark (Figure 11).

At the mithan sacrifice, last in the Feasts of Merit series of the southern group of the Western Rengma Naga, the animal is not given food or water on the day of sacrifice. Ropes are tied to its horns, and a blessing is offered by an old man at the home of the owner. The beast is exhorted to go in peace and is anointed with rice beer; then it is dragged through the village by the young men, all in full dress. In its passage, people pour water on the mithan and ask for its blessing.[7] Finally, it is tied to a post and an old man of the giver's clan "spears it feebly." Then one official grabs its tail and with another official hacks as much meat from the living animal as possible. When the mithan collapses, its stomach is slashed open and the young men fight over the meat. A more humane form of slaughter prevails among the northern group of the Western Rengma (Mills, 1937: 186–87, 193).

In earlier times the Lhota Naga, on ceremonial occasions, beat the mithan to death; and in the 1920's the Ao still gave the mithan a formal blow on the head (Hutton, 1921: 406; 1921a: 229). Beating the sacrificial animal to death, with a pestle, is also reported for the Purum Kuki of

7. The Northern Sangtam, too, lead or drag the sacrificial mithan through the village. As Stonor noted (1950: 9), superficially the practice resembles the scapegoat ceremony. In the Dafla "scape-goat ceremony" which he described later (1957: 15) —involving the sacrifice of a mithan to keep evil and sickness away from the village— the animal apparently is not led around the village.

Manipur. Even a sturdy animal succumbs after two or three strokes (T. Das, 1945: 87).

The use of a wooden stave, mentioned above for the Sema, Lhota, and Northern Sangtam, has been commented on by various writers, who have viewed it either as a taboo on the use of metal or as a persistence, for ritual purposes, of an early weapon, presumably from times before metal was known. It is possible, Stonor holds (1950: 9), that the ritual in which this is used symbolizes a time when the mithan was wild and wild animals were caught and dispatched with primitive weapons. To support this view he notes the ritual shooting of mithan with bow and arrow among the Lakher. Ritual shooting of mithan with bow and arrow is also found among the Dafla (Stonor, 1957: 15, 20) and among certain Burma Chin (Lehman, 1963: 181). The Northern Mru, says Löffler (pers. com., Oct. 18, 1966), have among their sacrificial paraphernalia an iron arrow which he thinks may be a survival from times when they used the bow and arrow in sacrifice; today, though imitation bows serve in certain rites, real bows have completely disappeared. The iron arrow, in Mru sacrifice, can be used like a spear in killing small cattle, but it is not used with a bow. Among those groups still using the bow and arrow in sacrifice, the Burma Chin in question dispatch the animal finally with an ax blow; the Lakher, with a blow from a heavy stick or an ax; the Dafla, usually with an ax blow and knifing.

The few accounts that are sufficiently explicit indicate that the brutality exhibited in mithan slaughter is related to religious belief, especially to fear of retribution by the spirit of the sacrificed animal. The Ao Naga believe that the animal's spirit would lie in wait to gore the feast giver's spirit on its way to the Land of the Dead. The deliberately cruel Ao ways of sacrificing mithan are intended to intimidate the beast's spirit and to prevent it from wreaking such vengeance (Smith, 1925: 103). Sometimes the feast giver appeals to the mithan for forgiveness, or tries to pass the blame on to someone else. Thus one Ao feast giver is reported as saying to the mithan: " 'Others tortured you, not I' " (Mills, 1926: 390). Or the sacrificer may undergo cleansing or punishment for the contamination of performing the act. The near kinsmen of the sacrificer, among the Mongsen clan of Ao Naga, actually stage a fight, which may develop into a free-for-all, in a feigned defense against the beating of the mithan.

Fear of retribution may also be at the root of certain customs, observed among the Ao, Rengma, and Lhota Naga, which require that the man who sponsors the sacrifice and in some cases his household avoid the flesh of the mithan killed. The Lhota (Mills, 1922: 138, 141) believe that should a feast giver or any member of his household eat mithan flesh he would go mad. In fact, a Lhota feast giver may avoid mithan flesh entirely for the year lest an enemy deliberately give him flesh of his own mithan to consume. There is even the one case of a Lhota woman attempting to poison her husband by mixing in his drink shavings from the horns of his sacrificed mithan.

Sacrifice and Keeping of Mithan and Conversion to Other Religions

Hinduism, especially through the Assamese and Bengali, has had an impact on some mithan-keeping tribal peoples—though unfortunately acculturation has gone almost unchronicled. The traditional Hindu, recognizing the mithan as a relative of common cattle, is shocked at the sacrifice of mithan and offended at the brutality so often involved. The result is pressure against mithan sacrifice and, where possible, modification of the traditional ceremonies requiring it. When tribal people are converted to Hinduism, they do, of course, give up such sacrifice.

The evidence of Christian acts against mithan sacrifice, though scanty, is better recorded. Verrier Elwin, for example, writes (1961: 78) that missionaries made many converts among the Naga, and interfered in Naga society and culture far more than the government could have, putting, to cite one instance, an end to the Feasts of Merit. At one time, he says, mithan flesh was forbidden to the convert because the animal was involved in sacrifices at "heathen" festivals. Hutton (pers. com., Jan. 25, 1966) adds to this: "Ao Naga Christians often refuse to eat mithan flesh as being 'meat offered to idols' (Acts, XV.29); Ao Christians are apt to be sanctimonious." P. Sentsi mentions the traditional Rengma Naga sacrifice of mithan and other animals to evil spirits to bring about the cure of sickness, then remarks that belief in such spirits is being quickly eliminated with conversion to Christianity (1965: 48). Today nearly 70 percent of the Rengma are Christians.

Among the Chin, too, Christian missionaries tried to eliminate mithan sacrifice. Initially this hindered conversion, for more than two decades ago Stevenson (1943: 161–63) wrote that the principal barriers to spread of the Christian faith of the American Baptist missionaries to the Burma Chin were the requirements of giving up beer drinking and feast giving. As a result, he observed, only 3 percent of these Chin had been converted to Christianity over a period of several decades. Following World War II, however, converts were more numerous, and by 1953 more than a third of the Chin enumerated in the Burma census professed Christianity, and presumably no longer performed Feasts of Merit. The abandonment of the Feasts, in turn, eliminated the most important incentive for mithan keeping and, one assumes, led to a decrease in mithan keeping among

Christians. This assumption is supported by data in the 1953 census. Haka, which had the largest percentage of Christians (55% of the total population) and lowest of animists (43%) of all subdivisions enumerated, also had the lowest percentage of households owning mithan (11%); while Kanpetlet, with the lowest percentage of Christians (1.4%) and highest of animists (76%), had the highest percentage of households owning mithan (23%) (*Union of Burma, First Stage Census, 1953,* 1957: 12, 20).

Sopher (1964: 113) has commented that keeping mithan for sacrifice has been dropped in the new Christian villages of Lushai and Pankhua in the Chittagong Hills. A survey conducted by H. J. Spielmann (pers. coms., Sept. 9 and Nov. 6, 1965) of 22 Bawm-Zo villages in the Chittagong Hills revealed, however, that none of the 450 non-Christians involved possessed mithan; all the owners were Christians! This curious reversal of the expected pattern, Löffler suggests (pers. coms., Aug. 20, 1965, and Oct. 18, 1966), may spring from the poverty of the non-Christians. The Khumi, southern neighbors of the Bawm, says Löffler, are untouched by missionary activity, yet keep no mithan. There are mithan skulls on Khumi walls, but people insist that, though mithan were kept by their ancestors, they are too poor to do so. The poor man has little enough land to use for crop cultivation, let alone for mithan, and he cannot afford to pay for the damages the mithan inevitably do to the fields of others.

The acceptance of Christianity sometimes results in a transfer of certain old practices to the new faith, and mithan may be slaughtered at Christian festivals instead of sacrificed at traditional ones. The Bawm, say Löffler and Spielmann, slaughter mithan and eat them at Christmas ceremonies (pers. coms., Spielmann, Feb. 7, 1966, and Löffler, Aug. 8, 1965). And J. K. Stanford (1946: 93) noted a mithan in northern Burma being brought in, presumably for slaughter at a feast and meeting of a Baptist mission. Such occasions scarcely provide the incentive for keeping mithan that sacrificial needs at the traditional ceremonies did. It may thus be significant that the NEFA tribes on the Himalayan slopes, who have been notably less disturbed by either Hinduism or Christianity, have the largest herds of mithan. In the Naga country and areas southward, missionaries have been numerous, traditional culture has suffered, and mithan are few.

18

Other Roles of the Mithan

In Exchange

The cash value of mithan varies considerably from place to place. Generally it has been increasing, in some places sharply. More important than specific cash values, however, is the position of the mithan as a pecuniary measure in the traditional exchange by barter. In many places ordinary money has been encroaching on barter, but barter still persists.

Various pecuniary measures[1] are or have been in use among mithan-keeping peoples, though they differ from group to group. Among the smaller measures mentioned for the Naga tribes are salt cakes or packets, iron hoes, dao blades, specially made large spearheads, round brass discs, conch shells, strings of conch shell beads, and thin strips of iron. One of the latter, known as *chabili*, was equal to a day's work among the Ao Naga in pre-British times.

Pecuniary measures are commonly incorporated into elaborate systems of value which generally establish, for each group, the values of commonly bartered items.[2] Stevenson (1943: 103) reports that for the old Tashon Chin of Burma the basic units were two items of equal value: the *tsi zawl* (a salt packet) and the *thir pek* (a piece of iron with a hole in it). Next came the *vawkthia seu* (a young pig of specified measurements), which was worth two of the basic units or one white blanket. The *khuai tsuai* (beeswax cake) was worth 2 vawkthia seu; and the *siapi* (mithan cow)

1. By Melville Herskovits' definition (1952: 245), these pecuniary measures are money. He regards money as "any kind of least common denominator of value, whether it be of metal, shell, stone, or other material, or, indeed, even if it itself is a consumption good, so long as it is regarded as a part of a system of graded equivalents, and is used in payment for goods and services."

2. See, for example, Mills, 1937: 72 for the Rengma Naga; Stevenson, 1943: 103 for the Tashon Chin; Lehman, 1963: 80 for the Haka Chin; Fürer-Haimendorf, 1962: 51–52 for the Apa Tani.

was worth from 40 to 60 vawkthia seu, depending on how numerous were the mithan herds, which were frequently decimated by disease. The Apa Tani have a different system, with named units—such as pachu, paroe, and puliang (see pp. 74–75)—and specified items understood for each. Mithan are not among these items, but the price of mithan and virtually all other objects can be expressed in the values of the Apa Tani table.

In most of those systems where mithan are found, they are the highest unit. They have sometimes been spoken of as currency because of their being present in the value systems and being used in exchange for land or in payment for ransom, tribute, fine, or bride-price. Among the Apa Tani, irrigated land generally is reckoned in mithan and can usually be purchased only for mithan and common cattle, though other items may be added to the basic payment. A man who has surplus grain and wishes to use it to purchase land usually exchanges his grain for mithan, then mithan for land. A well-located house site in an Apa Tani village can rarely be purchased for less than ten mithan; a fairly large bamboo grove outside the village costs perhaps three; a terrace of roughly half an acre of wet-rice land near the village may cost ten mithan or more; a half-acre terrace in distant side valleys as little as two or three (Fürer-Haimendorf, 1955: 58; 1962: 17–19, 21, 37, 52).

The best-documented accounts of mithan serving in ransom are those of Fürer-Haimendorf for the Apa Tani and Dafla (1955: 41–43, 66, 74–76, 79–80, 100, 138–39, 170–72; 1962: 107–10, 124–29). Individuals are seized for failure to repay debts; for sheltering escaped slaves; to rectify cheating, real or imagined, in trade deals; for other personal, social, or economic affronts or offenses; or with no provocation, simply for the sake of the ransom. The Apa Tani we have seen feel a particular obligation to ransom their people and mithan because their prestige is at stake. As one man observed, the spirits would be offended if mithan were not ransomed from the Dafla. Men of wealth and their families are special targets for capture, and the payment of ransom for them contributes to a redistribution of wealth. So does the ransom of kidnapped mithan. When a ransom includes mithan they are the most valuable part of an impressive array of goods. Payments to the intermediaries add notably to the cost of the transaction.

Though the payment of tribute has largely ended with the extension of national political control, it used to be common; and mithan were prominent in the payments. For example, J. Rawlins (1790: 190), reporting that mithan were killed for a feast celebrating the end of hostilities between two Kuki tribes in the Chittagong Hills, commented that had one tribe been vanquished and remained tributary to the other, mithan and other goods would have been paid annually to acknowledge vassalage.

Among various mithan-keeping groups the mithan can be used to pay fines for crimes. Even when the death penalty is invoked, a man is sometimes permitted to obtain his freedom by paying a fine in mithan. There are indications that British district officers sometimes followed native tradition in assessing fines in mithan. While J. P. Mills was deputy commissioner of the Naga Hills, he fined a Konyak Naga village two mithan for carrying a headhunters' trophy from one village to another, in the time after headhunting had been forbidden; he also assessed mithan from a village beyond his authority, for "involving British subjects" in headhunting raids (Fürer-Haimendorf, 1939: 50–52). In another headhunting violation by the Naga village of Tuensang, the government representative initially demanded the men who committed the act. "To this the Tuensang people replied, 'Does a hunter give away his hounds?' The next demand was for a fine in money. To this the reply was, 'We have no coins. We hear the Government makes coins. If they are short, let them make some more.' The final demand was for mithuns [mithan], the customary fine for head-hunting in British days, to which no reply was given, but the animals were quietly tied up outside the village gates" (Elwin, 1961: 72).

Wherever bride-price is customary, the mithan is apt to be part of it. Among the Lushai, early in this century, this meant from three to ten mithan or their equivalent in other goods, paid to the father or closest male relative, and additional sums to certain relatives of the bride; all these payments could be spread over many years. Despite the fixed customary bride-price, there was room for considerable negotiation over the down-payment, between the representatives of the bridegroom's family and the bride's parents. One side tried to keep the down-payment low and the other to set it high. Sometimes the husband died before fulfilling all his obligations, and it fell to his children to complete the payments of their mother's bride-price.[3] Now that the Lushai are Christians, the bride-price is paid in cash, not in mithan or other goods (Goswami, 1960: 44).

When T. T. Cooper visited the Mishmi country in 1869 he noted that the Mishmi, like so many other Assam peoples, displayed on house walls the skulls of mithan, common cattle, water buffalo, and various wild animals. The skulls were not only a measure of a man's wealth but also a sort

3. Risley, 1903: 224; *Imperial Gazetteer of India.* Provincial Series: Eastern Bengal and Assam, 1909: 462; J. Shakespear, 1912: 50–52, 82–83.

of currency. In fact the Mishmi word for "head" was used for any item given in exchange. If, for example, a Mishmi obtained a mithan in exchange for two mithan heads, a bear's head, an iron pot, and a piece of cloth, each of the items was referred to as a "head" (Cooper, 1873: 190).

Today coinage is universally in use among the Mishmi (Mills, 1952: 3); skulls, including those of mithan, no longer serve in exchange.

In Trade

Though unquestionably most mithan are kept without thought of trading them, some groups do keep them for that purpose. The trade in mithan of course is dwarfed by the trade in common cattle and water buffalo found in other parts of India.[4] The number of animals involved is many less. The organization of trade is less elaborate. And the distances involved are much smaller. For the most part, trade in mithan is local. Mithan may be purchased by one villager from another, or people of one village may purchase mithan from villages some distance away.

Intervillage trade has been encouraged by the inability or unwillingness of some groups to keep enough mithan for their needs. Among these are the Apa Tani, who not only have Dafla and Hill Miri care for some of their mithan but purchase additional mithan from them in return for rice and sometimes other agricultural produce.

A similar pattern prevails in the Naga Hills (Map 1). The tribes of the west (Ao, Lhota, Western Rengma, and Angami) keep few mithan within their country. There is evidence that they used to have more, but the damage the animals did to fields led to such problems that these groups have found other means of supplying their needs for sacrificial mithan. Some men place their mithan in the care of tribes to the east, and pay them for their effort. Others buy mithan as they need them. A trade has thus developed, with mithan passing from the Phom, Chang, Sema, Kacha Naga, and Kuki to the peoples west and north. In some cases, animals are passed from traders of one village to those of another. In others the purchaser may journey several days each way to obtain the mithan he needs. Two elements seem to have provided special impetus for the trade: differences in intensity of cultivation and in political organization. The Angami, for example, cultivate terraces of irrigated rice and other crops, and the mithan is too destructive for that form of agriculture. It is much more feasible for the Angami to purchase animals

4. For a picture of the trade in cattle, see *Report on the Marketing of Cattle in India*. Agricultural Marketing in India, Marketing Series No. [83?]. Delhi: Manager of Publications, 1956.

from groups having extensive forested areas at their disposal. While the Angami are strongly democratic people, others such as the Sema, Chang, Konyak, and Kuki have an aristocratic tendency. Among the aristocratic groups, the wealthy mithan owner is in a better position to ignore complaints about the damage his mithan do to crops; or—since he is also likely to be a large landowner—his fields may be the ones damaged, and he the only person involved.[5]

The most significant long-distance trade in mithan is that between NEFA and Bhutan, which was best described by J. P. Mills (1946: 10–11). At the two ends are the Dafla, needing ordinary cattle for meat and having a surplus of mithan, and the Bhutanese, with their surplus of common cattle and need of bull mithan for breeding purposes. (Though the hybrids of mithan and common cattle are stronger than purebred common cattle, the males are ordinarily sterile, so that there must be regular replacement with full-blooded mithan bulls.) For each young bull mithan that the Dafla trade to the Lamai (Miji), their neighbors to the west, they receive two or three head of ordinary cattle. The Lamai receive five or six cattle for each mithan from the Monba. And the Monba in turn trade the mithan to the Bhutanese.

There is a parallel westward trade in mithan among the Aka, Sherdukpen, Monba, and Bhutanese. The mithan that the Sherdukpen obtain from the Aka in exchange for cows (common cattle?) are passed on to the Monba and Bhutanese at a good profit (Sharma, 1961: 9–10). The Bhutanese in turn apparently trade mithan still farther westward, for purebred or half-breed animals have been reported in the Darjeeling area. Before the Chinese seized Tibet, there was also a trade of mithan from the Adi of Siang Division to the Tibetans. The Tibetans came south over the Kepung La with rock salt, iron, cloth, and other goods, which they exchanged for mithan and other local goods (S. Roy, 1960: 33). Other avenues of mithan trade to Tibet probably existed too.

Hybrid mithan were also reported as being brought for sale to the lowland town of Udalgiri (Oodulgheery) in Darrang District, Assam—a great meeting place, at the annual fair, of Assamese, Bhutanese, and Tibetan traders (Pollok and Thom, 1900: 101). Europeans among the purchasers apparently sometimes took the animals to Shillong in the hills south of the Assam Valley. Such trade must have been exceptional, for the value of mithan to the hill people is too high, as compared with common cattle, for Europeans to be much interested in them. The fact that mithan are not found around Shillong today bears out this view.

5. The above paragraph about Naga mithan trade is based on correspondence with H.-E. Kauffmann and J. H. Hutton and on their writings and those of J. P. Mills and W. C. Smith.

In Traction

Most mithan peoples traditionally had no plows, wheeled vehicles, or riding animals.[6] Hence use of mithan for such purposes would have been alien to their way of life. Apparently only in certain sections of western NEFA and in Bhutan were mithan or mithan hybrids put to the plow.[7] Mills (1946: 8–11) notes one such case, plowing by hybrids among the Monba of Dirang Dzong Valley, Kameng Division of NEFA. The Monba, a Buddhist people, are mainly sedentary plow farmers, cultivating wheat and barley, maize, millet, and rice. Their principal cattle are hybrids of mithan "and something else" (possibly dzo); hybrid bulls and hybrid bullocks are both used for plowing. The Monba obtain mithan bulls from the east and, using these and selected hybrid bulls, breed toward the mithan type. Mills noted that the Monba hybrids were the finest cattle he had ever seen in Assam. Whatever the ancestry of the Dirang Dzong hybrid may be, the most common mithan hybrid of Bhutan is of common cattle. This hybrid is a work animal which is docile, stronger than local common cattle, and better adapted to the cold, arid habitat than the purebred mithan would be.

In Fighting

Southeast Asia is noted for its varieties of animal fighting—pitting two animals of the same species against each other. Cock fighting, ram fighting, bull fighting, buffalo fighting, fish fighting, cricket fighting, and other forms occur, though they seem alien to Buddhist thinking and have sometimes been opposed by Western colonial governments. Ritual contests between two bulls or water buffalo have been reported for a vast area of the Old World, from Madagascar on the west to Japan on the east. They appear, says Carl W. Bishop (1925), to have been associated intimately with the complex of irrigated rice cultivation and with rites to promote crop fertility or to forecast yields. In its complete original form, the ritual bull fight included selection, preparation, and sometimes training of the bull, normally in the spring; arousing of the animal's pugnacity; the combat; triumphal procession for the victor; sacrifice of the victor to the god guarding the crops; bloodless killing of the animal by clubbing or driving a spike into its forehead; consumption of its flesh

6. For a discussion of the introduction of plow culture to the hill peoples, see H.-E. Kauffmann, 1934: 51.

7. George Harris was told by natives that the *gyall* (mithan) was used for tilling the ground in the Chittagong Hills (A. B. Lambert, 1804: 58–59). This report has not been confirmed by any later writer and almost certainly was incorrect.

at a communal banquet; and the exalting of the horns on a pole set up in a public place. Not all of the above elements occurred in any one area, so far as is known. In its degenerate form the complex became simply a form of amusement.

As we have seen, elements included in this complex—bloodless killing, consumption at a communal banquet, display of horns—occur in mithan sacrifice among certain hill peoples, but not mithan fighting itself. We have found only one record of a mithan fight anywhere within the range of mithan distribution. This appears in the account of Samuel Turner (1800: 160–61), who, while on a mission to Tibet in 1783, observed a fight in Bhutan staged by the Buddhist Raja of Tassisudon between two mithan. Turner indicated that they were not from Bhutan but from the east. The two mithan, firmly secured with strong ropes, were led between groups of Bhutia to the fighting ground. Men armed with bludgeons posted themselves in a circle, and the animals were released at either side. They broke the turf with their horns, raised their spines, and gave every symptom of rage. With the curious sideways advance of the breed, they circled and gradually approached each other. Finally they faced each other directly, dashed forward and struck heads with a great blow, and struggled for half an hour, alternately advancing and retreating. When one animal had almost won, they were separated, the loser was driven away, and the indignant winner was taken to his stall. Turner indicated that the animals were trained for fighting and that their owners were eager to save them for future sport. This clearly represents the degenerate stage of bull fighting as defined by Bishop.

An instance of a planned mithan fight (which ended as a fight between mithan and gaur) occurs in a folk tale of the Thadou Kuki (see W. Shaw, 1929: 135–36). Hutton, however, knows of no such setting of mithan to fight among the Thadou today (pers. com., Sept. 8, 1966), and we have uncovered nothing to suggest that the practice is current among them or other mithan-keeping groups. The nearest thing to it is the baiting of mithan described (p. 181) for the Ao Naga as part of their mithan sacrifice.

19

The Products of the Mithan
and Their Economic Use

Milk

Traditionally most of the mithan-keeping peoples were part of the Southeast Asian area of nonmilking, in which people neither milked their animals nor drank milk.[1] Some simply regarded milk with indifference. Some felt that taking the milk of an animal deprived its offspring of their rightful due. Some thought that the person who drank milk became like the animal from which the milk came. The extreme attitude was that milk was a dirty food; it disgusted people and nauseated them. In a few cases the rejection of milk was explained in folklore and supported by group pressures. The negative attitudes toward milk encompassed the mithan as well as other milkable animals, and there are abundant references to the failure of peoples to use the milk of their mithan.[2]

1. Curiously, though, milking was practiced at least in parts of Southeast Asia in early times. An important factor in this was the spread of Indian cultural influence into Southeast Asia in the early centuries of the Christian era, accompanied by the keeping of sacred temple cattle and use of milk and milk products for ritual purposes (see Wheatley, 1965). In the first half of the second millennium milking apparently disappeared, with the decline of the old Hindu and Mahayana Buddhist cults. This entire episode presumably never touched these hill tribes, who maintained their animist practices and had no religious incentive for milking.

2. Among the specific groups indicated as not milking their mithan are the Kuki of Chittagong (Hutchinson, 1906: 21; Colebrooke, 1808: 518); Purum Kuki of Manipur (T. Das, 1945: 65–66); Lushai (Lewin, 1870: 261–62; McCall, 1949: 21, 186); Lakher (Parry, 1932: 164–65); Chin of Burma (Stevenson, 1943: 47, 49; Wehrli, 1905–6: 116, 118; Thom, 1934–35: 109); Lhota Naga (Mills, 1922: 59–61); Konyak Naga (Fürer-Haimendorf, 1939: 52); Angami Naga (Hutton, 1921: 80); Sema Naga (Hutton, 1921a: 69); Kachari of the North Cachar Hills (Soppitt, 1885: 11); Mishmi (Dalton, 1872: 15; F. M. Bailey, 1911–13: 1071; H. Barua, [1954]: 129–30); Adi or Abor (Millington, 1912: 130–31; Bailey, 1911–13: 1071; Dunbar, 1914–15: 295; S. Roy, 1958: 147; Sen Gupta, 1954: 158, 166; Srivastava, 1962: 34–35, 47); Hill Miri (Dalton, 1845: 265–66; 1872: 34; Fürer-Haimendorf, 1946a: 52); Dafla (Fürer-

Some changes in traditional attitudes have occurred from place to place as contacts with milk-using peoples, facilitated by the Pax Britannica, have increased. There must have been some encouragement of milking by the Manipuri and other Indians. Notable stimulation of milking is known to have come from Christian missionaries, and Christian converts are sometimes reported as milking their animals. Also important, but virtually overlooked in the literature, have been the Nepali herdsmen who have migrated to the Assam hills and even to northern Burma. One example of their influence is found in the Sema Naga men who had been servants of Gurkha herdsmen near Kohima (in the Naga Hills) and who began milking their own animals (Hutton, 1921a: 69).

There are hints in the literature that where tribal people have taken up milking they tend first to milk animals like those of the group from whom they learn the practice, and that where mithan are involved, the hybrids are more likely candidates. The Kameng Frontier Division of NEFA, which has milking peoples to north, south, and west, provides an interesting example of this. Where milking for human consumption is practiced there, it centers on common cattle at lower elevations (Sherdukpen), yak and dzo at higher elevations (Tibetans), and hybrid mithan and dzo at intermediate elevations (Monba).

Striking changes in patterns of mithan care are not always necessary with the introduction of milking. Sanderson (1912: 249) noted, in the Chittagong Hills, mithan cows that were milked, without any modification in the traditional system of herding. They came with the other mithan to the village at night and went with them to the forest in the morning, after being detained a few minutes for milking.

Detailed studies have not been made of the quality of mithan milk. However, the milk of purebred mithan and of their hybrids with common cattle is reported as being as rich as cow's milk, sweet, and suitable for making butter. The Monba of Dirang Dzong make both butter and cheese from the milk of mithan hybrids (Mills, 1946: 10).

The data on milk yield are fragmentary and inconclusive. Hutton (pers. com., Sept. 8, 1966) has been told that that of mithan is significantly lower than that of common cattle and water buffalo. True, the specific published estimates of yield—roughly 4 to 8 pounds (2 to 4 seers) daily

---

Haimendorf, 1946a: 52); Apa Tani (Fürer-Haimendorf, 1948: 242; 1955: 37, 43; 1962: 117); Aka (Hesselmeyer, 1868: 200; Dalton, 1872: 38; Macgregor, 1884: 205–6). For further references on nonmilking peoples in the Assam hills and northern Burma, see H.-E. Kauffmann, 1934: 74. George Harris, writing of the Chittagong Hills at the beginning of the nineteenth century, says that the mithan was "used for all the purposes of the dairy" (A. B. Lambert, 1804: 58–59). This report, possibly based on native reports, is almost certainly incorrect.

for purebred mithan cows[3]—are significantly better than those of the average Indian common cow, which is notorious for its low milk yield (one estimate for India as a whole is that cows average 2 pounds per day during lactation) (*Report on the Marketing of Milk in the Indian Union,* 1950: 8–9). These estimates, however, are not comparable. Indian common cattle live in a wide variety of habitats, many of them unfavorable, whereas mithan live in a limited variety that are generally favorable. Indian common cows are often malnourished, whereas mithan cows are usually well fed. It is not indicated, moreover, whether the estimates for the mithan represent peaks in its lactation period, averages for the entire period, or what. It remains possible that the mithan—which has nowhere been bred for its milking qualities—may under similar conditions yield more milk on the average than some types of Indian common cattle. At the same time, it is almost certain that milk yields of mithan do not approach those of the better Indian milking breeds of common cattle. Good animals of the Sahiwal breed—one of the best Indian milch cattle—yield, under village conditions, 3,000 pounds of milk in a lactation period of 300 days; well-bred animals in some farms average almost twice that amount (India. Indian Council of Agricultural Research, 1961: 3).

Mithan Flesh

Though the blood of slain mithan is sometimes eaten, there is no indication in the record that mithan are bled in the way East African cattle peoples bleed their animals for food. Flesh, available chiefly at times of sacrifice, is the principal mithan product man makes use of. Whether the animal is sacrificed or simply killed for its flesh, there is concern among some people with the quality of the meat. The Chin of Burma believe that tying the mithan and giving it no food or drink for three days before slaughter will make the flesh tender.[4]

3. Early reports from Tippera (Tripura) and Cachar indicated that mithan cows yielded from 4 to 8 pounds (2 to 4 seers) of milk daily (Colebrooke, 1808: 521, 523). A report for the Darjeeling area indicated that mithan cows gave 6 to 8 pounds (3 to 4 seers) of rich milk, while hybrids between mithan and the Siri breed of common cattle gave less milk but of better quality (O'Malley, 1907: 69–71). An account on the Dirang Dzong area of NEFA states that good hybrid cows will give 8 to 10 pounds (4 to 5 seers) a day (Mills, 1946: 10). These hybrids, however, may be mithan/dzo (yak/common cattle) crosses. There is also a report, by N. K. Das, for the Lushai Hills, that "about 3 lb. of milk in one milking in one day was obtained" from hybrid cows (1945: 421).

Where yields were reported in seers, the amount in seers is indicated above in parentheses. In converting to pounds, we have assumed that the seer is the government or railway seer, which equals 2.057 pounds.

4. Sanderson (1912: 248–49) indicates that steaks taken from along the dorsal ridge of the gaur are best. Probably this is true also for the mithan.

When the mithan is slaughtered, usually its flesh is cut up and consumed without delay. Even dozens of animals killed at large sacrifices among the Apa Tani can be consumed readily (Fürer-Haimendorf, 1955: 73). At such times the village population is supplemented by visitors, all sharing the feast at the expense of those who perform the sacrifice. Mithan flesh that is smoked for preservation is gradually consumed at home.

Restrictions on women eating flesh food are widespread in the Old World. Though we cannot be certain of their origins, such restrictions are explained today in terms of women's susceptibility to illness or contamination which will affect the birth of healthy offspring.[5] There are a few references, in the admittedly scant mithan country literature on the subject, to mithan flesh—and certain other flesh foods—being forbidden to women. Among the Ao Naga, males are permitted the flesh of mithan and many types of animals, wild and domestic; females may eat only chickens, fish, and domestic swine (Majumder, 1925: 46). Men of the Idu Mishmi eat mithan and other flesh, but all meat except fish, rats, and small birds is strictly forbidden to women (Baruah, 1960: 37). In a Kom (Old Kuki) village in Manipur pregnant women are forbidden mithan flesh, as well as that of certain other animals (Hodson, 1911: 184). The Sherdukpen also have some curious prohibitions on eating the flesh of domestic animals. G. Paul (1958: 156) specifically lists beef, chicken and eggs, flesh of domestic pigs and goats as generally prohibited. Men are allowed mithan meat, but women would suffer headache and stomachache if they ate it. Sharma reports essentially the same general prohibitions, but mentions class rather than sexual differences in the permissibility of mithan flesh, as in the lower class, the Chhao, being free to eat mithan flesh while the aristocratic class, the Thong, may not (1961: 38, 52).

It would be interesting to determine the impact of Hinduism and Christianity on the consumption of mithan flesh. Though the literature is largely silent, there are indications that Hindus regard mithan as relatives of common cattle and urge the abandonment of mithan eating. The record also suggests that conversion to Christianity undermines the traditional beliefs surrounding mithan sacrifice; that it sometimes permits such sacrifice at Christian festive occasions but sometimes acts against eating mithan flesh because the mithan is associated with "heathen festivals," notably the Feasts of Merit (Elwin, 1961: 78). A parallel to this prohibition is the early Christian ban on horse eating for similar reasons in northern Europe (Simoons, 1961: 83–84).

Nothing in the literature suggests that mithan flesh is sold or that

5. For further information on women being singled out for food restrictions in the Old World, see Simoons, 1961: 12, 110, 115.

there is any substantial trade in mithan for beef purposes.[6] Such long-distance trade as exists is either to provide breeding stock or to provide animals needed for sacrifice.

Horns, Bones, Hide, and Tail

In India, according to George Watt (1908: 646, 733), the principal sources of horn for craftwork are the buffalo and gaur, because of religious objections to the use of horns of common cattle. In addition, the horns of mithan are used. Among mithan-keeping peoples the horns commonly serve as drinking cups, especially for rice beer. In nineteenth-century Bhutan, people were reported as carrying horns full of rice beer with them on journeys (Griffith, 1839: 269). The Angami Naga (Hutton, 1921: 58) use gaur horns for cups when they are obtainable, but prefer the larger horns of the mithan. They like the lower half of the cup to be black, grading upward into a transparent yellow rim. Right- and left-handed horns are distinguished, and the right-handed horn generally preferred. This horn should be so curved that when it is held in the right hand of the drinker the point is turned toward his left, and the flat—or back—side of the horn faces outward. A horn perfect in coloring and shape may cost an Angami as much as 40 rupees (at rates of exchange then prevailing, about $13).

Other uses mentioned for mithan horns are as powder flasks or nicotine-water flasks (Lakher)—which are decorated with patterns in metal and red and black lacquer—and as receptacles for storing valuables (Dafla). David Sopher (pers. com., 1965) observed mithan horns used for beating time at a hunting dance among the Pankhua of the Chittagong Hills. The dancer carried a boar's skull, and his dance was accompanied by the beating of a drum and the banging together of mithan horns. H.-E. Kauff-mann mentions a somewhat similar use in North Cachar (1934: 77–78).

The use of shoulder blades as implements occurs, though the practice must be rare. One example is found in the isolated Hill Miri villages of Mingö and Rute-Hate, where there is so little iron that people use hoes made of mithan shoulder blades for tilling (Fürer-Haimendorf, 1955: 195). Another is in Lhota Naga villages, which swarm with dogs, pigs, and cattle, and are full of filth which people scrape away from their doorways with "shovels made from the shoulder-blades of cattle or mithan" (Mills, 1922: 23). The skulls and horns of mithan and sometimes the shoulder blades also serve important uses in the prestige structure of mithan-keeping peoples.

6. Hans Spielmann (pers. com., Feb. 7, 1966) mentions one exception: the Bawm-Zo sell their mithan for slaughter to Moslem Bengali at up to 600 rupees apiece, and are eager to do so.

The hides of mithan seem not to be very skillfully utilized. The Naga, Hutton recalls (pers. com., Sept. 8, 1966), "generally slice up the hide with the flesh and cook and eat it, no doubt having singed off the hair first." Some mithan-keeping groups make hides into shields or chest coverings or small carrying bags. Some roughly dress the hides and use them to sit or sleep on. Strips of hide are made into straps for carrying the dao or for belts. Perhaps the most curious use of mithan hide was reported by Powell Millington (1912: 166–67) for an Adi (Abor) chief who had no facial hair but on important occasions wore "a pair of artificial whiskers." These were a "strip of mithan calf-skin with short hair upon it, that passed under the chin and extended from ear to ear." Such whiskers were worn only by important men. What Millington calls "whiskers," suggests Hutton (pers. com., Jan. 25, 1966), may actually be the hair fringe—commonly of bear's hair or yak tails—worn over the headpiece and chin strap of the Adi helmet.

We have found nothing to indicate whether mithan tails, like yak tails, serve as fly whisks, banners, or decorations, and, if so, whether they are traded. The single indication of mithan hair being used is for the Aka of NEFA, who make strings of tail hair for bow and fiddle (Macgregor, 1884: 202). Unfortunately, these and other economic uses of mithan products are not covered adequately in the literature.

20

The Mithan and Associated Symbols of Status and Fertility

Ownership of Mithan

Throughout its habitat, the mithan traditionally has been a focal point of the prestige structure and, together with items deriving from or associated with it, has been symbolic of status or fertility. Most basic is ownership of mithan, for the number of a man's animals is indicative of his social status and economic prosperity; often chiefs and other wealthy men have informed European travelers with pride about the size of their mithan herds. The mithan's importance in turn is related to its role in exchange, in paying tribute and ransom, in bride-price, and on ceremonial occasions, especially the prestige-bestowing Feasts of Merit.

With the breakdown of traditional culture, mithan ownership decreases in importance as a symbol of status. There may, of course, be persistences in attitude which are more pronounced in particular segments of the population. Among the Bawm-Zo, for example, Spielmann (pers. com., Sept. 5, 1965) reports that there seem to be more Panghawi, the former lower class, who own mithan than Sunthla, the former upper class. The Sunthla no longer need mithan for religious affairs, and mithan ownership has lost its role in conferring prestige on a man. The Panghawi in former times apparently had few mithan. Now, however, their economic position has improved and they may simply have taken to mithan keeping because this was formerly the privilege of the upper class. Such changes in class views of status symbols are common, and the reader may readily supply examples from his own culture.

Skulls and Other Items

Since among virtually all mithan-keeping groups the sacrifice of mithan is a notable act which brings prestige to the sacrificer as well as achieving the specific purpose of the sacrifice, many mithan-keeping groups have found ways to make it plain to all, long after the event, that a mithan has been sacrificed. Most often this is done by displaying the mithan skulls, with horns intact, in some prominent place, usually at the sacrificer's house. The skulls may be placed on the inside walls or house posts, on a bamboo rack in the house (Figures 12 and 13), on outside house walls or verandah walls, or on poles outside the house. The skulls of other domestic animals that have been sacrificed are frequently included in the display, as are skulls of wild animals killed in the chase. In the nineteenth century one Mishmi chief had several hundred animal skulls displayed on the walls of his house (Cooper, 1873: 190). In recent times, F. K. Lehman (1963: 182) commented that the house verandah decorated with as many trophies as possible is one of the characteristic features in the cultural landscape of a Burma Chin village.

Among some groups the priest who officiates at the mithan sacrifice also has rights of display. One Dafla senior priest we have mentioned (Stonor, 1957: 13) had about forty scapular bones of mithan hanging from the shrine on his front verandah. Each scapular bone represented an important sacrifice he had presided over. Also on display was a group of the large bamboo tubes which are used to catch mithan blood at sacrifices. Since a new tube is used for each sacrifice, the number of tubes is also a measure of status.

Among many groups, at the death of a man the skulls of mithan he sacrificed are removed from their place of display and put on his grave together with other of his valuables. The total exhibit indicates the status of the deceased. Dunbar (1932: 233–34) reported that usually there are two or three trophies at an Adi burial place. On one Adi headman's grave, however, he observed a screen 8 feet high and 18 feet long which was literally covered with trophies: swords, knives, bows and arrows, a helmet, a rucksack, and various skulls, including, of course, those of mithan. The Ao Naga put wooden imitations of the skulls of bovines sacrificed in the Feasts of Merit near the corpse-platform, and the real skulls are saved to be inherited by the dead person's heirs. Both practices testify to the value, both symbolic and intrinsic, of mithan skulls.

All Naga, one recalls, believe in the life-force inherent in the heads of human beings. Throughout the Naga country, both funeral customs and headhunting customs reveal concern with gaining and utilizing this life-force to acquire prosperity and fertility. Ao and Konyak examples illustrate an extension of the Naga fertility complex, in which the mithan skull assumes a significance approaching that of a human skull (Mills, 1926: 200, 205, 229, 257–62, 281, 376, 381, 392–93). The Ao and Konyak Naga believe that mithan skulls bring *aren* to the possessor. Aren is the same quality as the fertility-granting power or life-force that all Naga believe to exist in human heads. Mills notes an incident from 1923 that clearly illustrates the Konyak belief. Warriors of one Konyak village carried away the mithan skulls that belonged to an enemy village, certain that they would gain the aren of the skulls. Apparently it made no difference that the warriors had no connection with the sacrifice of the animals.

The Ao, at the time of the bull or mithan sacrifice in the Feasts of Merit sequence, turn the skull over to a priest, who hangs it in the morung. Hanging the fresh skull, laden with aren, in the place where unmarried men spend much of their time may well be an effort to transmit the fertility-granting power of the skull to a segment of society particularly in need of it. Only at the time of the next harvest does the feast giver bring the skull home and hang it on the wall of the front room of his house, in the firm expectation that it will bring prosperity not only to him during his lifetime but for long afterward to those who will inherit it. The Ao treatment of the skulls of bovines sacrificed at the Feasts is remarkably similar to the treatment of skulls taken in headhunting raids. Annually at harvest time, for example, exactly the same offerings of the first fruits, including flour ground from new grain, were made to both human and bovine skulls. Mills reports that the ceremonies were intended to assure good crops.

Although the idea of aren being present in mithan skulls is not expressly stated for other groups, we infer (from customs related to the treatment of the skulls and, in some cases, the use made of mithan horns) that the idea of some special quality attaching to them may occur more widely among the Naga, and possibly among the Chin. There is no clear evidence that the NEFA peoples make a direct association between mithan skulls and horns and fertility, though there are suggestions that the Dafla, for one, may regard them as more than mere items of display. The Dafla, to whom the mithan is the ultimate measure of wealth, display the skulls of sacrificed mithan on the most important inside house wall and forbid menstruating women to touch them.

The only hint in the literature that mithan skulls have some protective value is in a statement by W. C. Smith (1925: 98). The Ao Naga put the skulls of common cattle and mithan in trees behind the house at the season of greatest fire danger when the houses are dry and can burn readily. They believe, Smith says, that this protects the house from burning.[1] This recalls the bucrania, or ox heads, that were displayed over house doors in ancient Asia Minor to prevent evil spirits from entering.

Both mithan and buffalo horns figured in headhunting customs in two

1. Hutton (pers. com., Sept. 8, 1966) believes it more likely that the practice is based on the wish to protect the skulls—valuable items—from fire.

ways: they were attached to enemy skulls (Figure 14), and they were added to the headdress of a warrior, as the mark of a successful head-hunter (Figure 15). Disposition of the enemy skulls varied among the Naga. Generally, Naga west of the Dikhu River hung heads in a head-tree or displayed them on bamboo poles, where they remained until they fell down or disintegrated. The Ao, together with most Naga east of the Dikhu, stored enemy skulls either at the head taker's house, in the morung, in the chief's house, or in some other central place. The peoples who added mithan or buffalo horns to enemy skulls corresponded fairly closely to those who stored their trophies. The Chang, Konyak, some Ao, and probably the Phom, enhanced their enemy skulls with such additions.[2]

The purpose in adding the horns was to increase the fertility-granting power of the human skull. It is true that Mills was told that many Konyak and the people of the mixed Ao-Phom village of Yacham added the horns in order to make the skull deaf; that the soul of the man who had lost his head then would be unable to hear, or respond to, the calls of the relatives who were searching for him; and they, not knowing who was responsible for the death, would be unable to avenge it (Mills, 1926: 205; Hutton, 1922b: 113). Hutton thinks that although such a reason was given, the people involved had forgotten the true significance of the horns, which was "that of a fertility emblem, and associates the victim with the first fruits of the earth" (Mills, 1926: 205 n.). He gives interest-ing and convincing support for his idea. Some Phom and Konyak, if they had wounded an enemy but had not taken his head, would hang up as the trophy a cow's skull to which buffalo horns were attached. As Hutton observes, there would be little point in attempting to deafen the skull of a cow for the reasons given by the Konyak and the men of Yacham. On the other hand, adding the horns as a fertility emblem is plausible. The warrior, though his feat was imperfect, might still be entitled to limited recognition from his fellows and to limited benefits of the "prosperity" of his foe.

The addition of horns to ceremonial headdresses has a wider distribu-tion than the addition of horns to enemy heads. The headdresses were decorated sometimes with mithan horns, sometimes with buffalo horns, and sometimes with representations carved from buffalo horn, gaur horn, beak of the hornbill, or occasionally from light wood or bamboo. There

2. Fürer-Haimendorf, 1939: 143; Hutton, 1928: 404, Plate 42; Mills, 1926: 205. Hutton (1922b: 114) commented that the Chang apparently do not decorate enemy heads with mithan or buffalo horns, for he often saw unadorned human skulls hanging in Chang morungs. Fürer-Haimendorf (1939: 143), however, did see, in the Chang village of Chingmei, an impressive collection of such skulls with horns of both mithan and buffalo added.

are reports of this custom for the Kalyo-Kengyu (Khiemnungam), Konyak, Angami, Lhota, Western and Eastern Rengma of Nagaland; and for the Tangkhul and Mao of Manipur. For the Kalyo-Kengyu, Konyak, and Angami, the use of the horns in the headdress was definitely the mark of a man who had taken a head, and thus served the dual purpose of revealing status and symbolizing fertility. For the others, we can only infer from incidental details provided, that the purpose was the same.

Some of the Konyak and Phom apparently employ the fertility symbolism of the buffalo horn in the form of certain buildings. In the Konyak village of Yungya, Hutton (1929a: 7–8, 11) noted and sketched one of the large field houses constructed by men who enjoyed outstanding harvests. The roof line, he felt, "probably represents buffalo horns"—and the resemblance is certainly striking. In the Phom village of Urangkong he observed even more impressive horn-shaped roofs on shelters built to protect the effigies of dead men. He suspected they indicated the association, so common in the Naga Hills, of the dead with crops. We have uncovered nothing to indicate that mithan horns serve in a similar way as roof construction models, though they may well do so; but we shall find them (in the following section) represented in roof decoration among various Naga groups.

House Decoration and Dress

The sacrificer of mithan among at least two groups, the Naga and Lushai, has certain prerogatives in decorating his house (Figures 16, 17, 18, 19). The Lushai, for example, consider side windows in their houses as unlucky unless the owner has purchased this right "by killing two mithan and feasting the village," presumably in connection with the Feasts of Merit (Risley, 1903: 224; Shakespear, 1912: 27). The Ao Naga performer of the Feasts of Merit has successive rights in house decoration. When he gives the Sichatang sacrifice, highest of the Feasts of Merit, he leaves the scaffold, used for sacrificing the mithan, in front of his house permanently, constructs "triangular roofs" on the house, and fastens wooden birds to the roof. He is also permitted certain other decorations (Majumdar, 1924: 75–76; Majumder, [1925]: 23, 27–28). The performance of the highest Feast of Merit among the Lhota Naga and "dragging a stone" (erecting a memorial stone) more than once earns the man the right to decorate his roof with crossed bamboos which represent mithan horns (Mills, 1922: 34). Such "house horns" (Figures 19 and 20), sometimes with wooden birds perching on them, are found also among the Rengma and Angami Naga (Hutton, 1921: 51; Mills, 1937: 63). It is often possible to tell exactly the progress a house owner has made in the

Feasts of Merit by the shape and ornamentation of his house. The poor man's house front, among the southern group of the Western Rengma, for example, is flat and has no semicircular projection of the eaves. The man who has performed the first Feast adds a front porch and eave above it, both semicircular in shape. The final sacrifice sees the addition of both planks and a post on the porch, the post carved with human and mithan heads (Mills, 1937: 62–63). In some villages of the Northern Sangtam Naga, the performer of the third Feast, which involves sacrifice of a mithan and a common bull, is permitted a fringe of thatch, symbolic of the mithan's dewlap, on the projecting house roof (Stonor, 1950: 3). The pattern of privileges in house decoration varies from group to group and village to village. Wherever such decoration is found, however, it serves the same purpose: to provide recognition to the man who has performed the Feasts.

Dress is particularly important among the Naga and groups to the south of them as indicative of social status. Individuals may gain rights to wear body-cloths of particular patterns (Figure 21), and other forms of dress and decoration, through feats in hunting, in war or headhunting, and by performing Feasts of Merit. Performance of the higher Feasts, with their sacrifice of mithan, brings the greatest rights. A woman is commonly given special rights of dress and ornamentation according to her husband's progress in the Feasts of Merit. A Lhota boy may wear any cloth to which his father is entitled. When he marries and establishes his own household, however, he is permitted only those to which he is himself entitled (Mills, 1922: 9 n.). Stonor describes how rights of dress and ornamentation may be progressively added among the Northern Sangtam Naga (1950: 2–4). The first of the Feasts of Merit series, known as Yungti, involves the slaughter of four pigs and the supplying of beer to the guests. The feast giver enjoys the privilege of wearing a special cloth with alternate broad stripes of red and blue-black. Across the center of the cloth is a patch of small rectangles, symbolic of the ferment used in the beer making. The Yungti Feast is repeated after a certain time, usually one or two years. The third Feast, the Anitz, requires the sacrifice of single specimens of mithan, common cattle, and pig—all preferably male, and the supplying of beer. Performance of this Feast earns a man the right to wear a special black cloth with several narrow red stripes, which is "embroidered in red with symbolic representations of mithan horns"; also two hornbill feathers in his ceremonial headdress. His wife too has her rights: to add a fringe to her body-cloth; to wear an elaborately striped red-and-blue skirt with a narrow center strip of white. She and other women of the giver's household and his female descendants forevermore may wear certain jewelry: cornelian bead necklaces, crystal earrings, and large white conch shell discs. The fourth sacrifice is a repetition of the Anitz except that two mithan and a pig are sacrificed. The only privilege acquired in dress is the right of the giver to wear a third hornbill feather. The fifth and final Feast, Tchar Tsu, involves the sacrifice of two mithan and the providing of beer. The giver qualifies for wearing a special cloth, known as *tsungkotepsü*, purchased from the neighboring Ao Naga. Dark blue, with broad and narrow red bands, this cloth has a central narrow white band painted in black with a pattern which often includes mithan as well as human heads.[3] Thus, just as mithan are associated with the later and more prestigeful Feasts, so mithan horns or heads are associated with the cloths which can be worn by performing those higher Feasts.

Although mithan head tattoos are mentioned for the Lushai, Lakher, Chang and some Konyak Naga (Shakespear, 1912: 12; Parry, 1932: 58; pers. com., Hutton, Sept. 8, 1966), there is no suggestion that they are other than decorative.

Forked Posts

In the southern range of the mithan, another way of indicating that one has sacrificed mithan is to erect a post, usually Y-shaped or forked, but in a few cases straight. Commonly one post is set up for each animal killed, and it is left standing afterward. The erection of such posts almost always occurs in connection with the Feasts of Merit. Thus in many cases an observer can tell at a glance a man's progress in the Feasts, which also reflects his prosperity and status. Among the groups that erect such posts, some actually tether the sacrificial animal to the post, but others do not.

In the northern range of the mithan, the Feasts of Merit are not found, and forked posts are rare. Where the posts do occur, their significance has only been speculated upon by European observers. Fürer-Haimendorf reports that the Minyong Adi erect posts, often Y-shaped, at the time of their Sholung feast (see pp. 95–96 above). All mithan are brought into the village at that time and each is tied to an individual post near its owner's house, where it remains overnight. Each mithan owner prays and makes offerings for the health and multiplication of his mithan. The wooden posts, though short and unworked, are left standing after the end of the festivities. That they are more than utilitarian in function is evident from the fine charged for damaging one: an entire mithan or its equivalent. Though he could find nothing to connect them with ceremonies that

3. Cloths decorated with mithan heads are found not only among Ao and Sangtam but also among the Lhota.

increase a man's prestige, as the Feasts of Merit do, Fürer-Haimendorf was certain that the number of posts put up for the Sholung indicated the number of mithan owned by a man, and thus his wealth (1954: 597–98). Both Fürer-Haimendorf (1955: 155) and Stonor (1957: 7) have also observed Y-shaped posts among certain Dafla; in all cases observed, the posts were erected on special occasions involving mithan sacrifice. It is possible that these peoples may have taken up the use of forked posts when mithan were introduced, but did not adopt the entire Feasts complex.

Forked posts are also found in the nearby hills beyond the range of the mithan, used in the sacrifice of buffalo or common cattle: among the Garo of the Garo Hills of Assam and the Kachin and Wa of Burma; in peninsular India, where they serve in buffalo sacrifice; and, in a degenerate form, in Bengal, for goat sacrifice. Such posts also occur from East Africa and Madagascar on the one hand to Melanesia on the other (Risley, 1903: 219; Mills, 1922: xxix; Hutton, 1922: 55; Heine-Geldern, 1928: 283; and H.-E. Kauffmann, 1960: 416).

The shape and size of the forked posts erected for the Feasts of Merit vary considerably (Figure 22). Most are from 7 to 10 feet high. Usually they are made directly from a tree, shaped sometimes roughly, sometimes carefully, into a rounded form and Y-shape. Some are relatively slender; others are of impressive girth. Some Chin, instead of fashioning posts straight from a tree, make them of planks that are split and carved at the top to form a Y. The posts may be entirely unadorned, or carved or incised with designs. Among the common Naga motifs are mithan heads and hornbill feathers or heads[4]—symbols of wealth, fertility, and bravery.

Among certain Naga, the sacrificial posts themselves are symbolic of fertility. This is most evident in the Angami posts erected in their next-to-highest Feast (p. 111 above); one post is phallic in form and the other, a forked post, is symbolic of the female sexual organs. Often those Naga who tether the sacrificial animal to the post use ropes made of the bean creeper *Entada scandens*, whose association, for the Naga, with fertility Hutton has noted (Mills, 1926: 116 n.).

Displaying the head of the sacrificed mithan on the forked post for a short time—usually a day or two—is reported for four Naga groups: the Chongli Ao, Northern Sangtam, Chang, and Eastern Rengma (Figure 22b). No explanation of this practice appears in the literature, and whether it too is part of the fertility cult has not been discussed.

4. The hornbill (*Dichoceros bicornis*) is impressive not only for its size and huge bill but because of the loud whirring of its wings in flight. Among many Naga tribes, hornbill tail feathers on headdress or shield are the special mark of the man who has taken heads, the insignia of the successful warrior.

A few Naga and Chin groups put up stone memorials in connection with the Feasts of Merit. Among these memorials, erect stones are most common. Such stones can be set up, among the Naga, only by a man who has performed all the ceremonies of the Feasts of Merit sequence, the highest of which in most cases involves mithan sacrifice. The reasons for erecting monoliths have never been investigated systematically, but there is little question that the Naga monoliths, like the wooden posts, are symbols of both status and fertility. The Angami, for one, we know believe that after death some of a person's life-force attaches itself to the monoliths he has set up during his lifetime.

Hutton has pointed out, in several publications, the remarkable similarities between the forked posts and monoliths of the Assam hills today and the monoliths at Dimapur (1922 and 1922a, 1929b; Mills, 1922: xxx). Dimapur, situated on the Dhansiri River at the southwestern foot of the Naga Hills, was the capital city of the Kachari Kingdom. The Dimapur monoliths (Figure 23) are believed to have been constructed by Kachari and to date from before A.D. 1536. Some of them are round in cross-section, with domed tops; others are squared and Y-shaped. Both types are similar in form to the present-day wooden memorials that various Naga use in the Feasts of Merit. Hutton states that the Y-shaped monoliths represent the female sexual organs while the round domed stones are phallic symbols. He argues that the modern Assam forked posts are related in origin to these Dimapur monoliths; that the original use of the forked posts as symbols of fertility has been lost by most groups, who now view them simply as symbols of prosperity.

In investigating the question of forked posts further, we find that they go back at least to later Vedic times; they are mentioned, for a particular type of sacrifice, in the Taittīriya Saṃhitā (ii, 1, 9; Keith, 1914, 18: 143). The post was forked because two deities, Mitra and Varuṇa, were the objects of sacrifice. Two animals were sacrificed, a black cow to Varuṇa and a white one to Mitra. The account is not explicit, but one wonders whether one animal was tied to each fork of the post. The sacrifice in question, if we accept one interpretation of the passage, was made at the time the planted seed first received water, and was motivated by the sacrificer's wishes for plentiful food and prosperity. Probably, as among the mithan keepers of today, the forked post itself also was symbolic of prosperity. Similar sacrifices were made to Mitra and Varuṇa in an effort to cure illness.

Thus we have the occurrence of forked posts in later Vedic times, and among certain Assam-Burma hill peoples today, some 2,500 years later; the Vedic association of bovine sacrifice, sacrificial post, and wishes for crop fertility and prosperity still existing among the hill people today!

The megalithic complex of which Hutton (1922, 1922a, 1928), Heine-Geldern (1928, 1959), and others have written may be related to this Vedic association. This megalithic complex is believed to have embraced in early times scattered groups in Southeast Asia and India. It is supposed (Lehman, 1963: 186) to have been a fertility cult centering on the sacrifice of cattle, headhunting, and the construction of monoliths and/or wooden memorials for persons of high status and prosperity. The complex is thought to have been based on the belief that the power, riches, and other qualities of a dead man, or of a man still living, could be transmitted to the village and could assure crop fertility and human well-being. Monoliths and posts—which, appropriately, sometimes took phallic form—were presumably set up in commemoration, or to assure the soul of the deceased continued connection with the living and to assure the living the power and wisdom of the dead. The people concerned, it is held, believed that the life-substance is centered principally in the head, and that taking a human head benefited the headhunter's village. An epidemic or poor harvest was a sign that more heads had to be taken to renew the supply of fertility.

In modern times this megalithic complex is believed to be most fully manifest among the Naga, and it corresponds with what we have termed the Naga fertility complex. It encompasses not only the Feasts of Merit and the memorials put up to commemorate them but also the memorials associated with the dead. Among other peoples, some elements of the complex have persisted and others have been modified or lost (see Löffler, 1954).

Mithan Figures on Village Gates

Fortified villages are or were common among many mithan-keeping peoples and other hill groups of Southeast Asia. Among the Ao, Rengma, and Sangtam Naga the wooden gates that provide entry to the village are occasionally carved and painted in a rudimentary way; but among the Angami all village gates are elaborately carved and painted with figures and designs (Figure 27). Most common among the Angami motifs are large bovine heads or bucrania, human heads, concentric circles, full-figured warriors (including one "phallic man"), full-figured bovines, and women's breasts (some designate these "rice-basket covers"). The bovine heads represent sacrificial cattle, which among the Angami are mithan. The human heads represent enemy heads taken by headhunters. The concentric circles probably represent the sun or moon. The themes of the carvings, Kauffmann observes, are related either to the Feasts of Merit or headhunting, and the gate motifs in one way or another symbolize fertility and prosperity. The village gate itself is erected amid religious rites, is sacred, and is an effective force in bestowing fertility on the village as well as affording protection against human enemies and evil influences and spirits (H.-E. Kauffmann, 1955).

The association of the bucranium or bull head, women's breasts, and human heads in symbolizing fertility and prosperity is to be mentioned again, in considering the domestication of common cattle.

Part IV

The Domestication of Mithan and of Common Cattle

21

Domestication of the Mithan

From the earliest days of exploration writers have been struck by this curious position of the mithan that we have been observing among the Assam hill peoples: a free-ranging animal, used for sacrifice on festive occasions, intimately involved in ritual and religious belief and in the prestige structure; figuring in the exchange system and used in payment of political, legal, and social obligations—yet having a minimal role in the realms of traction and dairying, for which common cattle are so valued among Hindu Indians. It is true that domestic animals much alike in form and temperament often play widely divergent roles among the world's peoples. Nevertheless, that a bovine animal should be kept for purposes so distinctive and under a system of husbandry so different from its relatives in nearby areas makes it seem worthwhile to reexamine the widely held view that bovines were domesticated for their flesh, their milk, and for traction, and that in the earliest days of domestication they were confined and herded.

In this chapter we will take up the domestication of the mithan and in the succeeding one the domestication of common cattle; but first we will see how the mithan meets the criteria for domestication.

The Mithan: A Domesticated Animal?

There has been considerable discussion in the literature, at least since the time of Darwin, about the criteria that can be used to distinguish domesticated from wild animals. Various writers, puzzled by the freedom enjoyed by the mithan, by the loose ties it has with man, and by man's failure to feed or breed it, have said that it is "semiferal," "semidomesticated," or "not properly domesticated." It may be useful here to consider the main definitions of "domestic" and see how the mithan fits them.

First, there is what Robert H. Dyson (1953: 661–62) calls the "osteo-logical" definition. One form of this definition (Thévenin, 1947: 7) holds that a domesticated animal is one which, raised from generation to generation under the surveillance of man, evolves in this manner so as to constitute a species or at least a race different from the primitive wild form from which it is descended. Involved here are both surveillance and physical divergence from the wild ancestor. Using this definition, one can not only distinguish among domestic and wild forms today, but one can presumably identify them archeologically on the basis of osteological differences.

A second type of definition views domestication in terms not of modi-fication of the animal physically but of its relations with man. This "cul-tural" definition is found in many forms. One is that a domestic animal is "one which breeds in captivity and is of some use to the human group." Another is that it must both breed freely in captivity and be able to accept man's proximity and handling. A third form, proposed by J. F. Downs (1960: 24–25), establishes four criteria for domestication:

> 1. Man must have a recognized need or desire which can be satisfied by controlling, protecting, and breeding animals.
> 2. Man must control the animal population in question to the extent neces-sary to satisfy this need or desire.
> 3. Man must devote himself, to a greater or lesser extent, to protecting and nurturing the animals.
> 4. Man must be involved, again to a greater or lesser extent, in the selec-tion of breeding individuals from the population he has brought under control.

The mithan fits quite well the criteria of the "osteological" definition. Certainly it is under the surveillance of man. Certainly it has differen-tiated physically from its wild form sufficiently to constitute a distinct race, though there is overlapping in certain traits between the two.

The mithan fits the cultural definitions of domestication, too, but with qualifications. Under the first definition quoted, a domestic animal must be of use to the human group. The mithan is. The animal, by both the first and the second definitions, must breed in captivity. The mithan does, provided that one defines captivity in broad enough terms to encompass the forest where, beyond man's presence and immediate control, the breeding takes place. The mithan also meets the criterion that the animal accept man's proximity and handling. Downs's definition, which he ar-rived at after considerable care and weighing of alternatives, creates greater problems. Admittedly men felt a need to enter a relationship with the wild ancestor of the mithan, to place it under "control" (loose control), and he does "protect," "nurture," and "breed" the animals, but only in a broad sense. Among those groups whose mithan return to the village each evening, the animals receive the protection of the human settlement. They sometimes also receive shelter. Those groups who permit their animals to stay out for weeks or months at a time provide much less protection and no regular shelter, but even with them a mithan cow and her newborn calf may be brought into the village, sheltered, cared for, and fed. This gives both cow and calf valuable help at a critical juncture of existence. The fact that all mithan are more or less in the vicinity of human settlement affords a measure of protection for them, too, for some predators avoid the presence of man, and others, through man's efforts, will be fewer near human settlements. Men also perform various rites for mithan protection and fertility, and they give medicines to sick mithan. All of these acts reveal a concern with protection, though admittedly mithan keepers offer less protection than many other groups provide their domestic animals. For most mithan, the only nurture (in the sense of food) that man regularly provides is salt, but since this is given primarily to bind the animal to its owner it is doubtful that it should be considered nurture in this sense. Downs feels that in its simplest form the breeding criterion requires that "each domestic generation be descended from a domestic generation," and that man consciously or unconsciously select the animals that will breed. This may be done, says Downs, simply through man's choice of animals for slaughter, or may involve more conscious control over breeding animals, such as castration of males or deliberate crossing of particular males and females. In mithan country proper, no "breeding animals" are consciously singled out within the mithan population, nor is there any conscious selection through castration or other means. There is, however, unconscious selection, as in choosing mithan for sacrifice. Therefore the mithan qualifies under this part of the criterion. It does not, however, qualify so well under the part requiring that "each domestic generation be descended from a domestic generation." There is ample evidence that in the past mating between mithan cows and gaur bulls was commonplace, and under those conditions each domestic generation was not descended solely from another. Such interbreeding of mithan and gaur, however, has largely come to an end and at the present day mithan can with more validity be viewed as descended from domestic stock.

Thus the mithan qualifies under enough of the above criteria to justify considering it within the domesticated category. Though it does not fit without qualification under all criteria, this is also true of certain other animals that almost universally are viewed as domesticated.

The Mithan and Related Animals in Ancient India

In the Indus Valley

No mithan or gaur bones have been identified in sites of the Indus Valley (Harappan) Civilization (*c.* 2500–1700 B.C.),[1] though the possibility remains that some bones designated simply *Bos* may be from these animals. J. H. Hutton's inclination (pers. coms., Feb. 6, Sept. 8, and Sept. 29, 1966) to look for mithan domestication in the ancient Indus Valley or in the Indo-Persian borderlands is based on seals from Mohenjo-Daro depicting an animal that may represent the gaur. Similar seals also occur at Chanhu-Daro and Harappa. The seals depict a bovine animal with horns and what appears to be a dorsal ridge similar to those of the gaur.[2] Ernest Mackay, who described the seals uncovered in the first Mohenjo-Daro excavations, called the animal (along with one of another type) "the short-horned bull" (Figure 24b), but did not identify it further. However, Sir John Marshall, director-general of archaeology in India, under whose direction those excavations were carried out, insisted that it, and probably one figurine as well, represent the gaur (1931, 1: 29, 70, 72; 2: 385). Mackay later (1937–38, 1: 326–27) expressed doubt that the animal of the seals is the gaur, and wondered whether it may be a hybrid between gaur and common cattle, like, he said, the mithan of today. Still later (1943: 147, 157), in discussing similar Chanhu-Daro seals, he described the animal in one place as a short-horned bull or "bison" (gaur) and in another said that it "appears to be a bison." It seems that he was partly won over by Marshall's idea. M. S. Vats, excavator of Harappa, designates the animal without question as a gaur (1940, 1: 323).

On almost all the seals the animal's head is lowered, as if it is displaying or eating, and it is facing what Marshall calls a "food trough," Vats a "feeding trough," and Mackay a "manger." Marshall argues that the gaur was among the animals sacred to people of the Indus Valley Civilization and that the troughs probably symbolize food offerings to it.

The "trough" has a strange form: flat bottom, low sides, and hornlike protrusions at each end. It is possible that it is not a food container at all but a device of some other sort, perhaps a cult object. There are, besides

1. Early dates in this book, where possible, are based on 1) the already published fascicles of the forthcoming *Cambridge Ancient History*, Rev. Ed., and 2) R. W. Ehrich, 1965. Where carbon-14 determinations are used in arriving at dates, they have been computed at the new mean radiocarbon half-life value of 5730 ± 40.

2. Marshall, 1931, 3: Plates CX: 308–25; CXI: 326; CXV: 536, 557b; Mackay, 1937–38, 2: Plates LXXXII: 689, 701; LXXXIII: 50; LXXXIV: 90; LXXXV: 123, 129, etc.; 1943: Plate LI: 13–15, 17; Vats, 1940, 2: Plate XCI: 235, 238, 241–45.

the "trough," other bits of evidence that hint at the relationship between man and the animal in question, and whether it was wild or domesticated. One is the occurrence on several seals of a collar, garland, or necklace around the animal's neck. Another is the occurrence of trappings on one Chanhu-Daro animal. Still another is a Chanhu-Daro seal which pictures the animal trampling a prostrate human figure that wears a strange headdress and seems to be trying to fend the creature off. The "troughs" and the garlands do not prove domestication, and may simply indicate that man fed and decorated the wild animal he had captured, or they may represent artistic license.

The most reasonable conclusion, from this fragmentary and conflicting evidence, seems to be that the animal in question is the gaur; that the gaur, like certain other animals, had religious import; and that people may have captured gaur for cult purposes. We view the evidence as revealing only a predomestication relationship between gaur and man, and are inclined to look elsewhere for mithan domestication. Our conclusions are generally in agreement with those of Heinz F. Friederichs (1933: 14–15, 19, 44), who carefully considered the animals depicted on the Mohenjo-Daro seals. Friederichs identified the animal in question as a gaur, not a mithan; and he considered it a sacred animal of the Indus Valley people that was tamed or at least kept in captivity.

The question may be raised whether any of the pre-Harappan peoples of the area knew and perhaps interacted with the gaur. So far as we know, the only hint that any earlier group may even have known the gaur is the occurrence, on a seal of the Amri culture, of a curious composite animal with three heads emerging from a single body (Figure 24d). The horns of the lower head resemble those of the gaur, though the head itself is not much like the "gaur" of the Harappan seals. Gaur bones or figurines have not been reported for Amri, though those of common cattle have.[3] Since archeologic knowledge is increasing rapidly for the Iran-Afghanistan-Pakistan area, there is hope that further light will be cast on the presence or absence of the gaur in that region in ancient times and on its relations with man. The mithan, however, seems out of the picture.

In the Vedic Records

The Vedic records (composed *c.* 1500–500 B.C.?) contain many references to the *gaurá,* a wild forest animal sometimes apparently captured

3. *Bos taurus* bones are found in the earliest subperiod of Amri I, and were the only bones of domestic animals uncovered by J.-M. Casal for that subperiod. Though the chronology of Amri culture is unsettled, this subperiod may date from early in the third millennium B.C. The discussion of Amri is based on Casal, 1964, 1: 157–58, 164–69; 2: Figure 116–No. 27; 124–No. 2; Plate XXVII–D, XXX–7.

for sacrifice. The gaurá is universally believed to have been the gaur. Also mentioned in the Vedic accounts is another animal, the *gavayá,* which most Sanskritists identify as *Bos gavaeus* or "gayal."[4] We have seen that *gayal* is a Bengali word used for both mithan and gaur, and also that *Bos gavaeus* is one of the synonyms for *Bos frontalis,* the mithan.[5] It seems, therefore, that if one accepts the Sanskritists' identification, one must conclude that the mithan was known to the Vedic Indians.

To make certain, let us examine the Vedic records themselves, to determine the characteristics of the gavayá and to see whether or not it was domesticated. The word *gavayá* occurs in just one passage (iv, 21, 8) of the earliest text, the *Rigveda.* In that passage the word is linked with gaurá (the gaur). Though many have argued that the passage denotes two animals rather than one, this cannot be ascertained from the passage itself. Neither does the passage tell us much about the animal in question. It is true that another passage of the *Rigveda* (iv, 58, 2) mentions the gaurá separately as a sacrificial animal; and still others mention it as a wild animal, hunted by man. One cannot say with assurance whether or not the hypothetical gavayá of the *Rigveda* shared these qualities. In later Vedic sources the gavayá and the gaurá are clearly distinguished as different animals. Like the gaurá, however, the gavayá is described as a wild forest animal which also served for sacrifice.[6] There is no account which portrays the gavayá as a domestic animal.[7] The con-

4. See, for example, Monier-Williams, 1899: 351; Macdonell and Keith, 1912, 1: 222; Macdonell, 1929: 83; Wackernagel, 1954: 214; Mayrhofer, 1956: 331.

5. The eminent orientalist and Sanskritist H. T. Colebrooke (1808: 512, 524–25) first used the term *Bos gavaeus* for the "gayal," the animal of northeastern India which in his day was reported in both a wild and domestic form. Colebrooke also first associated the "gayal" with the gavayá of the Vedic records. Though Colebrooke nowhere considered the question of whether the gavayá may have been domesticated in Vedic times, his quotations of Vedic passages indicate that a wild animal was being referred to. Nowhere in his account does he suggest that the gavayá was domesticated. The reader will recall the early linguistic confusion that surrounded the terms "mithan" and "gayal," which led many observers to believe that there was a wild "gayal" similar to the domestic "gayal." It was only later that naturalists came to the conclusion that there is a domestic bovine, the mithan, and a quite different wild relative, the gaur. Sanskritists, however, seem to have persisted in using Colebrooke's terminology: "gayal (*Bos gavaeus*)."

6. *Sāṅkhāyana Śrauta Sūtra,* xvi, 3, 14; *Vājasaneyi Saṃhitā,* xiii, 49; xxiv, 28; *Taittirīya Saṃhitā,* iv, 2, 10; *Kāṇva Saṃhitā,* xiv, 4 and 5; *Kāṭhaka Saṃhitā,* xvi, 17. Acknowledgment is made to Prof. J. A. B. van Buitenen for his helpful comments on the gavayá of the Vedic accounts, and to Stefan Anaker for translating various Sanskrit passages.

7. One passage (*Taittirīya Saṃhitā,* ii, 1, 10) vaguely hints at a resemblance between the gavayá and the mithan of today. To quote Keith's translation, "He [a man] whom men calumniate though he has slain no one should offer a Gayal to Vāyu [the

clusion seems inescapable that the gavayá was a wild creature which had ties with man.

If the gavayá was wild, what may it have been? Was it a bovine or some other sort of animal? Some Sanskritists, it is true, have taken the gavayá to be a deer because its name, like that of the gaurá, is sometimes coupled with *mrga*, a word which in later times came to mean deer. Originally, however, mrga meant wild animal in general, and the coupling of gavayá and mrga has been taken by most authorities to mean "wild gavayá." The possibility remains that the gavayá was a deer, an antelope, or some other nonbovine species. In present-day India, the *nilgai* or "blue cow" is a species of antelope (*Boselaphus tragocamelus*), despite its name. On the other hand, it is more likely that the prefix *gava-*, which in Sanskrit is derived from *gáuh* or *gó*, cow or bull (the buffalo, a related animal, is thus designated *gavala*), indicates that the gavayá was a bovine animal. Adding support is the Rigvedic linking of gavayá with gaurá, suggesting that the two animals were closely related bovines. The famous fourteenth-century commentator Sāyaṇa's description of the gavayá as "a species of forest-dwelling wild animal resembling the cow" (Śāstri, 1915: 68) seems to us the most reasonable conclusion.

There are four primary candidates among bovines, if that is what the gavayá was: 1) the aurochs, wild ancestor of common cattle, now extinct in India; 2) some other wild bovine now extinct there; 3) the arni, or wild buffalo; and 4) the gaur. The aurochs was known in Mohenjo-Daro and other sites of the Indus Valley Civilization, and very likely survived into the Vedic period. The possibility cannot be eliminated that another wild bovine now extinct was found in India in Vedic times: perhaps the banteng, which today does not occur regularly west of the India-Burma border. One might be tempted to advance the cause of the hypothetical wild ancestor (different from the gaur) of the mithan, too, were it not for the lack of any concrete evidence that it ever existed and for the determined opposition of certain reputable zoologists who view the gaur as the ancestor of the mithan and deny the need for the hypothetical wild mithan. The remaining candidates, the gaur and water buffalo, both of which are known wild in India today, have distinct Sanskrit names, *gavala* and *gaurá*, but it remains possible that one of them may

---

god of the wind, purifier of the gods]; impure speech comes to him whom men calumniate though he has slain no one; the Gayal is neither a domestic nor a wild animal; he [the man] is neither in the village nor the forest ["neither fish nor fowl"] whom men calumniate though he has slain no one" (1914, 18: 144). It is the statement that the animal is neither domestic nor wild that is suggestive of the mithan. The statement could, however, equally well apply to various wild animals that frequent human settlements or fields.

have also been called *gavayá*. That the gaur and water buffalo are known by a variety of names in India today lends support to the idea that the Indians of Vedic times, too, could have used two names for the same animal. It might also be that the Vedic Indians recognized more than one race of gaur and called one gaurá, the other gavayá. If so, this might explain the Rigvedic linking of the names of the two animals. Today the Assamese and certain other people distinguish two types of gaur, a larger type of the hills and a smaller one of the plains. The Europeans who report these native distinctions are not all convinced that they are valid; nor, one should add, are the European reports themselves altogether clear (see Pizey, 1940: 658; Milroy, 1934–35: 103; Hermanns, 1952: 138).

About all one can safely say about the gavayá is that it probably was a wild bovine, which was sometimes sacrificed by man in religious rites. The Rigvedic linking of its name with that of the gaur suggests that it may have been either a gaur or form of gaur, or a closely related animal such as the banteng.

If the gavayá of the Vedic records were the domestic mithan, it would offer exciting prospects indeed. The mithan would be pushed far back in time, into the Vedic period. The Aryans could, in that event, already have been in contact with the Assam hill people. Or the mithan could have occurred in areas well beyond its present distribution. Unfortunately, the evidence indicates that the gavayá was a wild, not a domestic, animal. The Vedic records do show clearly that man was using the gaur and the gavayá for sacrifice. In at least two places, the two are specifically mentioned as substitutes for domestic animals, including common cattle, in a sacrifice to the god Agni. This raises the question (p. 262) whether the gaur may have been domesticated to serve a sacrificial role originally occupied by common cattle or some other bovine.

Native Traditions of Mithan Origin

If we turn to the traditions of the tribal people who keep mithan we find many interesting legends, with certain ideas occurring repeatedly. Stonor (1957: 5) reports that the Adi (Abor) have a legend that everything was given to them by the sun "on the horns of the tame bison" (mithan). This suggests that the Adi consider the mithan to be an early domesticate. The belief is repeated in more elaborate form in a myth of the Minyong Adi. Sedi-Botte, the earth, and his sister and wife Melo-Nane, the sky (who are commonly linked as the dual deity Sedi-Melo), first produced two sons. Then Melo-Nane gave birth to a third offspring, a mithan. The mithan grew fast, had large horns, and was dangerous to man; for this reason, his brothers killed him and planted his sexual organs in their field. From the planting grew a creeper which had large pumpkins on it. When a pumpkin was cut open, a silk worm emerged; and to it the dual sun-moon deity Doini-Polo (Donyi-Polo), who was consulted, affixed the head, horns, and legs of the dead mithan. Thus a new mithan was created, smaller and more tame than the original one. There was a quarrel about its ancestry, and the village council decided that it was the offspring of Doini-Polo (Elwin, 1958: 400).

In this Minyong myth we find the original mithan, presumably the wild gaur, derived from an incestuous relationship between earth and sky. Burial of its sexual organs in the field has strong fertility connotations. The domestic mithan was created by the sun-moon deity from parts of a large and dangerous ancestor. There is no hint of hybridization with common cattle in creation of the mithan. The Adi traditions are especially interesting when one considers again that common cattle are never used in Adi sacrifice and indeed have only recently appeared among the Adi at all.

The Idu Mishmi (Baruah, 1960: 87) also have a story of how the mithan came under domestication. After men came into existence, animals were created. They were asked by their creator to live in the forest, which was ruled by the god Gallan. Gallan permitted the tiger, elephant, deer, and other creatures to stay but drove "the mithan" out of the forest because it had large horns. Subsequently the mithan "came to live with human beings." This story clearly reveals the tradition that the mithan springs from a wild forest creature, and there is nothing to suggest its origin in hybridization between gaur and common cattle.

The Dafla, who believe their ancestral home to be somewhere in the Eastern Himalayas and whose southward migration in Subansiri Frontier Division has been documented, have a tradition that among other things they brought with them, to the hills they now occupy, the mithan and pig and the arts of weaving and agriculture (Shukla, 1959: 4–5). A Dafla myth tells how the Dafla began keeping mithan. Two spirits, Gyomane and Himane, who were husband and wife, produced a baby girl. One day the father became irritated with the child and said, "Become a mithan, become a mithan." As he spoke, she changed into a mithan. Teni, ancestor of the Dafla, was the first to see the girl after she became a mithan; thus all of his descendants keep mithan (Elwin, 1958: 394). Again, nothing in these traditions suggests an origin of mithan through hybridization. Moreover, as is true in the Adi Hills, common cattle occur today in Dafla country only in areas that border the Assamese plains.

The Bugun, or Khowa, a small group living in Kameng Frontier Division, have a story to account for the mithan among their neighbors the Aka. The sun and moon, who were married, had two children, a boy and a girl. When they were about sixteen years old the brother and sister had sexual intercourse, and the girl became pregnant. Fearful of the reaction of their parents, she hid in the clouds until the baby was born. It was not a child but a mithan, and the young people threw it down to earth so their parents would know nothing about it. The mithan fell on a great rock in a lake and was afraid to cross the water to shore. An Aka hunting party discovered the mithan and tried to tempt it to cross the water by offering it grass, but the mithan would not leave the rock. The Aka then collected fresh green leaves for the mithan. When it saw them it came across, whereupon the Aka captured the mithan and kept it at home (Elwin, 1958: 394). This story too views the mithan as having been domesticated from a wild animal, attracted to men by leaves; again common cattle are not mentioned.

The Aka themselves have a parallel myth that is both more elaborate and more revealing. Buslu-Ao had three sons and three daughters. Since the children were unable to find mates, he decided that his sons should marry his daughters. Two of the brother-sister couples were perfectly happy, but the third daughter refused to accept her brother as her husband and would not work for him in the fields. Goaded beyond endurance, one day he beat her, and she lay down in a corner of the house and sulked. When everyone had gone to the fields, she collected her bamboo tubes and a gourd and went to the river for water. There she attached the various containers to her body to resemble horns, a tail, and legs. Then she ate her clothes. By these acts she turned into a mithan, and went into the forest to live.

Her brother-husband, informed that she had become a mithan, searched for her, caught her, and brought her home. The assembled family agreed that she could not be permitted to wander in the forest. They tied her to a pillar with a cane rope and gave her food and water, but she refused them and stood there crying. Her father, taking pity, asked his daughter what could be done; she asked to be released so she could seek a suitable husband. When he turned her loose, she returned to the forest, and finally found an animal that was like her in color and form—a male mithan. They mated and soon had two calves.

Meanwhile her brother-husband had become ill, and the priest declared that he could be saved only by sacrificing a mithan. The other two brothers sought and found a mithan herd, on the distant bank of a river of hot waters. They tried to entice them across by calling and holding out leaves and salt. According to Elwin's version of the myth (1958: 397–400), when the mithan saw the salt they began to cross the river, but the heat was so great that only one female and her two calves arrived. The brothers took them home and tied them at the front of the house. Buslu-

Ao's wife recognized the female as their daughter and protested vigorously against sacrificing her. Buslu-Ao replied that it was true the mithan had once been their daughter, but that since the gods desired her they had no choice but to sacrifice her. There were certain difficulties in carrying out the sacrifice, and the parents had to tell their mithan-daughter that now that she was a mithan it was her duty to die. After that they succeeded in killing her with their daos.

This story, besides touching on themes that occur in the other myths, introduces quite dramatically the idea of the need of mithan for sacrifice. Several additional ideas are included as well: that the sacrifice is to save a human life; that the gods wish the sacrifice; that it must be carried out despite the cost to the family of the sacrificer; and finally that it is the duty of the mithan to die at this time and in this way. Elwin in his collection of myths of the North-East Frontier (1958: 355) says that often the stories about the mithan, buffalo, and pig emphasize the role of these animals in sacrifice and contain suggestions that they were created for this purpose. In the Aka myth the idea is again presented of the wild animal being lured to man with leaves and salt. Eating the clothes is interesting because mithan have been reported as doing this, attracted to the salt deposited by human perspiration. Again there is no indication of the mithan deriving from the hybridization of a wild animal and a tame related form such as common cattle. In fact the continued search by the girl-mithan for a suitable mate, a creature like herself, might well be taken as evidence to the contrary.

In a myth of the Miji (Elwin, 1958: 395–96), neighbors of the Aka, Kan-Nui-Nuchu, a deity, appeared on earth and could find no living being except himself. Apparently for company, he made a huge horned animal of wood, plastered it with mud, and covered it with plantain leaves. While the god, pleased with his effort, slept, the creature came to life, as a female mithan. She ate the god's clothes and drank his rice beer. Then, realizing that the god would be angry when he woke, she ran away and followed the footsteps of a man to a settlement. The brother of the man, on seeing her, thought how tasty the flesh would be, and ran for his bow and arrows. Before he could shoot, however, the mithan begged him not to kill her and told him she had come to live with him, to help him and his children. Convinced, the man tied her with a rope and took her to his house, where she gave birth to many other mithan. The god, upon awaking, followed the mithan's prints to the settlement and saw her tied up there; annoyed, he made the man's children sick. A priest instructed them to offer beer and cloth to the god to quiet his anger. The practice has been continued until today: the Miji still offer cloth and beer to Kan-Nui-Nuchu, who in return protects humans and their cattle. The mithan in this myth presented itself to man for domestication. Rather than kill it for its flesh, man decided to keep it at home. Again, one notes, the eating of clothes appears.

The Hill Miri have a somewhat parallel story (Elwin, 1958: 396–97). Two brothers lived together and cleared land in the forest. The elder brother, Nikkum, cut one clearing a day, but the younger one, Sukkum, cut three; the elder had to drink often, the younger but once a day; Nikkum had to sleep as other men do, but Sukkum worked both night and day. Resentful that he could not match his brother, Nikkum decided to kill him. Finding a pretext and occasion, he went to Sukkum with a wooden dao, since there was no iron in those days. "Don't kill me," said Sukkum. "I will have children and they will serve you. Tie me up with a rope and tether me outside your house. I and my wife will both serve you." At first Nikkum was tempted to kill Sukkum anyway, but just then Si-Duinye came by and urged him not to: "When you are ill," Si-Duinye said, "you can sacrifice his children; when you want wives, you can buy them with his children." Nikkum was persuaded and tied his brother, who was the first mithan, outside his house. Even today, the myth goes, when a mithan is sacrificed, the priest tells it not to be sorry, that by an old agreement the gods will eat half of its flesh and men half. Sometimes, it is said, tears fall from the mithan's eyes on hearing this. This story shows the belief that the mithan is not only tied closely to man but related to him, and was brought into his service for purposes of sacrifice.

Another tradition is that of the Kachari of the North Cachar Hills (Soppitt, 1885: 23–24). According to a Kachari legend, when the world was yet young the God of Plenty, disguised as an old woman, visited the earth. Going from house to house and begging alms, he was refused, though the people were prosperous and had full granaries. Eventually reaching the home of an aged widow and her son, he was given food and rest and urged to stay as long as he wished. When the food supply of his hosts ran short, the god identified himself and had his hosts build a large granary, which he filled with rice. Before departing he told the son to go to a certain place in the forest a week afterward, where he would find cattle which he could drive home and use. The son found there hundreds of buffalo and mithan. In the process of driving the animals home, however, there was a stampede. Some mithan and buffalo were secured, to become the basis of domestic herds; others escaped to the forest, to form the wild herds that still exist. The widow and her son, as the reader can guess, had plentiful harvests ever after, while the neighbors had to endure blight and locusts. In this Kachari legend the mithan is the gift to man from the God of Plenty, to provide him with sustenance. Striking are the clarity and simplicity with which it shows that the wild and tame mithan are different lines of one ancestor. The Kachari, we note, still employ the same word, *mithang*, for both *Bos gaurus* and *Bos frontalis*.

Still another tradition is found among the Rengma Naga (Mills, 1937: 208). Among the Rengma, a young man pays part of his marriage price in cattle and part in cash. But, says Mills, the marriage price "must never include an animal from the plains." This is apparently supported by a story that originally men, mithan, Naga cattle (hill cattle), and plains cattle emerged in that order from a hole in the earth. As they came out, the hole gradually reduced in size. When the plains animal finally emerged, the hole closed behind it and took off the end of its tail. The use of plains cattle in marriage price might, as a result, lead to the extinction of the clan. For the Rengma, the mithan preceded common cattle; and there is no hint in the story of origin through hybridization.

According to the Thadou myth of creation, their ancestors originally lived inside the earth. They emerged to the surface through a hole, bringing with them the cultivated plants millet and Job's tears, and one mithan. Subsequently this mithan was killed for a feast. Later another one was captured and domesticated. The chicken and pig were also found and domesticated, as was rice (Shaw, 1929: 24–29, 40, 73). This account suggests the Thadou belief in the mithan as an early domestic animal, perhaps the earliest, as well as the belief that they had captured and tamed it, possibly from a related wild form. Their names for the animals support this: the mithan is known as the *shiel*, the gaur as *jang-shiel* (presumably "wild or jungle" mithan) (Shaw, 1929: 135). Common cattle are not mentioned among the domestic animals of the Thadou.

A final tale, not a tradition of origin, is that by Macrae, already cited, of how the Kuki of the Chittagong Hills used salt to attract "wild gyalls" and then gradually led them home with the domestic "gyall" (mithan). Though the story is of questionable validity, it nevertheless reveals the Kuki informant's view that the wild and domesticated "gyall" were the same and that the wild form could be converted into the domesticated one.

The native traditions of origin we have considered above, taken together, contain various interesting points. First is the belief that the mithan is a domesticated form of a related wild animal. Second are the statements that man used salt and green leaves to attract the animal to him, and that the mithan eats human clothes for their salt deposit. Third is the belief that the mithan is an early domesticate which was closely tied to man and the gods, and was even born of incestuous relations. Fourth is the feeling that the animal was brought under the control of man to provide a creature for sacrifice. Fifth is the belief that the mithan was given to man to provide him with flesh, with plenty. And finally, in one story, there is the sowing of mithan genitals in a field, possibly to assure crop fertility. Nothing in these stories suggests that mithan horns were important in any way, nothing ties the animal to a universal deity, nothing suggests that it is a recent domesticate springing from the hybridization of common cattle and gaur.

Contrary traditions are reported only for the Chin of Burma. According to Carey and Tuck (1896, 1: 180–81), the Chin claim that the mithan is not distinct from the gaur; that their mithan result from a cross between gaur bull and common cow; that they purposely drive domestic cows to the habitat of the gaur to bring about mating; and that only in the fourth generation of back-crossing is the mithan stage reached. H. J. Wehrli (1905–6: 118) heard similar statements on the upper Chindwin regarding the origin of the mithan. The Carey and Tuck statement has provided some of the principal support for those who view the mithan as a hybrid between common cattle and gaur. Four decades later, however, Stevenson (1943: 48) found no instances in the Falam Subdivision of Chin herding common cattle to encourage crossing with gaur; gaur indeed had long been exterminated in the area, except for an occasional animal that wandered in. All breeding in Stevenson's time was either within the mithan group or between mithan and common cattle. Stevenson himself questioned the assumption that mithan necessarily developed as hybrids between common cattle and gaur, basing his opinion on certain physical and behavioral resemblances and differences with these and on the fact that mithan are common in the Nung Hills of northeast Burma where common cattle are recent introductions and where the nearest gaur are several days distant. Still another argument against Carey's and Tuck's statement comes from Hutton (pers. com., Jan. 25, 1966). He points to the absence of a similar tradition of origin among both the Thadou Kuki and Lakher, related groups who would be expected to know of it.

> What has happened, I fancy, is that either Sir Bertram Carey or Mr. Tuck, or both, misunderstood the Chins when they told them that mithan cows were released where the gaur bulls of the jungle would have access to them, taking the cows to be plains kine whereas they really meant . . . [mithan] cows, since it is a well-known fact that the Thado at any rate regard an occasional infusion of wild blood as greatly improving the domesticated breed, in spite of making calves of the first generation a bit difficult. Indeed Carey and Tuck's tale about the mithun is on a par with the inference to be drawn from an earlier paragraph on the same page that the woolly-haired hunting dogs were tamed from the wild dogs by the Chins. The breed is well known from Tibet and throughout the Naga Hills, the Lushai Hills, and Manipur, but it was more probably tamed in Anau, or earlier, than by the Chins or their ancestors. It was assuredly never derived from the local wild dog.

However one interprets the Chin evidence, it seems insufficient to out-weigh the traditions of origin of the groups mentioned above, all of which view the mithan as a domestic form of a related wild animal.

Names for the Mithan as Clues to Its Domesticators

The word "mithan" appears to have come into English from the As-samese, Indo-Europeans of the Indic subfamily who occupy the Brahma-putra Valley.[8] The transliteration of the Assamese word into English should be "mithun" (always, however, pronounced míthᴈn), but the spelling "mithan" has come into such general use in English that its re-placement by "mithun" is unlikely.

There are various possibilities for the origin of the Assamese word *mithun*. One is that it is of Assamese or Indic origin. The second is that it is of Sino-Tibetan origin. The third is that it is of Mon-Khmer origin. The fourth is that the Assamese or some other group may have applied to the animal the name of the first mithan-keeping group with whom they came in contact.

The first possibility seems remote. The Assamese word *mithun* does not seem to have Sanskrit roots, nor is it found among other Indic peoples except where it can be explained in terms of borrowing. The Assamese themselves, besides using *mithun* for the domestic animal, sometimes use other synonyms that are clearly of Indic origin. The Bengali, the other Indic language group directly bordering mithan country, use Indic words exclusively for the mithan and gaur. They commonly call both *gayal*. The gaur is sometimes further distinguished as *aseel gayal* ("true gayal"), as distinct from the domesticated animal, the *gobbah gayal* ("village gayal"). The gaur, which is also found in other parts of India, is known by various names to the groups involved. In Hindi, it is usually known as *gaur* or *gauri-gai* or sometimes, strangely, as *jangli khulga* ("jungle buffalo"). For the mithan, Hindi speakers use *gayal*, *mithan* (*mithun?*), or *gavai*, all probably picked up from Bengali or Assamese, and the latter, like *gayal*, related to the Sanskrit. Though a variation of *mithun* appears among at least one other Indic group (the Nepalis, who use *mithun gāi* for the gaur), it seems likely that the word *mithun* was introduced to the Assamese and other Indic peoples from some non-Indic group.

The second possibility, that *mithun* is of Sino-Tibetan origin, has

8. Acknowledgment is made to E. J. A. Henderson and his colleagues at the School of Oriental and African Studies, University of London, for comments and suggestions on the possible origin of the word *mithan*. The authors, however, are responsible for analysis of the data.

serious drawbacks. It is true that the Kachari, who belong to the Sino-Tibetan language family, have a word *mithang* (said by some to mean "the muscular animal"; from *mi* = animal, *thang* = muscular); and that they apply *mithang* both to *Bos gaurus* and *Bos frontalis*, with the prefix *hagrani*, "of the jungle," for the wild animal and *noni*, "of the house," for the domestic form. It is also true that until the end of the last century the Kachari kept domestic mithan. However, among the Sino-Tibetan peoples of mithan country proper the word *mithun* apparently is not native. Indeed, an altogether different word (or variants of it) is used from one end of the animal's range to the other. The word is indicated in the literature as *sia, she, shial, sü, esso, esho, cha, chai,* and so forth. Though different words also occur, variations of the above are by far the most common. A few of the peoples involved use similar words to refer to gaur, common cattle, buffalo, or mithan, but with prefixes or suffixes added to distinguish among them. Thus, the Mru of the Chittagong Hills refer to common cattle and mithan collectively as *cia;* and to the mithan as *cia-nöm* ("the true *cia*") (pers. com., L. G. Löffler, Aug. 20, 1965). In the Dulien dialect of Lushai the mithan is *shial* or *she* (a contraction of *shial*), and one name for the gaur is *ram-shial* or "forest mithan" (Lorrain and Savidge, 1898: 61, 168, 169, 179, 180, 181, 248, 278).[9]

The above suggests that the word *mithun* is neither of Indic nor of Sino-Tibetan origin, despite its occurrence among the Assamese and Kachari. If this is so, from where may it have come? One possibility is that the Kachari, Sino-Tibetans who once ruled the Assam Valley, or the Assamese, who occupied it later, simply applied to the animal the name of the group from whom they first gained knowledge of it. There is, it should be noted, a mithan-keeping Idu Mishmi group called Mithun, meaning "the people of the Ithun River" (just as Midri means "people of the Dri River"). The people of the Ithun River, which is a tributary of the Dibang, are one of the first groups encountered on entering Mishmi country from the plains; and the Dibang Valley has long been a major artery of trade between the Assam Valley and Tibet.

Another possibility, and to us the more likely one, is that the word *mithun* is of Mon-Khmer origin. It is widely held that the Assam hills were once occupied by Mon-Khmer groups, related to the Khasi who today live in the hills west of the Naga. The Khasi, it should be emphasized, use a similar-sounding word, *mynthyna*, for gaur or "wild bull." Moreover, as H. L. Shorto observes (pers. com., April 1, 1966), the

9. Prefixes or suffixes are also commonly added to indicate sex or other characteristics among mithan. For the Haka Chin, the word *sia-te* is used for baby mithan, *sia-pi* for fertile females, *siapi le siate* for a mithan cow with offspring, and *ki-kawng* for bull mithan (Lehman, 1963: 80).

"*-thun*" of *mithun* could by "a wild shot" relate to the Mon-Khmer, possibly Austric, word, which in Khmer is pronounced khti̱:ŋ and means "hump, humped cattle," and in Theng, kti̱ɲ and is used for "wild ox"; and it may possibly be related to the Java Malay word *banteng.* Our hypothesis is that the word *mithun* has Mon-Khmer roots; that the Khasi *mynthyna* is one form still used by a Mon-Khmer group of the area; that the word spread to the Kachari, the Angami Naga (whose word for common cattle, curiously, is *mithu* or *mithoo*), and then to the Assamese, certain other Indic peoples, and to the British. The word, however, was initially used, in the sense of "wild ox," for the gaur, and only later came to be applied to its domesticated form, the mithan.

There is nothing in this hypothesis to suggest that the Mon-Khmer peoples, widely believed to have been the ancient inhabitants of much of present-day mithan country, knew the domesticated animal. Indeed, the fact that the mithan does not occur today among the Khasi or any other Mon-Khmer people suggests that it was domesticated by the Sino-Tibetan migrants who succeeded them. That the animal is known widely among the Sino-Tibetan peoples by forms of a single word, *sia,* which is apparently of Sino-Tibetan origin, adds strength to the view that they carried out the domestication. Detailed study by a linguist competent in Sino-Tibetan and other languages of the area is needed before final answers can be obtained to the questions considered above.

Time, Place, and Means of Domestication

There is little concrete evidence on which to base conclusions about the time of mithan domestication. Virtually no archeologic excavation has been carried out in mithan country. Moreover, under the conditions of heavy precipitation—among the heaviest in the world—that characterize much of the region, skeletal material and wooden carvings of mithan decay with alarming rapidity. Caves and rock overhangs might seem to be hopeful places for survival of remains, but unfortunately village sites in the Assam hills do not occur in such places, nor can one assume that since Paleolithic times they have ever done so. Probably the hills will never reveal an abundance of archeologic material of use. Nor is there anything in the archeology of other parts of India or Burma that can with assurance be identified with the mithan. There are, it is true, the Indus Valley (Harappan) seals which depict a bovine that seems to be the gaur. This animal, moreover, probably had ritual importance for the Indus Valley people (*c.* 2500–1700 B.C.), as the mithan does today for the people of the Assam hills. J. H. Hutton infers from the seals that gaur were probably captured and possibly tamed by the people of the Indus Valley

Civilization, and is inclined to look for mithan domestication "in the Upper Indus basin or on the Indo-Persian borders before the desiccation of Afghanistan and Baluchistan set in" (pers. coms., Jan. 25, Feb. 6, and Sept. 29, 1966). We think that the seals indicate a predomestication relationship between gaur and man, but not domestication itself. The view that gaur were captured and tamed has much merit, for various Vedic statements suggest that in those times gaur were captured for sacrifice. It should be emphasized, however, that at that time the hill peoples of Assam also may have been capturing and taming gaur, or they may already have moved from capture and taming to domestication.

If the Indus Valley people domesticated the gaur, use of the domesticated animal would have spread eastward across India to reach the Assam hill country, the only part of India where it is found today. One might expect to find evidence along the route of diffusion, places where the animal is found in small numbers today, or where it was found in past times. No such evidence is known. One might also expect the Aryans, who presumably invaded India about 1500 B.C., to have recorded the presence of such a domesticated animal in the Vedic accounts. There is no such record. It is true that there are puzzling references to the *gavayá*, a wild forest animal and probably a bovine, and that the gavayá, like the *gaurá* (gaur), seems to have been captured and sacrificed to the gods. It is also true that most Sanskritists have identified the gavayá as "gayal," or *Bos gavaeus*, terms also sometimes used to designate the mithan. Nothing in the Vedic accounts suggests, however, that the gavayá was a domestic animal, nor is there anything substantial to tie it to the mithan. Since it is linked with gaurá in the earliest account, the *Rigveda*, and for other reasons, we conclude that the gavayá probably was a type of gaur or some other closely related wild bovine, but not a mithan.

The etymology of the word "mithan" and the forms of *sia* by which the animal is known to the hill people offers little support for the animal having been introduced to the hills by the Aryans or other Indo-Europeans. The words apparently are Sino-Tibetan or Mon-Khmer in origin, not Indo-European. And there are strong suggestions that the Assamese, Indo-Europeans of the Brahmaputra Valley, borrowed their word for mithan from some hill group.

The deficiencies of archeology, history, and etymology leave us largely dependent on zoologic, ethnographic, and related data in developing a hypothesis on the time and place of mithan domestication. A factor of relevance to the time when domestication took place is the difference in physical appearance between the mithan and its presumed wild ancestor, the gaur. While the animals are similar enough to lead zoologists to believe they are wild ancestor and domestic offspring, the differences in size, horn shape, and other features are notable. Admittedly, rapid changes in physical characteristics of domestic animals such as the rabbit, mink, and fox have occurred in modern times under conditions of careful selection. However, under the loose system of care that has prevailed in mithan country—with maximum opportunity to continue breeding with wild relatives, and with no effort at controlled breeding—it is very unlikely that such differences would develop over a short period of time. Though selective factors operate, there is little to indicate that they would rapidly alter the physical appearance of the animal. Whatever selective factors have operated have done so gradually.

Looking next at the place of the mithan among the hill tribes, we acknowledge the rapidity with which newly introduced domesticated plants and animals can become integrated in recipient cultures: in their traditions of origin, folklore, and social, ceremonial, and religious life. Nevertheless, there are sometimes indications that a particular plant or animal was recently introduced or domesticated. Such indications for the mithan may indeed be found among certain Naga groups. Most of the mithan-keeping groups however look on the animal as among their earliest domesticates; and no animal today is more deeply involved in their social, ceremonial, and religious life than the mithan. Very little of the foregoing conflicts with the view that the mithan is an animal of some antiquity.

Why, we may ask, if the mithan was an early domesticate, does it have such a limited distribution today? Some of the probable reasons are already evident to the reader. Since the animal does not adapt well to the hot lowlands bordering its homeland or to the cold uplands of Tibet, those important avenues of diffusion were blocked. Common cattle have become so widespread because of their adaptability to varied environments. Water buffalo have been less adaptable than common cattle, but more so than mithan. Another possible reason for the mithan's limited distribution may be that the animal's habits and needs do not suit it to conditions of sedentary cultivation. Indeed, as we have seen, it gives way when shifting cultivation is replaced by sedentary farming. This would bar the mithan from much of the country adjacent to the hills. A third reason is that the neighboring Buddhist and Hindu groups are opposed to sacrificing an animal such as the mithan (it was not always so in India), so it had no value as sacrifice for them. A final possible reason is that the ecological niche the mithan might have filled among shifting cultivators was already occupied by another well entrenched domesticate such as the water buffalo, which slowed mithan diffusion.

Hutton (in Mills, 1926: 78 n.; 1932; 1965: 29, 33–34; pers. coms., Feb. 6 and Sept. 8, 1966) has expressed the view that in Assam domestic water buffalo were early; that they were originally associated with Mon-Khmer cultures there and with wet-rice cultivation; that subsequently, before mithan were present, buffalo were introduced to hill peoples who did not cultivate irrigated rice. He regards the occurrence of buffalo among certain Naga groups—the Tangkhul, Eastern Rengma, Chang, Konyak, and Phom Naga—as the remnant of what once was a broader distribution; and points, for support, to the bovine representations, which resemble buffalo heads, in the art of certain Naga groups (Ao, Angami) who today keep no buffalo. Hutton also mentions that the Memi (Mao) Naga of Manipur keep mithan today, but wear buffalo-shaped horns, either of real buffalo horn or of wood, in ceremonial costume; and that in Lephori, an old Eastern Rengma village where there are both buffalo and a few mithan, the buffalo is the senior animal in sacrifice (Hutton, pers. coms., Feb. 6 and Sept. 8, 1966; Hodson, 1911: facing 6, 120; Mills, 1937: 91).

Also of significance, in our view, is the occurrence of free-ranging buffalo among various groups in mithan country and in a cultural context similar to that of mithan. Further there is the presence of free-ranging buffalo among hill peoples east of mithan country in Southeast Asia (see Appendix B); their traditional use among these peoples in sacrifice but not in milking or plowing; and their association, among some of these groups, with other traits, such as forked posts, which, in Naga and Chin country, are linked with the mithan (see Löffler, 1954). Common cattle also are found in such free-ranging situations in Southeast Asia, but buffalo are the more widespread and apparently the earlier bovine to be so used there. It may be that free-ranging buffalo and the complex associated with them preceded mithan in the Assam hill country as well as in the hills of Southeast Asia.

If the buffalo was the earliest bovine in the hills of the Indo-Burman borderlands, the mithan may have come largely to displace it because of its gentle quality under free-ranging conditions. In modern times, with security and increased trade with nearby lowland areas, the buffalo has been introduced, or reintroduced, in some places.

It is Hutton's feeling (in Mills, 1926: 78 n.; Hutton, 1932: 10–11, and pers. com., Sept. 8, 1966) that the mithan was introduced to its present habitat by "Tibeto-Burmans," specifically the ancestors of the Kuki-Chin, who brought mithan in their early migrations from the Himalayas, down the Chindwin Valley and into the present Kuki-Chin homeland at the southern margins of mithan country. From there, he postulates, mithan moved northward again, through the mountains west of the Chindwin in later Kuki-Chin migrations, and displaced the buffalo among the Naga in many places.

It does not appear to us likely that the ancestors of the Kuki-Chin introduced the mithan into the southern hills in the way suggested; the hot, low valley of the Chindwin, which is unsuited to mithan and where they are not found today, does not seem a plausible migration route for the animal. Our review of the evidence suggests an alternative hypothesis: that at some undetermined early date the mithan was domesticated by representatives of the Sino-Tibetan language family within the hills where it is found today, and that after domestication it spread through the hills from one group to another. Our further feeling, for reasons that will emerge in Chapter 23, our Conclusion, is that mithan domestication occurred in the southern range of the animal (Naga and Chin country).

Certain observers have been skeptical that the strong, wary gaur could have been domesticated by primitive hill tribes. On the other hand, as Downs has noted, not all individuals of an animal species are the same. Some are intractable and incapable of domestication. Others are able to adjust to man's presence and are ready for domestication. There must have been such differences among the gaur with which the early hill people had contact. A simple form of economic organization, moreover, would not have hindered domestication. As Francis Galton observed a century ago (1865: 138), there is no reason to suppose that the initial domestication of any animal [presently domesticated?], with the exception of the elephant, requires that the domesticators have a high civilization. Looking at the question from another point of view, it must have been such hill tribes who accomplished the domestication of the gaur. The mithan is found only in the hills. There is no clear evidence that it was formerly present elsewhere. Nor has anything been found to indicate that the hill peoples ever were more advanced than they are now.

Equally unknown is just how the domestication of the mithan may have occurred. Theodore Hubback's observations on the gaur in Malaya (1939: 10–11, 14–15) suggest one promising avenue of inquiry. The Malayan gaur, notes Hubback, frequently appears at the edge of clearings to feed, and makes liberal use both of the grasses that spring up there and of the leaves of trees in the secondary forest. Hubback argues further that the gaur is probably a relatively recent migrant from the north into Malaya, and that its migration followed the spread of shifting cultivation into the peninsula. If he is correct, it may be that in mithan country the gaur first came into continuous contact with man at the forest clearings made by early shifting cultivators. Not only was contact made between man and gaur, but the disturbance created by man's agricultural activities may have resulted in vegetation which better nourished the gaur and favored its multiplication. Of relevance here is the Thadou myth

(Shaw, 1929: 73) of the capture of a mithan, presumably wild, grazing in a man's millet fields.

Also of significance in the question of how domestication came about is the curious salt tie, which so reminds one of the reindeer's tie with hunters and herdsmen in northern Eurasia that doubtless contributed to reindeer domestication. Early hunters lurking along game trails or at salt licks would have been acutely aware of the gaur's craving for salt. In certain tribal myths of mithan domestication the animal is attracted to men by salt and leaves, or it is pictured as eating clothes, which contain human salt. Hunters could have used salt or salty earth to entice gaur into ambush, and then brought the surviving young to the village.[10] Nothing in the literature suggests that gaur—like reindeer—are attracted to human settlements by the salt in human urine. But there is the Mru myth, reported by Löffler (pers. com., Oct. 18, 1966), in which a wild boar and an elephant come to the village at night to bathe in the urine of a young woman. If these wild animals were attracted to human settlement by urine, why not the gaur, which is known to crave salt? Löffler mentions the practice, common among the hill people, of urinating, at least at night, from an outside corner of the raised house platform; in the morning, one may see the common cattle, he says, licking the bamboo supports of the platforms. If the cattle do not sleep, he adds, and are "near a urinating human, they try to let the urine flow right into their mouths." There are also J. Shakespear's observations (1912: 68, 112) that among the Lushai mithan lick up the urine under the bachelors' dormitory, and that there is a myth of a man who enticed a gaur—by what means is not indicated—under his house to kill it.

In the hypothesized case of salt being offered to wild gaur, the less wild animals would be the most likely to approach man. This in itself would be a selective factor. Survival of their relatively gentle young that were not killed along with the parents might have been assisted by proximity to human settlements, which were avoided by wild dogs and tigers. When the young were old enough to browse in the forest, they might have been drawn back to the village by human urine, or men might have maintained the tie as they do now, periodically providing the animals with salt. The gentle offspring would remain and multiply, but those with inherited wildness would return to the deep forest and the wild state. Since mithan bulls are most commonly sacrificed, wilder bulls

10. The parallels between reindeer herders and mithan people need further investigation. The Uriankhai Soyot, for example, permit their reindeer to graze unattended. At night, the reindeer return to the encampment of their own free will, and find their way to the tents of their owners. Then they wander among the tents begging for salt, and are so tame that they permit small children to mount them.

were probably dispatched young, and gentler ones survived to breed. This also contributed to development of a gentle quality. Though this is a process of selection that involves a vastly longer time span than the systems of close control envisaged by many theories of domestication, it does seem feasible.[11] The sacrifice of mithan among certain tribes even today involves a ritual suggestive of hunting. One of the strongest and most wary of hunted animals thus may have become domesticated through its liking for salt, to fill the role of sacrificial animal. What the broader associations of mithan sacrifice may have been will develop in the succeeding chapter on the domestication of common cattle.

11. That the process may have taken an even longer time is suggested by a practice of the Lamet of Laos. The Lamet keep water buffalo and permit them to wander loose in the woods. Under those conditions a buffalo sometimes becomes wild and dangerous. In such cases the Lamet entice the animal into an enclosure and leave it to starve until it is gentle. Only then is it permitted to join the herd. Such an alternative, which could also have been applied to troublesome mithan, would permit wilder animals to survive and would slow the development of a gentle quality in succeeding generations.

22

Notes on the Domestication of Common Cattle

Bovine Keeping: "Southwest Asian" and "Southeast Asian" Traditions

There are two principal traditions of bovine keeping among settled people in southern Asia today. One probably developed in Southwest Asia and was first associated with common cattle. It is not known where the other tradition developed, but today it is found mainly in Southeast Asia, where it is associated principally with water buffalo and mithan. There are profound differences between the two traditions. The "Southwest Asian" tradition usually involves herding or confinement of bovines, their use in plowing and other traction, and the consumption of their milk and flesh. The "Southeast Asian" tradition involves free-ranging bovines and the use of bovines in sacrifice and the consumption only of their flesh. The Southwest Asian form has been involved with an agricultural type, the plow-cereal complex, that has had a profound effect on the life of the region, has spread widely, and, sometimes in modified form, has had a strong impact wherever it has traveled. The Southeast Asian form is not widespread. On the contrary, it survives mostly in hill regions among primitive tribal people. In the rest of Southeast Asia a modified Southwest Asian form, generally without milking, prevails.

Carl O. Sauer (1952) views the free-ranging Southeast Asian household animals (pig, chicken, and dog) as the earliest animal domesticates. According to his hypothesis, the earliest cultivation, based on vegetatively reproduced crops, is also Southeast Asian and preceded animal domestication. He views alert fishermen, living in a rich and varied environment and using plant materials in their fishing activities, as the agents who accomplished the first plant domestication. The Southeast Asian complex of vegetatively reproduced plants and household animals, Sauer feels, spread westward into more arid regions. There, seed plants (the cereals and pulses) came under domestication as well as the herd animals (sheep, goats, and common cattle) to evolve into the plow-cereal complex. Another, more widely held, hypothesis, based on the archeologic excavations of Robert Braidwood, Kathleen Kenyon, and others in the Near East, is that the earliest plant and herd animal domestication occurred in Southwest Asia; and that among the animals were common cattle, presumably the first bovine to be domesticated.

Whether one supports the Sauer hypothesis or the more popular one, the mithan represents a most interesting example of a bovine animal which, because of tradition and ecology, lives in a way quite different from its relatives elsewhere in India and western Asia. Despite the differences in the two traditions—Southwest Asian and Southeast Asian early man must have faced similar problems in both areas in accomplishing the domestication of the strong, wary bovines. He may also, though we cannot be sure, have had similar motives for attempting domestication. It may well be profitable, therefore, to view the domestication of common cattle in Southwest Asia in the light of what we have learned about the mithan.

Near Eastern Archeology and the Time of Cattle Domestication

As mentioned above, it is widely held that the earliest gropings toward agriculture and animal husbandry occurred in the Near East.[1] The hunting-gathering peoples who seem to have carried out early domestication lived at different altitudes and in a variety of environmental zones besides the open woodland in which the greatest number of potential domesticates occurred. There is clear evidence that certain Near Eastern hunting-gathering peoples lived in permanent or semipermanent settlements, some having hundreds of inhabitants. These peoples were either in regions with an abundance of game and/or fish and gathered foods, or they controlled some resource (i.e., salt, obsidian) which they could trade for food. They may have had an increased specialization of labor, leisure, and opportunities to domesticate plants and animals. Whether such sedentary peoples actually are to be credited with domestication or not, there may, as some suggest, have been an additional stimulus or trigger to domestication, such as increased trade and movement of plants and animals into new environmental zones. In any case the general importance of hunting was such that one could advance a "thesis of the

1. See Braidwood and Reed, 1957; Braidwood and Howe, 1962; Perrot, 1962; Zervos, 1962–63; Solecki, 1963; Butzer, 1964; Flannery, 1965; Mellaart, 1965; Weinberg, 1965; Hole, 1966; van Loon, 1966; Braidwood, 1966.

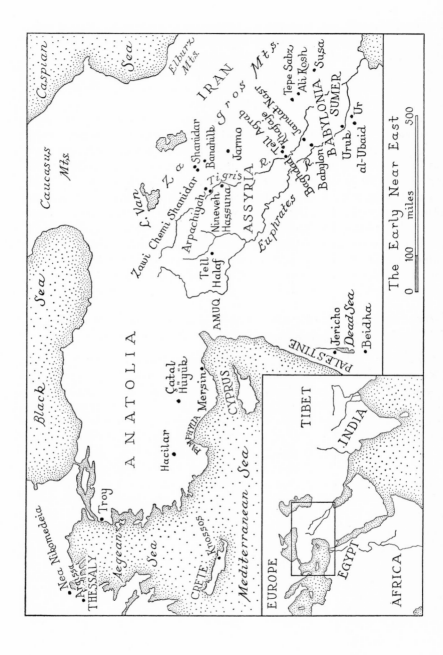

The Early Near East

0   100   500
         miles

Map 7

alert hunters" as a local counterpart of Sauer's "thesis of the alert fishermen." The peoples involved manipulated the potential plant and animal
domesticates and brought them under control one by one.[2] Though
many feel that agriculture preceded animal husbandry, present evidence
supports the view that domesticated sheep and goats were known before
plant domestication. In any event, not too long after domestication there
arose a distinction between pastoralists and village farmers.

The first bones of clearly domesticated herd animals uncovered, dating
from about 9000 B.C., are those of sheep. Later, following about 7000 B.C.,
sheep are joined by goats, pigs, and common cattle.[3] If one accepts both
the judgment of competent zoologists and dates mostly based on C–14
determinations, it seems that the earliest-known clearly domesticated or
probably domesticated cattle are those of Argissa in Thessaly (in the
Aceramic Neolithic levels, pre–6100 B.C.?; see Map 7); of Otzaki in
Thessaly and Nea Nikomedeia in Greek Macedonia (for both, in Early
Neolithic levels dating from *c.* 6100–5600 B.C.?); of Çatal Hüyük in
Anatolia (Level VI B: *c.* 6050–5950 B.C.); of Tepe Sabz in southwestern
Iran (Sabz phase, *c.* 5500–5000 B.C.); of Ghar-i-Mar (Snake Cave) in
the hills of the Hindu Kush in Afghanistan (occurring in levels having
one C–14 date (Hv–428) of *c.* 5270 B.C. and another (Hv–429) of *c.* 5080
B.C.); of Hódmezővásárhely-Bodzáspart and Maroslele-Pana in southeast
Hungary (late in the sixth millennium B.C.?); and of the Halafian site of
Banahilk of northern Iraq (*c.* 5000 B.C.?).[4]

2. For an excellent review of recent advances in our knowledge of the origins of
agriculture, see Harris, 1967.

3. *Sources:* This section is based on many sources, among them the following:
Argissa and Otzaki: J. Boessneck, 1956, 1960, 1961, 1962; Nea Nikomedeia: E. S.
Higgs in R. J. Rodden, 1962; R. J. Rodden, 1965; Çatal Hüyük: pers. com., D.
Perkins, Jr., March 27, 1967; Tepe Sabz: F. Hole, K. Flannery, and J. Neely, 1965:
105–6; pers. coms., F. Hole, Dec. 28, 1966, and May 29, 1967; pers. com., K.
Flannery, May 25, 1967; Ghar-i-Mar: L. Dupree, 1964, and pers. com., Feb. 14, 1967
(basing his views on identification by D. Perkins, Jr.); the southeast Hungarian sites:
S. Bökönyi, 1964, and pers. com., Aug. 1, 1967; Banahilk: C. A. Reed, 1961. Other
sources used: C. A. Reed, 1959, 1960; C. S. Coon, 1951: 44–45; F. E. Zeuner, 1963;
F. Hole and K. V. Flannery, 1962: 126–33; D. Stronach, 1961: 124; D. Perkins, Jr.,
1964 and 1966: 66–67 (in D. Kirkbride); and pers. com., R. J. Braidwood, March 3,
1967.

4. There are no C–14 dates for Banahilk. There are none for either of the two
Hungarian sites; these sites, however, contained only materials of the earliest Hungarian Neolithic culture, Körös, which for other sites has provided a few C–14 dates
(Bln. 75, Bln. 86, Bln. 115), ranging from *c.* 5332 to 4611 B.C., both ± 100. The
assumption here is that domesticated cattle were present in earlier Körös times,
possibly late in the sixth millennium B.C.

There are no published C–14 dates for the Aceramic Neolithic levels at Argissa,
though there is a date (GrN–4145) for the early ceramic phase: 5775 B.C. ± 90.

There are, however, many uncertainties surrounding C–14 dating, and scholars have voiced repeated warnings against uncritical acceptance of C–14 dates and against viewing them in precise calendar terms. For this reason the dates recorded above should be viewed with wariness. Together they provide at best a rough approximation of a historical sequence. There is particular uncertainty among archeologists about the relationships between and sequence of early Near Eastern cultures on the one hand and East European cultures on the other. Archeologists generally view the Neolithic cultures of early Eastern Europe as border manifestations of developments that centered in the Near East, and feel that usually they followed comparable Near Eastern cultures by at least a century or two. Some view early C–14 dates in Eastern Europe with suspicion, and feel that there may be some yet unknown element that makes such dates earlier than they should be. This would mean that dates for Eastern Europe and the Near East cannot be directly equated, that the domesticated cattle in the European sites mentioned above are later than indicated, and that the Çatal Hüyük domesticated cattle are the earliest presently known. Final solution of the overall Eastern Europe–Near East problem must await further discoveries; for the present it seems a wise course to withhold judgment.

There are claims of "early" domesticated cattle (5000 B.C. or earlier)

Apparently there are no dates for Otzaki. The first C–14 date published for Nea Nikomedeia (Q–655) was 6475 B.C. ± 150, obtained from charcoal near the original ground level of the site, which falls in the Greek Early Neolithic. Typologically the Aceramic Neolithic levels at Argissa are earlier than the Early Neolithic of Nea Nikomedeia, whereas the Early Neolithic levels (the second and third phases of EN) in which domesticated cattle are found at Otzaki are of roughly comparable age. That first date, however, was felt by such authorities as S. S. Weinberg (1965: 30; Weinberg in Ehrich, 1965: 310; pers. com., May 5, 1967) and V. Milojčić (pers. com., May 23, 1967)—the excavator of Argissa and Otzaki—to be too early. This was supported by various evidence: typological comparisons of pottery with that from other Greek sites; and C–14 dates from such sites, most notably the recently excavated, stratified site at Sidari on Corfu (GXO–771, GXO–772, and a date published in *Kerkyraïká Xronikà,* 11 (1966), pp. 141–48), where the transition from aceramic to pottery-bearing levels (the primary occupation level at Nea Nikomedeia is pottery-bearing) is dated at about 6000 B.C. Subsequently three additional C–14 dates (GX–679, P–1202, P–1203A), of 6063 B.C. ± 270, 5833 B.C. ± 91, and 5549 B.C. ± 74, have been indicated for the Early Neolithic at Nea Nikomedeia. Even with these, dating problems remain. If, however, the earlier date of 6475 B.C. is disregarded and the others accepted, the Nea Nikomedeia cattle would fall somewhere within the period roughly from 6100 to 5500 B.C. The Otzaki cattle would be of comparable age, and those of Aceramic Argissa would be earlier, pre–6100 B.C. Thus, the Greek and Anatolian cattle would seem to be of roughly the same age, allowing for various uncertainties in dating, in identification, and in the need for a time span over which domestication was carried out.

for other sites, too—among them are Belt Cave and Sialk in Iran and the Amuq in Syria; C. A. Reed (1960: 143), however, views these claims as doubtful. At the time of this writing, the cattle bones of Horse Cave in Afghanistan (probably pre–6000 B.C.) are still being studied. Should some prove to be of domesticated animals, as Louis Dupree thinks possible (pers. com., Feb. 14, 1967), we would have still more evidence of early cattle. Whatever the results may be, domesticated cattle are now known to be much older than at the time Reed published his first survey (1959) of archeologic evidences of animal domestication in the Near East. The probable occurrence of early domesticated cattle from Afghanistan to Hungary[5] also creates a far broader arena in which domestication may have occurred. It is particularly interesting that there were "early" domesticated cattle in Afghanistan, so close to the Indian subcontinent, though there is no presently available archeologic evidence that cattle were of such antiquity in Baluchistan, the Indus Valley, or eastward in the Indian subcontinent. Since the early domestic cattle (not considering the Saharan pastoralists, about whom dating remains uncertain) appear among settled people, and since it is unlikely that pastoralists could accomplish cattle domestication, we assume that settled people, probably farmers,[6] and not pastoralists were responsible for the achievement.

5. Early domesticated cattle may have been even more widespread. One possible place of occurrence is the Sahara, where ancient rock drawings of cattle and herdsmen are widespread. Some specialists have believed that the "cattle pastoralist" period represented by the rock drawings in question may have lasted from about 4000 B.C. to 2000 B.C. (Lhote, 1964: 214; pers. com., Feb. 28, 1967). This is well after cattle are known to have been domesticated in Eastern Europe and Southwest Asia. Recently, however, there have been suggestions that domesticated cattle may have been kept in the Sahara earlier than previously suspected. In his excavations in the Acacus hills of the Fezzan, F. Mori (1964) found, in association with pottery and bone implements, abundant bones of animals, among them cattle, sheep, and goats; and the cattle are believed, after osteological examination, to have been domesticated. Mori also regards it as probable that the excavated remains are those of the people who made the rock drawings. He mentions two C–14 dates, one about 3500 B.C. and the other about 5500 B.C., from the site. His final conclusion is that pastoral people keeping cattle lived in the Sahara certainly by 3500 B.C., and possibly about 5500 B.C. Additional charcoal samples were being processed at the time Mori wrote, so that we should soon have greater assurance about his dates. New evidence is coming in from the Sahara, and when it is more abundant and certain, it may well have important implications for our knowledge of cattle domestication. The question is raised by K. W. Butzer of possible "independent" domestication of cattle in Africa. Though the Saharan people in question are pastoralists, it has been argued that they used primarily the meat of their cattle, for in the rock drawings the udders of the cows are not emphasized.

6. In the levels of Snake Cave where cattle bones were found, writes Dupree

V. Gordon Childe and the Desiccation Theory

V. Gordon Childe popularized the idea that post-Pleistocene desiccation in the Near East drove men and herd animals to the permanent sources of water and led to both animal and plant domestication there.[7] R. J. Braidwood, C. A. Reed, H. E. Wright, Jr., and K. W. Butzer have all cast doubt on this so-called "propinquity" or "riverine-oasis" theory of domestication.[8] Some of them have argued that the desiccation theories of Childe and others are meaningless because they assume that the agricultural revolution occurred in arid lands. Instead, they have contended, the evidence points to the Southwest Asian hill-lands as the places where both agriculture and animal husbandry developed, and these are not deserts. Rather, they are well-watered woodlands which in those times, too, formed a generous environment that included a variety of potential domesticates. In the hill-lands, the argument went, pluvial-interpluvial climatic fluctuations would have only a limited ecologic impact. Even with variations in precipitation, there would be only slight changes in ecology, and a variety of ecological niches would remain available to men and animals.

Recently there has been increasing evidence that the earliest village-farming communities occurred more widely and in a greater variety of environments than was earlier suspected. Sites are now known even in the Zagros area that are clearly lower and more arid than the hilly flanks, or clearly above them. The period of incipient domestication also may have begun earlier in some places than was initially thought. For these reasons, it seems prudent to withhold judgment on the possible role of climatic fluctuation as a stimulant to the first plant and animal domestication. At the same time, present evidence indicates that bovines were domesticated later than sheep and goats and after the village-farming community had been established. Under village conditions, climatic pressures are not needed to bring man and bovines into contact. Our knowledge of the mithan, for example, shows that man and the bovines came into contact regularly without such pressure. Their most frequent

---

(pers. com., Feb. 14, 1967), there were "many sickle blades, indicating at least the collection of wild grains." Since the botanical analysis is not yet complete, he believes it is best to call the levels "gathering of grains with flint sickle blades, grains *may be* domesticated." The Snake Cave cattle may prove to have been kept by settled hunters-gatherers; or it may be that the Snake Cave cattle keepers were cultivators, like the other early cattle-keeping peoples now known.

7. Childe, 1928: 42 ff. The theory was repeated later in similar forms by Childe and others.

8. Braidwood, 1957: 77–78; Reed, 1959: 1637–38; 1960: 122–23; H. E. Wright, Jr., 1960: 71 ff.; Butzer, 1964: 435–37.

meeting grounds, in Southwest as well as Southeast Asia, probably were the fields that man had fashioned from the wild. The fields attracted the animals because of the tasty, nutritious plants available in quantity. This is in keeping with Zeuner's inclusion of cattle in his "crop-robber" category of domesticated animals. Even after the farmer abandoned his field, perhaps to clear a new, more fertile swidden, the volunteer plants that sprang up were sufficiently attractive to draw the bovines into man's orbit. Though at present we cannot say whether or not climatic fluctuation played a role in the earliest phases of plant and animal domestication, such fluctuation was not needed to bring early farmers and cattle into contact.

Confinement vs. Free-Ranging

The idea is widespread that confinement is necessary for the full domestication of cattle and other animals, and that it is under such confinement that the animal becomes different from its wild ancestor. F. E. Zeuner (1963: 57–59, 63), for example, postulates five stages in the process of domestication. The first stage involves loose contacts between the animal and man, and free interbreeding with wild relatives. In this stage the species remains close morphologically to its wild ancestor. The second stage sees the subjection of large numbers of the species, and their confinement to make them totally dependent on man and his society. During Zeuner's second stage there is little if any interbreeding with wild relatives, and in it there develop the characteristics of domestication: reduction in body size and horns, changes in color, and so forth. The third, fourth, and fifth stages involve selective breeding of the animals by man to obtain desired qualities, the development of standard breeds of animals, and the persecution or extermination of wild ancestors. The case of the mithan raises doubts that confinement is necessary to bring about the notable morphological and temperamental changes associated with domesticated animals. The mithan seems to be in Zeuner's first stage—without confinement—but is strikingly different in morphology and temperament from its wild relative.

Looking back to ancient Southwest Asia and Eastern Europe, one wonders whether man found it necessary under all ecological conditions to confine common cattle, or whether under some conditions he permitted them to range freely. The wild aurochs was a formidable animal which preferred wooded country. Its domestic offspring probably were able to hold their own against most predators, and could have done quite well if permitted to graze alone during the daytime or for longer periods in the open wooded hills. Such free-ranging would also free the early farmers from the burden of providing feed for their cattle, or of sending herdsmen with them. This would save considerable labor for food crop cultivation and other tasks.

It should be emphasized that free-ranging domesticated animals occur not only in South and Southeast Asia (see Appendix B) but in parts of the Near East at the present day.[9] Xavier de Planhol (pers. com., Jan. 22, 1967; see also de Planhol, 1958: 285–86; 1964: 50–56) observes that the free-ranging of cattle is very common in all the regions of Anatolia and Iran with which he is especially familiar. In one section of the Elburz Mountains of Iran, milk cows are constantly herded, but oxen remain "on vacation," without surveillance, in high mountain valleys throughout the summer, until the time of sowing. Domestic equids which serve as beasts of burden are permitted such free-ranging, too, but for a shorter period. Both oxen and equids, de Planhol observes, can protect themselves quite well against wild animals. In the Pamphylian Plain of southern Anatolia, he notes further, livestock are permitted to wander freely around the village from the time the harvest is finished until the next sowing. This period of *bozuk*, or negligence, lasts for varying periods depending on the time of harvest and on the type of crops cultivated. In the case of villages where only winter cereals are cultivated, it can be close to six months. In the uplands of south Anatolia, free-ranging is more rare because of the presence of wild animals, but de Planhol has found cases even there.

Writers on cattle domestication in the Near East and Eastern Europe have overlooked the possibility that the earliest domesticated cattle were permitted free-ranging. This is understandable for, from the time of the first written accounts, of the Sumerians, cattle are mentioned as being herded and confined. Judging from the fragmentary pictures on seals and pottery for periods immediately preceding the Sumerians (see, for example, Van Buren, 1939: 69; Frankfort, 1965: 20–21), cattle were herded and confined in those times, too. The records just mentioned, however, pertain to an arid lowland characterized by irrigated agriculture, where special problems (high density of agricultural land, shortage of suitable grazing areas, need for cattle to be constantly available for traction and milking) made such confinement necessary. The earliest

9. We have found nothing to indicate that free-ranging pigs are found today in the Near East, but one wonders whether they ever were kept in that tradition. The open forests in the hills of Southwest Asia and the Mediterranean region have long been used for feeding pigs, which consumed the acorns, beechnuts, roots, and truffles that grow there. The record indicates, however, that the pigs in question were herded. For one account of contemporary pig herding in the oak woodlands of southwestern Spain, see J. J. Parsons, 1962.

domesticated cattle were probably found in or near woodland, the favored habitat of the aurochs, where ecologic conditions were quite different from those of arid Sumer. The time of domestication, moreover, was probably at least 3,500 years before the Sumerian written accounts.

We suggest that confinement was not necessary to accomplish cattle domestication; that the first cattle to be domesticated may have been permitted to range free; that present-day cases of free-ranging in the Near East represent survivals of the ancient pattern in particular ecological situations. In at least three of the four earliest sites where domesticated cattle were found (Argissa, Çatal Hüyük, Otzaki), there were no sheds or other structures that clearly could have been used to shelter cattle. C. Zervos (1962–63, 1: 78), writing of Greece, says that the house plans of Aceramic and later Neolithic times (including Argissa and Otzaki) provide no trace of cattle sheds; nor, he adds, are there any traces, near the houses, of animal excrement mixed with litter. This leads him to suppose that the livestock were not kept in sheds but lived either in enclosures or in the open, guarded by herdsmen and watched by dogs. J. Mellaart similarly found nothing in Çatal Hüyük to show that animals were kept within the settlement; he thinks that they may have been kept at the edge of the settlement, in corrals. As an alternative to these suppositions, we suggest that in Greece and at Çatal Hüyük common cattle may have been free-ranging, with the same loose ties with man that are found today in much of the mithan country. It may also be significant that Bökönyi (1964: 93) found at Maroslele-Pana several cattle bones intermediate in size and appearance between those of aurochs and domestic cattle. In his view this hints either at a local domestication of cattle or the presence of aurochs/domestic cattle hybrids. If there were hybrids, it shows that the aurochs gained access to domestic herds, and raises the question whether the Maroslele-Pana domestic cattle were free-ranging.

If the earliest farmers of Eastern Europe and the Near East permitted their cattle to range free, what may have led so many of them to change their pattern of husbandry? Among the mithan-keeping peoples, we have seen that the Central Chin are virtually the only people to herd their mithan, and they do so only for fear of crop destruction by the animals. Penalties levied against the mithan owner whose animals damage the crops of others discourage ownership of mithan by any but the wealthy who can withstand the losses and other problems involved. In our hypothesized case of early free-ranging cattle in Southwest Asia and Eastern Europe, various factors could have forced the change: population increase, greater density of fields and settlement, destruction of the upland grazing areas, increased losses to predatory animals and nomadic or other human raiders, innovations (i.e., plowing and other forms of trac-

tion, milking)[10] which required close control of the animals, or movement into new environments (the alluvial lowlands) with changed
ecological conditions. Under the changed conditions, free-ranging would
no longer be suitable. J. F. Downs (1960: 23) has commented on changes
in practices of cattle keeping in the United States which are similar to
those we have hypothesized for Southwest Asia. In the days of open range
in the American West, it was not necessary to confine cattle, but increasing population pressure and increasing value of land and of cattle made
fencing necessary.

Eduard Hahn on Human Motives in Domestication

The German economic geographer Eduard Hahn, who was cited in
our Introduction, was a powerful voice against the economic rationalism
of his day. He argued effectively against the tendency of modern Westerners to view the whole range of domestication in terms of the economic
considerations that dominate their thinking. Instead, he insisted that we
look at the life and beliefs, especially the religious beliefs, of those early
men who accomplished domestication. Specifically he argued that common cattle were the first herd animals to be domesticated; that they were
domesticated in Mesopotamia, to supply animals for sacrifice in fertility
rites to the lunar mother-goddess;[11] that the resemblance men noted
between the crescent-shaped horns of cattle and the new moon made
cattle seem to them especially suited for lunar sacrifice. As he went on to
discuss the origins of other important traits that came to be joined in the
plow-cereal complex, Hahn argued that the practice of milking and use
of the wagon and plow sprang from religious ceremonies associated with
the lunar goddess and intended to assure crop fertility; the economic
uses of cattle were secondary results of a domestication that was essentially religious in motivation.

The Place of Cattle among the Sumerians

Hahn's argument has had an amazing persistence; for that reason we
will treat it here in the light of our information about the mithan and of
the evidence that has accumulated concerning Southwest Asia since

10. Milking does not always require that milk animals be herded—as with the
Chittagong Hill people who continued to permit the mithan cows they milked to
range free during the daytime.

11. For recent restatements of Hahn's position, see Boettger, 1958: 33 ff.; Isaac,
1962: 197 ff.

Hahn's day. The mithan, as we have argued above, was probably domesticated for sacrificial purposes. There is, however, nothing among mithan-keeping people to suggest a concern with crescent-shaped horns, as Hahn hypothesized for common cattle in the Near East. Nor is the mithan tied to a specific spirit or deity, and certainly not to a lunar mother-goddess. In mithan country, indeed, the higher gods tend to be remote from the affairs of man and less likely to receive animal sacrifices than the minor gods who are closely involved with man's everyday activities. Sacrifice is made to get results, not to honor some remote, inactive being. It is thus the priest, who is the intermediary between man and the spiritual world, and the circumstances of the individual situation that determine the nature of the sacrifice. One thing that is prominent in sacrifice is the desire of the individual and group to gain or continue a state of well-being, "fertility" in a very broad sense. The fertility concerns become most explicit in the Naga Feasts of Merit, though other elements, religious, social, and economic, are involved, too. One wonders whether the ancient Southwest Asians also may initially have been interested in cattle for sacrifice because of concern with general well-being or fertility; and whether or not in the earliest days of domestication there was a specific tie between cattle and a lunar mother-goddess.

At the time Hahn advanced his hypothesis, in 1896, a good deal was known about Babylonia and Assyria, but these great states were late in Mesopotamian history, from about 1800 B.C. on. Unknown in 1896 were the Natufians and other early hunting-gathering peoples of the period of incipient domestication. Unknown were the early village-farming communities of the Near East, and the early history of settlement in the arid Tigris-Euphrates Valley. Still largely unexcavated were the Sumerian archeologic sites of lower Mesopotamia. The Sumerians may first have settled in Mesopotamia following 3500 B.C., but the historical age of Sumer begins about 2700 B.C., still almost a millennium before the rise of Babylonia. The Sumerians, from whom later Mesopotamian civilizations borrowed so liberally, themselves took their city names and probably other culture traits from the groups who preceded them in the valley. It was the Sumerians who fashioned the cuneiform system of writing into a usable tool, and we are dependent on them for the first clear accounts showing the position of cattle in human life.

Cattle were the most useful of the Sumerians' domestic animals.[12] They enjoyed a position in economic life that, with some modifications, was to be found widely among other Near Eastern and Mediterranean peoples

12. Our material on the Sumerians is based largely on C. L. Woolley, 1928, 1965; C. J. Gadd, 1929, 1964; S. N. Kramer, 1961, 1963; S. H. Hooke, 1953.

for many thousands of years. Cattle carried loads, plowed, and pulled carts and threshing sledges. They were turned into irrigated fields after the water had drained off, to trample the earth and thus kill weeds and level the surface. And, finally, their milk, flesh, and hides were used. Cattle were not as well adapted to arid lowland conditions as sheep and goats, for sheep and goats could get along better on the natural vegetation available, whereas cattle needed more supplementary feed.

Thorkild Jacobsen has written (1963: 474–75) that though the civilizations of Mesopotamia were major advances in man's ability to feed himself, permitting large numbers of people to gather in cities, theirs were fragile economies, visited regularly by famines. For this reason, he insists, concern with "fertility, produce, and food" was in one way or another behind Mesopotamian cult activities. The gods were taken into the cities to live with men, were provided for, and were expected to assure continued harvests and new generations of animals and men.

Sumerian deities were honored throughout Sumer, but each city had its special deity; and each man, in turn, had a tutelary deity, a minor figure to intercede in his interests. Both mother-goddesses and male deities were important for the Sumerians. Notable among the manifestations of the mother-goddess—listed in order of their supposed origin—were Ki, the earth goddess; Ninhursag, the goddess of birth (also known as Ninmah and Nintu); Ningal, wife of the moon god Nanna; and Inanna, goddess of erotic love, who became the Babylonian Ishtar. Significant male deities were An, the heaven god; Enlil, the air god; Enki, the water god; Nanna, the moon god—the leading Sumerian astral deity who later came to be known by the Semitic name, Sin; and Utu, the sun god. The Sumerians believed that the first deity created was the goddess Nammu, who represented the sea. Then were born An, the male heaven god, and Ki, the earth goddess, and subsequently the other gods. As a source of food and clothing for themselves, the gods created plants and animals; when the arrangement proved unsatisfactory, man was created to care for the plants and animals. Man's function on earth was to serve the gods, to provide "them with food, drink and shelter." Sumerian temples were the shelter of the gods, provided by man. The offerings and sacrifices were their food and drink. Within the context of Sumerian religious beliefs, the services and products contributed by cattle, then, were ultimately intended for the gods. The cattle themselves, like other animals, were sacrificed to the gods, and both the god and the participants in the rite shared the flesh.

Judging from Babylonian and Assyrian records as well as those of Sumer, cows and bulls were not deities in their own right, but were identified with or symbolic of certain deities. Several deities were referred to as "bull," and their strength and size of horns were extolled. This probably derives from the importance of the bull as representative of masculine virility. There was also the "heavenly bull," a powerful creature which was associated with particular deities.

The cow, in its turn, seems to have been identified with various of the mother-goddesses, notably with Ninhursag. C. J. Gadd (1929: 56–57, 62–65, 236–37), on whose account we rely, says that Ninhursag seems to have been depicted as a cow and, in any case, the cow was her symbol. In Sumerian mythology, she had participated in the initial creation of man and was involved in the birth of each new generation of men. At Ninhursag's temple center at al-Ubaid (dated at about 2600 B.C.) near the city of Ur, and at Lagash, too, herds of Ninhursag's cattle were maintained. Servants of the temple at al-Ubaid are shown milking the cows and converting the milk into butter. One cannot be certain whether the bulls of the temple herd enjoyed a sacred position but it is assumed that the cows did. The Sumerian kings in particular called attention to their tie with Ninhursag; they boasted that they were her children, and almost all of them include as one of their titles "fed with the holy milk of Ninhursag." Gadd points out that the crescent symbol which appears at the temple is an allusion to Nanna or Sin, the moon god of nearby Ur, who is often referred to as "bull," and whose symbol is the crescent moon. This presumably led Gadd to an imagined reconstruction, based on later Mesopotamian examples, that at least once a year Ninhursag was taken from her temple at al-Ubaid to be married to the moon god. In a solemn procession, he supposes, she was carried to the city of Ur where she was received by the king and another procession accompanying the moon god. The two deities were taken into their shrine and joined together while outside sacrifices and chants were carried on. Upon these nuptials, writes Gadd, the fertility of all life depended.

Whether or not Ninhursag actually was ceremonially wedded to Nanna or to any other deity cannot be proved by presently available data. There is reason to believe, however, that such holy marriages occurred in all the major Sumerian cities, and that they were intended to assure fecundity and prosperity. The main holy marriage, however, "was not that between the city-god and his wife, but between the demi-god Dumuzi (or some king . . . representing Dumuzi) and the goddess of love, Inanna (represented by a specially elected hierodule)" (pers. com., S. N. Kramer, May 25, 1967). It is also known from Sumerian accounts that at least one other goddess, Nidaba (goddess of writing, accounting, and wisdom), had milking animals, including a cow, at her temple. What seem to be sacred herds of cattle also appear on cylinder seals in earlier Mesopotamia during the Uruk and Jamdat Nasr periods (*c.* 3500–2900 B.C.) (Frankfort, 1965: 20–22; Mallowan, 1965: 73).

Sumerian religion seems to have been concerned primarily with extending and improving life on earth. At the same time, Sumerians believed in an afterworld to which men go at death, and that one's position there is related to one's status on earth. There are indications also that the sun god Utu and the moon god Nanna decided the fate of the dead and that a man's city god and personal god "were invoked on his behalf." Though the details are not indicated, the individual on earth could gain the goodwill of the gods—for this life and the afterlife—through performance of religious rites, including sacrifices of animals. The Sumerian kings never tired of indicating that they had not been derelict in such performances.

The Sumerian evidence, incomplete though it may be, does not support Hahn's theory of a special tie between common cattle and a moon goddess. The moon, on the contrary, was a god among the Sumerians, not a goddess. There was, however, an involvement of cow with mother-goddesses and of bull with male deities. There were also associations between various of the male and female deities; and prominent in Sumerian ritual and sacrifice—including bovine sacrifice—was concern with prosperity and the continuing fertility of man, his animals, and his crops.

Cattle in Early Fertility Cults from the Eastern Mediterranean to India

The association of cattle with well-being and fertility was not unique to the Sumerians, and later documents attest to its widespread occurrence in the Old World. The tie of cow and mother-goddess is revealed in Hathor of Egypt, Anat in Syria, and Lakshmi and Parvati in India, among others. The bull was important in the religion of Minoan Crete, and elsewhere in the classical world.[13] It is not, however, with the successors of

13. For a well-documented survey of the bull in classical religion, see Malten, 1928. A popular but not entirely reliable account is Conrad, 1959. Malten, referring to Egypt, Southwest Asia, and Crete, suggests that in early times men may have recognized the power of the bull; and that in sacrificing the bull, the power and fertility of the animal was believed to pass on to man and his fields. From this, a close tie developed between the bull on the one hand and sky, sun, and rain on the other, three elements vital for agricultural growth and increase.

Malten and other scholars agree that the bull played an important role in religion in Minoan Crete; but they differ as to whether there was a bull cult, involving a bull god and worship of him. For a recent survey of the differences, see Guthrie, 1964: 21–22. Guthrie himself supports the view that bull worship existed in Crete.

Sumerian tradition that we are most concerned here, but with the predecessors, particularly at the time and place in the Near East where cattle
were presumably first brought under domestication.

The human concern with fertility has deep roots. From the far recesses
of the Paleolithic there survive figurines of women with exaggerated
breasts and buttocks, the so-called Venus statuettes. It is widely held
that these figurines were associated with cult activities intended to bring
about continued fertility among humans. One school of thought holds
that this cult, with the development of agriculture and animal husbandry, evolved directly into the cult of the mother-goddess, a many-
sided person who assumed responsibility for fertility and who also was
widely represented in figurines.[14] Certainly the beginnings of agriculture
and animal husbandry see the rise of both mother-goddesses and male
deities. The eminent historian of religion E. O. James (1959: 47–48; 1960:
46 ff., 292 ff.; 1963: 13, 20–21) argues that with domestication males were
assigned as consorts to the mother-goddess because it was increasingly
recognized that males, too, contributed to generation. He also documents
the widespread occurrence since Neolithic times of a sky god as the
supreme male deity which, in one form or another, was behind the higher
religions from the Eastern Mediterranean to India. The sky god was
usually tied to the mother-goddess in assuring fertility. The cult imagery
varied with time and place, but everywhere there was ritual depicting
copulation between the goddess and her consort, generally symbolized by
the cow and the bull, earth and sky, and in some places by moon and
sun. If this view is correct, the Sumerian moon god Nanna was probably
a later counterpart of the sky deity (in Sumer known as An); Nanna, as
gods were wont to do, took on many of the sky god's functions and characteristics. Also of interest are the fragments of evidence among certain
present-day mithan-keeping peoples of a tie among cattle sacrifice, sun
and moon, and fertility concerns (see Appendix C).

Within the broad region where cattle domestication was accomplished
can be found many fragments of evidence relevant to that domestication.
First are the rock carvings, apparently made by early hunters, which
were discovered in the 1930's at the early oasis of Kilwa, east of Aqaba in

14. The differing views expressed by scholars about such figurines are reviewed by
G. F. Dales, Jr. (1960: 250–65), who made a detailed comparison of the female
figurines of Mesopotamia and nearby areas. His research, it should be noted, showed
that stylistically the earliest Mesopotamian figurines, from Jarmo, were descended
from the Venus statuettes of the Old World Paleolithic; that stylistic differences
subsequently arose with time and place, but that stylistic parallels link various parts
of the Near East and Aegean, and a few link Mesopotamia with early India. See also
S. S. Weinberg, 1950, for resemblances between certain Aegean Neolithic female
figurines and figurines of Asia Minor and north Syria.

Palestine. Though scholars differ on the precise dating of the carvings, all assume they fall somewhere in the period from the late Paleolithic to the Neolithic, roughly 10,000–4500 B.C. The most common figure among them is the ibex, sometimes appearing in herds and sometimes alone. One carving shows an ibex from whose mouth run two lines, possibly streams of blood. On its back is a small human figure with arms raised in a posture which some have called "adoration." Rhotert, who has studied the carvings, believes the scene represents the sacrifice of an ibex; and Bodenheimer (1960: 33–35), on whose account we rely, thinks that ibex may have been captured by hunters and kept for sacrifice on solemn occasions —a practice which may have led to the domestication of certain animal species, though the ibex itself proved unsuitable for domestication. If the interpretations of Rhotert and Bodenheimer are correct, we have evidence of the capture and sacrifice of wild animals by an early hunting group well within the region where the first indications of animal domestication appear in the archeologic record. Though the people in question were hunters, their concern with the capture of animals for sacrifice could well have persisted into the time of the primary village-farming community where cattle domestication seems to have taken place.

Our next evidence, which indicates early man's concern with fertility, is the discovery by Kathleen Kenyon (1956: 186–87; 1957: 59–65; 1960: 50–54) in the Pre-Pottery Neolithic B levels (*c.* 7000–6000 B.C.) at the Jericho site of mother-goddess figurines. She also found that in some cases human heads had been carefully removed from corpses. One skull of an elderly man had been set upright beneath the floor in the corner of a room. On certain skulls, faces had been molded in plaster and eyes of shell had been added. Her conviction was that the inhabitants of ancient Jericho had a "cult of skulls," that the skull ritual was concerned with preserving for the family the wisdom and spiritual faculties of the person who had died. Thus we may have here a parallel to the Naga headhunters' conception of the head as the repository of a man's life-force.[15] The early Jericho people, like the Naga, may have been concerned with accumulating for the benefit of the living the power, wealth, and fertility of the dead. Since Miss Kenyon's discovery, evidences of a cult of skulls have been found in certain other sites of roughly comparable age: at Beidha in Palestine, at Hacilar and Çatal Hüyük in Anatolia, and at Lepenski Vir in Yugoslavia.

The most amazing evidence of all comes from southern Anatolia, especially from the recent excavations by James Mellaart at Çatal Hüyük

---

15. For a further discussion of the cult of skulls and other uses of skulls by early and modern man, see James, 1960: 55 ff.; Hays, 1963: 26–31.

(about 6750–5650 B.C.).[16] Çatal Hüyük is the largest Neolithic site uncovered in the Near East (32 acres), and the most spectacular. A town of rectangular, one-story, flat-roofed, sundried-brick houses, it was located on a river in the center of an alluvial plain at an elevation of about 3,300 feet. In the Neolithic there seems to have been a woodland in at least some sections of the plain. The people depended on hunting (aurochs, red deer, wild donkey, boar, leopard, etc.) and gathering to a considerable extent, but they also cultivated crops (most important were einkorn, emmer, naked barley, and pea) and seem to have kept domesticated animals: dogs, sheep, goats, and, later on, common cattle. Mellaart writes (pers. com., Jan. 25, 1967) that "the large horn cores used in building levels VII and VI [*c.* 6200–5880 B.C.] are those of wild animals [*Bos primigenius*]. There is, however, a decrease in horn size as time goes on and it is possible that its domestication was in progress." The osteological examination has not been completed, but the zoologist Dexter Perkins, Jr., writes (pers. com., March 27, 1967) that he "found a skull of the *brachyceros* type" in Level VI B (*c.* 6050–5950 B.C.) which he is quite certain was domestic. Thus in Level VI at Çatal Hüyük there were both wild and domestic cattle.

The remarkable thing about Çatal Hüyük, from our point of view, is that the forty village shrines uncovered contain indisputable evidence of a rich fertility cult. Some of the evidence comes from the magnificent wall paintings, often polychrome, that appear on shrine walls and include, among other things, hunting scenes, vultures eating headless human corpses, and single large red or black aurochs bulls (one over six feet long). Two shrines, from different site levels, are devoted entirely to hunting or baiting scenes. Each features prominently a large bull, surrounded by men. The bull, in both cases (and wherever else it appears in the shrines), is on the north wall, which faces the Taurus ("bull") Mountains to the south. Many of the men surrounding the bull wear garments or hats of leopard skin. In the earliest of the two "hunting shrines" (Figure 25) a naked woman with exaggerated sexual features appears prominently below the bull (such a woman also appears on certain other scenes from that and other shrines). There are indications in that scene that the animal is not being shot but baited. One man has even jumped on the bull's back.

It is very difficult to interpret the meaning of the paintings in the two "hunting shrines." Mellaart at one time was inclined to view them as connected with wishes to assure good hunting. Later he rejected that

---

16. This section is based on the works of Mellaart cited in the bibliography, and on a personal communication, Jan. 25, 1967.

idea and the view that the animals were being worshiped, and suggested that the scenes represent heroic feats of dead hunters, either in this world or the afterworld. The association elsewhere at Çatal Hüyük of the leopard with the mother-goddess may deserve attention. Can it be that the men attired in leopard skins are her priests participating in a religious (fertility) ceremony? May the naked woman be a female representative of the mother-goddess, or indeed the goddess herself?

Whatever the answer may be, hunting scenes of one sort or another occur in the earlier site levels but are absent in the latest two periods. Mellaart feels that the complete domestication of cattle probably occurred over the span of Çatal Hüyük, and that the decline of hunting may have made hunting scenes superfluous.

Also notable in the shrines are figures, usually of animals, some of them bulls or cows, which are partly reliefs on the plaster and partly cutouts. There are also straightforward plaster reliefs of the mother-goddess, animals, and other things. Where reliefs of bull or ram heads occur, they incorporate real horns and frontal bones (Figure 26). Some bull heads are accompanied by clay representations of women's breasts; many breasts in their turn incorporate "the lower jaws of wild boars, the skulls of fox, weasel or the griffon vulture," a curious combination of symbols of life and death. The symbols used remind one strongly of the Angami Naga village gates considered by H.-E. Kauffmann (1955) which include bovine heads, human heads, representations of women's breasts, and "phallic men," among other designs (Figure 27). Several Çatal Hüyük pottery cups also have the bull head or bucranium design and the ram head.

Most interesting of all in Çatal Hüyük shrines are the bull horn cores set in clay (Figure 28), some in groups or in rows on benches, and still others in "bull pillars."[17] There are also horns with stylized bull heads drawn between. On the floor in some shrines were human skulls. In the shrines there were also figurines of mother-goddesses (sometimes accompanied by a leopard) of the sort that in later times evolved into distinct deities (i.e., Ishtar) who were associated in one way or another with fertility.

As if the above were not enough, Çatal Hüyük also revealed figurines of a male deity, in some cases as son or consort of the mother-goddess and in others as an older, bearded man. In the latter form he is often shown seated on a bull, the deity's sacred animal. There are also repre-

17. Though there is no evidence for it from Çatal Hüyük, one wonders whether bucrania, or bull heads, were displayed outside the houses, too. The display of bucrania over the doors of houses, to prevent the entry of evil spirits, was prevalent in later times throughout ancient Asia Minor.

sentations of the mother-goddess giving birth to a bull's head or a ram's head. Both of these animals are symbolic of male potency and, Mellaart asserts, symbolic of the male deity. All of this led Mellaart to an imagined but reasonable reconstruction that tied elements including the mother-goddess, symbolized by the leopard, and her consort, usually symbolized by the bull, into a cult concerned with maintaining fertility and abundance.[18]

There is no evidence at Çatal Hüyük of animal sacrifice; if it occurred, it apparently did not take place in the shrines. Nor is there clear indication at Çatal Hüyük of the uses of common cattle, which were domesticated during the later period of the town. Their meat was certainly eaten, though, and bovid shoulder blades, as with certain mithan-keeping groups, were used as shovels.

The Çatal Hüyük evidence, overwhelming in variety and amount, reveals a fertility cult of great richness that altered through the various levels of the site. Both bull and ram were involved, though the bull seems to have been most closely associated with and symbolic of the male deity. The bull, wild or domesticated, was certainly a more impressive symbol of male potency than the ram, and probably this was reason enough for it to come in historic times to be dominant in that role. The leopard was associated with the mother-goddess; and wild boars, vultures, and other animals were also involved in the cult, perhaps as symbols of death. As in mithan country, the people of Çatal Hüyük may have viewed the head, human and animal, as the repository of the special qualities of the organism.

The mother-goddess—sometimes with the leopard—the male god (depicted as child or consort), and bull head designs and figures are also found in houses in the earlier levels of the Late Neolithic at Hacilar (c. 5700–5600 B.C.), a site almost 200 miles west of Çatal Hüyük. Our most significant later evidence, however, occurs not in Anatolia but in northern Iraq, in sites of the Halafian Period, which has also produced some of the earliest clearly domesticated cattle (c. 5000 B.C.?). In Halafian sites there are both female figurines (some painted with crosses, still a symbol of fertility in present-day Anatolia) and evidences, in ram head and bull head representations (Figure 29) on pottery and other items, of a fer-

18. At both Çatal Hüyük and Hacilar mother-goddess figurines were "found in deposits of grain or in grainbins, evidently for reasons of sympathetic magic" (pers. com., J. Mellaart, Jan. 25, 1967). There is similar evidence of an association between agriculture and a mother-goddess for the much later Tripolye Neolithic people of the Ukraine (c. 3000–1500 B.C.). Tripolye sites contained female figurines believed to have been tied to a fertility cult, and in them were found grains of wheat (Mongait, 1959: 107–9).

tility cult (Mallowan and Rose, 1935: 79–81, 154–55; Mellaart, 1965: 124). Equally important may be the occurrence on bull head representations on the earliest Halafian pottery at Tell Arpachiyah of what Mallowan and Rose call "a solid circle or disk" between the horns. None of the other naturalistic or stylized bull designs of the early or late stages of the Tell Halaf pottery includes such circles; and Mallowan and Rose believe they may be "an addition to the design without any ulterior significance." One wonders, however, whether the disk may be the symbol of a god, perhaps a sky deity. If so, the view would be strengthened that the people of Arpachiyah associated bulls with a fertility cult, and this would provide a link between Çatal Hüyük (where the bull was tied to a male deity) and Sumer (where it was tied to various gods, including the moon god Nanna). Also of importance here is E. O. James's observation (1959: 23–25; 1960: 293–96) that the Arpachiyah female figurines occurred not only with the bull's head but with the double ax, the dove, and the serpent. These three were among the characteristic emblems of the mother-goddess in Minoan Crete. There, too, she was involved with the bull, which may have been sacrificed, James notes, on the horned Minoan altars in fertility rites.[19] He also notes that at Arpachiyah mother-goddess figurines are numerous, though they were not so in pre-Halafian times.

Both elements in Sumerian religion that are related to cattle are present at Arpachiyah: representations of the bull and indications of a bull cult; and concern with a mother-goddess. Coupled with the evidence from Anatolia, this strongly suggests that in the early days of cattle domestication there was a real and powerful association of bulls with human fertility rites.

Pertinent materials were also unearthed in Iraq east of Baghdad at Tell Agrab and Khafaje (Khafajah) in the 1930's. At Tell Agrab, on a vase fragment of Early Dynastic Sumerian age (about 2900–2400 B.C.), a zebu bull is depicted within a building, standing at what appears to be a manger (Frankfort, 1936: 434, Figure 10); it has been suggested that this was a sacred bull. A man on another fragment of the vase is typically Mesopotamian, but the form of expression and bull motif are not; perhaps, it has been argued, the vase originated not in Mesopotamia but in Susa in southwest Iran. The Khafaje material (Frankfort, 1936a: 524, Figures 4–5; 525, Figures 9–11; Delougaz and Lloyd, 1942: 18, 28–29, 81–82), which cannot be explained away in this manner, comes from a temple, probably of the moon god Sin, and dates from the Jamdat Nasr

19. The fertility cult spread widely in the Aegean and Eastern Mediterranean and in later times the bull, sometimes surmounted by a god, is often shown with the double-headed ax. The Çatal Hüyük male deity too is frequently depicted on a bull.

Period (*c.* 3100–2900 B.C.). Most important is the base of a stone offering stand. On a lower tier are two bulls, immediately surmounted by two naked female figures (mother-goddess figures?). Second is a bull-shaped libation vessel with a spout rising from the middle of its back. Such libation vessels are also known in a bird form from this site (the dove was widely associated with the mother-goddess). Third is a female figure in stone. It is naked from the waist up, has prominent breasts, and resembles the female figurines of earlier times. Another Khafaje temple of Early Dynastic II age (*c.* 2750–2600 B.C.) contains a statuette of a bearded cow which the excavators, Delougaz and Lloyd, believe to be the symbol or image of the mother-goddess Ninhursag. This information further suggests an early fertility cult, and an association between bull, cow, male god, and mother-goddess.

Turning to Predynastic Egypt, we find that E. J. Baumgartel (1960–65, 2: 144–50; 1965: 33) regards the mother-goddess as "one of the most important if not the most important deity." She was already known in Badarian times (*c.* 4400–4000 B.C.), though the evidence is less complete than one would like. The evidence becomes more abundant in Naqada times (following *c.* 4000 B.C.) and shows an association between the mother-goddess and a male god (her son and lover) and her identification with the cow. On Naqada remains, she is sometimes symbolized with hands on breasts; she is apparently depicted on one vase with her head "flanked by two cow's horns"; one of her standards is "cow horns mounted concentrically on sticks"; and on still another vase she is shown being joined in sacred marriage to the male god, who was linked with the bull. Baumgartel notes also the assumption of divinity by the kings of dynastic Egypt; the king as lover and son of the mother-goddess; the king called in historic times "the bull of his mother" or "the strong bull"; the king's role in assuring the fertility of Egypt; and the displacement of the bull god by the god Horus. Not to be overlooked is the clear association, in early Egypt, of the mother-goddess with the cow, and the male god with the bull, all tied to a fertility cult. The parallels between Egypt and Çatal Hüyük are made even more striking by the occurrence of bucrania remarkably like those of the Çatal Hüyük shrines: clay heads—including the horn cores of actual bulls—that were found in a long row on a bench outside the tomb of a First Dynasty Egyptian king (*c.* 3100 B.C.) (Emery, 1954: Plates VI and VII).

Of relevance, too, are Johannes Maringer's observations (1960: 142–50, 198–200) about the Danubians, an early farming culture of central Europe (beginning in the fifth millennium B.C.). The first clues to Danubian religious beliefs, dating from the end of the third millennium, reveal, according to Maringer's interpretation, a fertility cult embracing mother-goddess and her male consort. He occupied a secondary role and was rarely represented in human form; instead, he was commonly conceived of as a bull, symbolic of male virility, and was presumably sacrificed in fertility rites.

In the Indus Valley Civilization (*c.* 2500–1700 B.C.) we find further parallels. That civilization probably had sea contacts, and possibly land contacts as well, with Mesopotamia. Kramer (1964) suggests that the Indus Valley may actually be the Sumerian paradise land of Dilmun, settled by the Sumerians' predecessors in Mesopotamia, the Ubaidians. In every case, the Indus seals that depict bovines (Figure 24)—whether "aurochs," zebu, water buffalo, or "gaur"—are of bulls rather than cows. Basham (1954: 22–24) and Gordon (1958: 68–69) both think that the religion of the Indus Civilization centered on the worship of a mother-goddess and a horned god; that the pipal tree (*Ficus religiosa*) was sacred; and that the bull was involved in ritual. Basham believes that the bull was sacred, but the evidence seems to us too slight to warrant that conclusion. More convincing is Gordon's statement that certain seals represent "bull and buffalo sacrifice, bull-baiting and bull-leaping in connection with a shrine enclosing the sacred tree, in which is embodied the sacred pillar crowned with the horned headdress and braided hair of the god."

It is also relevant that the device which characteristically stands in front of the "aurochs" on the seals has been tied by Koppers (1946) to offering stands used today in fertility rites in central India, and by Hutton (pers. com., Sept. 29, 1966) to offering platforms to spirits, made by present-day Assam hill tribes. In Indus Valley sites there are also limestone phallic emblems and what some have called "female rings." This, with the evidence mentioned above, suggests that the early Indus people had a religion concerned with fertility, one in which mother-goddess and horned god were prominent, and in which bulls of various bovines were probably sacrificed.

In the earliest decipherable Indian writings, the Vedic accounts (composed *c.* 1500–500 B.C.?), we find that common cattle—bulls, cows, and oxen—are mentioned more often than any other animal; they and their dairy products were regarded as wealth, were appreciated for their utility to man;[20] and they were important in sacrifices to the gods. Though all forms of common cattle were sacrificed and eaten, there were objections to such sacrifice, especially of cows, perhaps because of their greater utility. Neither the bull nor the cow was sacred. The bull was symbolic of

20. This paragraph is based on A. A. Macdonell, 1963: 21–22, 54–66, 88, 120–23, 150–51; E. O. James, 1959: 101, 112–13; and W. N. Brown, 1957.

masculine virility, and the cow was associated with fecundity, maternity, and plenty. Thus in the *Rigveda* the great Indra, weather god and war god of the Aryans, is called a bull; so, less often, are other gods. In one Vedic work, "a bull is addressed as Indra," and in another "the bull is stated to be Indra's form" (A. A. Macdonell, 1963: 150). The goddess Aditi, sometimes identified in the Vedic accounts with the earth, is commonly called "cow" and is seen as the mother of various deities. The primeval sky deity and father of Indra, Dyaus Pitar, is the only deity who has roots in Indo-European times. His consort is the earth goddess Prithivi. Dyaus is depicted as a bull in a few passages of the *Rigveda* and, as such, he fertilizes the earth, Prithivi; Prithivi, on her part, yields milk and other benefits for her worshipers.

The later development of the cow as a sacred animal in Hinduism need not concern us here,[21] but it should be emphasized that the Vedic identification of bull with male deities and cow with female deities, their association with fertility and fecundity, and their role in sacrifice is remarkably similar to that found in the early Near East. The rich and abundant milk of Prithivi is paralleled by the holy milk of Ninhursag.

If indeed related early cults embracing common cattle extended from Mesopotamia to India, there should be indications of their existence in archeologic sites in the intervening lands of Iran, Afghanistan, and Baluchistan. It is well established that ties existed among the early village cultures of those lands, and that there was an overall spread of culture traits from west to east. It is sufficient here to mention just a few relevant items. First to be noted are the clay humped-bull figurines that occur in southern Afghanistan at Mundigak (starting in Period I, which began late fourth or early third millennium B.C.?), one of the earliest known villages of the Afghanistan-Baluchistan area; that there are affinities in style between the Mundigak figurines and those of Hissar in Iran (which itself had contacts with Sialk in Iran and ultimately with Ubaid in Mesopotamia); and that the Mundigak figurines seem to be the predecessors of the higher quality bull figurines that occur there and in northern Baluchistan in later times (G. F. Dales, in Ehrich, 1965: 261, 275). The humped bull also appears in Baluchistan as a motif on painted pottery; at Rana Ghundai during Period II A (designated the "Bull period": beginning in the first half of the third millennium B.C.?) there was such a concentration of well made pots bearing the bull motif that the excavator, E. J. Ross, strongly suspected that they had religious significance; and D. E. McCown, observing striking similarities between this

21. The interested reader is referred to W. Norman Brown's excellent article, "The Sanctity of the Cow in Hinduism" (1957).

type of pottery and pottery of northern Iran, deduced that the culture of Rana Ghundai II A was an offshoot of that of Hissar (E. J. Ross, 1946: 289–91, 303). For somewhat later times, starting perhaps the latter half of the third millennium B.C., there is more certain evidence in Baluchistan and southern Afghanistan of a fertility cult in which common cattle were prominent. The remains of this cult, designated by W. A. Fairservis the "Zhob cult," include mother-goddess figurines; painted bull figurines, some with ovoid "female" patterns between the horns; and structures, presumably cult centers, erected in commanding places (Fairservis, 1961: 7–13, 20–24, 27, 32). In Fairservis' view, the cult probably included ritual bathing, and human and animal sacrifice; it had affinities with early Indus Valley cultures and with Harappan Civilization; and it was a reflection more of Indian than Near Eastern religious views.

For a much later time, there is literary evidence, about the followers of the traditional religion, "the Lie," that preceded Zoroaster (c. 628–551 B.C.) among the Iranian peoples. Prominent among the practices of the "followers of the Lie" was the sacrifice of common cattle, including bulls, to ancient deities, apparently to assure fertility and immortality (Zaehner, 1961: 34–40, 84–88).

23

Conclusion

The archeologic record reveals the plow-cereal complex—and the Southwest Asian form of bovine keeping—fully developed in the fourth millennium B.C. in the Near East. There is no archeology bearing on the Southeast Asian free-ranging form, though we are inclined to view it as ancient. Whatever their antecedents, the widespread distribution of the one form and limited present-day occurrence of the other are rooted in ecology. The Southeast Asian form is an adaptation to areas of plowless shifting cultivation where bovines are not milked and where there is an abundance of forest available for browsing. The Southwest Asian form is an adaptation to a variety of ecologies, many of which require the close control of bovines for plowing and other forms of draft, for milking, or because there is insufficient open range to permit bovines freedom. Whatever the differences between the two traditions today and whatever their sequence in time, we believe that in the early days of bovine keeping there were basic similarities in the problems that man faced in these areas in bringing about domestication. We also think that there were parallels in the human motives for bovine domestication, and perhaps in the processes by which it was accomplished and the ways in which the animals were initially kept.

In the early village-farming communities of Southwest Asia and Eastern Europe, if we understand the situation aright, the aurochs, lusty and powerful ancestor of common cattle, was regarded as destructive, as an enemy to be driven away, rather than as a potential domesticate. Was it economic motivation, as many contend, that led the farmers to change their minds? Did the desire for animals for traction, plowing, milking, or flesh dominate their thinking? We have learned that the mithan owner does not see things that way. He does not use his animals for traction, plowing, or milking. He does not keep herds of mithan primarily for their flesh. Indeed, ownership of mithan tends to be not general but concentrated in the hands of the wealthy and prestigeful. The herd of such a man is a symbol of his status. When he slaughters an animal, his principal motivation is not to get flesh for himself and his immediate family; in some cases he and they are not even permitted to eat the flesh of the sacrificed animal, which instead is distributed to others. He seeks other benefits: among them to placate deities and spirits; transmit his fertility to the entire village, its fields, and its domestic animals; enhance his status in the community; and assure his position in the afterworld. It is true that the group as a whole eats the flesh of the slaughtered mithan, and that a series of reciprocal obligations provides the sacrificer with economic and other benefits. But the motives of the sacrificer are not economic in the narrow, usual Western, sense.

We can quite easily eliminate certain economic motivations for the early Southwest Asians or East Europeans who presumably carried out common cattle domestication. There is, for example, no acceptable evidence that plows were known or draft animals used there before late in the fourth millennium, some 2,500 years after cattle are known to have been domesticated. It is likely that plow and draft oxen were used earlier, but cattle domestication too must date back beyond the time for which we now have evidence. The first known milking of cows, in a religious context, is of comparable age to plowing. There still remains the possibility that early men in Southwest Asia or Eastern Europe domesticated cattle to have a supply of flesh ready at hand. We should bear in mind, however, that the domesticators of cattle quite likely already had in their villages domesticated animals such as sheep and goats, which constituted a ready source of meat and were easy to manage. Should they have wanted beef, moreover, there were wild cattle about, and—judging from the abundant aurochs remains at Çatal Hüyük and other early Neolithic sites—men were skilled at hunting them. These circumstances would seem to provide no great incentive for attempting the domestication of the formidable aurochs, and we suspect that other motives were also involved. Our opinion is that these motives must have been compelling, that man was driven by something more than a desire to have an additional handy source of meat. Let us turn to the religious life of the early farmers to see whether it may have provided such motives.

The earliest detailed material evidence, for the early Neolithic site of Çatal Hüyük, and the earliest written evidence, for the Sumerians, suggest that they were not as different from the mithan-keeping people of today in their religious beliefs as all of them are from Westerners of today. The people of Çatal Hüyük, Sumer, and the mithan country focused on those aspects of religious belief intimately associated with life, death, and the afterlife. Their concern was with those supernatural beings who take possession of a man, make him sick, keep his wife from bearing children, cause his domestic animals to become ill and die and his crops to wither. The domestication of bovines must be viewed against this background, for it is with such problems that man first viewed animals as potential domesticates. In Çatal Hüyük, attention was directed to various animals in cult activities, but all were related in one way or another to life, fertility, and death. The bull aurochs was prominent among them, was symbolic of and sacred to the male deity, was depicted as being born of the mother-goddess who was so prominent in the cult. We have here the earliest representations of a male deity, as offspring and consort of the mother-goddess; and the bull was associated with him. We also find that the Halafians of northern Iraq, one of the early peoples who had domesticated cattle, had both a bull cult and a mother-goddess. In Sumerian times, the bull was tied to various male deities, including the moon god Sin, and was involved in fertility rites. In Sumer, too, cows were kept in sacred herds, were tied to the mother-goddess Ninhursag, and their milk was viewed as sacred. Ninhursag's cult may have been linked with that of Sin, and she may have been ceremonially married to him from time to time to assure continued fertility. All of this reveals a strong tie in Southwest Asia between bovines and fertility rites, first the bull with male god, then the cow with mother-goddess. Where animals were sacrificed in Sumer, some of the flesh was presented to the deity and the rest was consumed by the worshipers.

The Indus Valley (Harappan) people had a mother-goddess and horned god prominent in their religious life; they had ritual embracing various bovine bulls ("aurochs," zebu cattle, water buffalo, "gaur"); and these probably were involved in fertility rites and sacrificed. In Vedic times, too, bulls continued to be sacrificed to various deities, and to be symbolic of masculine virility. Though cows were sacrificed also, there was greater objection to this. The mithan country furnishes further striking parallels, this time with Çatal Hüyük—in spite of the distance in time and space. The parallels are most notable for the Naga peoples (see Table 2), and are almost all related in one way or another to fertility. This, and other evidence mentioned above, leads us to the conclusions that there was a widespread and early fertility cult; that though it took various forms, it was commonly tied to bovines and initially to male animals; and that across a wide belt of the Old World bovine domestication was carried out to obtain animals for sacrifice in the cult.

The archeological evidence at present available suggests that the earliest bovine domesticates, found from Afghanistan to Hungary, were common cattle, and that these were the first domesticated bovines in-

TABLE 2

Bovines at Çatal Hüyük (6750–5650 B.C.) and in the Naga Country (Recent)

	Çatal Hüyük	Naga Country
1. Bovines important in religion	+	+
2. Association of bulls with fertility rites	+	+
3. Association of bulls with mother-goddess or male deity	+	−
4. Association of bulls with moon god or moon goddess	−	−
5. Bovine horns and skull displayed	+	+
6. Bucranium motif an art form	+	+
7. Women's breasts depicted with bucrania	+	+
8. Bull baiting	+	(+, Ao)
9. Sacrifice of bovines	?	+
10. Forked sacrificial or memorial posts	−	+
11. Free-ranging of domestic bovines	?	+
12. Ritual surrounding human skulls (headhunting or cult of skulls)	+	+
13. Skulls of animals possess special qualities	?	+

volved with the cult. If common cattle were indeed earliest, the domestication of the water buffalo and gaur in India was probably in imitation of common cattle. We believe that the mithan was first domesticated in imitation of water buffalo; that the domestication was carried out somewhere in the Naga-Chin country, by ancestors of one of the present-day groups or by some "Tibeto-Burman" group that preceded them; and that fertility concerns and sacrificial needs were important in the domestication.

If this hypothesis is valid, one might reasonably expect to find survivals of the fertility cult in other parts of the Indian subcontinent. This is most to be expected in areas where Islam, Hinduism, or other religions have not completely eliminated the cult. Only further investigation will show whether there are widespread survivals. One of the most promising areas for investigation is South India, where sacrifice of buffalo and common cattle has survived among certain non-Hindu tribal peoples; where buffalo sacrifice has persisted among some low-caste Hindus as well; where common bull and buffalo baiting and racing occur; and where indications exist, at least in some cases, of a tie between these practices and fertility concerns (Allchin, 1963: 118–25).

Here we can only note that surprising parallels with the early Near East on the one hand and with the Naga country on the other existed among the nineteenth-century Kafirs of the Hindu Kush, a pagan people who have since largely become Moslem.[1] The homeland of the Kafirs is about halfway between Naga country and Mesopotamia. For the Kafirs, common cattle were the principal bovine animal, and served in various economic ways: in dairying, plowing, as a standard of value in the prevailing system of barter, and in payment of fines. They were also the most prestigeful sacrificial animals. Both bulls and cows were sacrificed in various contexts, among them death ceremonies, peace pacts between individuals, and offerings to various deities. For the war-god Gísh, only bulls or male goats were suitable. For Imrá, the creator god, "cows" (females of common cattle?) were sacrificed, and Imrá was depicted in temple carvings as preparing butter. Bulls were also sacrificed in connection with feasts closely resembling the Naga Feasts of Merit. The main goal of sacrifice to deities seems to have been assuring prosperity and fertility in the broad sense, as was true of the Naga and early Near Eastern peoples. Like certain Naga, the Kafirs erected wooden effigies of the dead. Also like the Naga, they erected monoliths, some as memorials to dead ancestors. Such stone memorials are for the Naga the means of dispensing the fertility of the dead to the living. There are hints, in the Kafir sacrifices made at both monoliths and effigies, that for them too these structures were more than purely commemorative. Other hints include the observations that offerings at an effigy were made by sick men, apparently in the hope of a cure; and that the Kafirs believed that removal of an effigy from their country would bring on bad weather.

Accumulated evidence leads us to the conclusion that simple economic explanations of earliest bovine domestication do not fit, that man did not domesticate the first bovines to obtain a source of milk, or to have an animal to aid in their agricultural labors. Instead, men's motives seem to have been quite broad, but centered on a desire to assure, through sacrifice, fertility and well-being on this earth and a satisfactory fate after death. The meat of the sacrificed animals was certainly welcome (and later the milk, and the strength of cattle in traction), but man quite likely was moved to domesticate bovines by more than wishes for a convenient beef supply.

The methods by which the domestication of common cattle was accomplished remain obscure. Important men who could obtain help from other villagers seem the most likely promoters of cattle domestication. Domesticating cattle need not entail, contrary to the contention of various writers, the capture of animals by corralling; any method of killing the adult wild cattle would suffice. The young, on being brought home, could be confined with other domestic animals or tied nearby. They could be

---

1. For details of the parallels, see Appendix D.

provided milk by goats or sheep. As they matured, they could be given salt to bind them to man, and could be permitted freedom to seek their own feed in the woods nearby, thereby saving man effort. We have seen the importance of salt in binding the mithan to man and have speculated on its possible role in mithan domestication. Common cattle are attracted to salt too, and man could have used salt equally well to bring about their domestication. It is curious that Hahn and others have overlooked this possibility.

We feel, as Hahn did, that man's initial interest in cattle was to obtain sacrificial animals—though crescent-shaped horns, the cow, and the lunar-goddess do not seem to us to have been important initially. Unlike Hahn, we believe that man did not at first find it to his advantage to bring cattle under complete control, to confine them. Population pressure and short-age of land alone may have been sufficient to bring about the hypothesized confinement of Southwest Asian bovines; but we wonder whether man's devising other uses for bovines that necessitated their daily presence—the providing of milk or draft power—was not the climactic factor in bringing confinement about. That time never came to mithan-keeping people, and the mithan remains free-ranging, feeding itself, with only limited contact with man. In the case of common cattle, in the Near East and elsewhere, milking, plowing, and other traction soon became so im-portant that the sacrificial function was obscured; but in the case of the mithan, remote in the hills and mountains of the Indo-Burman border, milking and plowing were never adopted, and sacrifice remained para-mount.

Appendices

Appendix A

The Lisudu and the Kwakiutl
Potlatch Compared

Though there were notable differences in the potlatch from group to group, the classic type is the Kwakiutl potlatch described by Franz Boas (pp. 341–58 in "The Social Organization and the Secret Societies of the Kwakiutl Indians," *Report* of the U. S. National Museum for 1895; Washington, D.C.: 1897). The Kwakiutl potlatch (herein referred to as "the potlatch"), like the Apa Tani lisudu, was concerned with the validation of social position. The potlatch involved holders of fixed, ranked, and named "social positions" (though in later times so many positions were available that all individuals could have one). Men, women, and even children had potlatches. Only slaves were excluded. The lisudu, by contrast, does not involve persons with fixed social positions. Any offended wealthy man may start a lisudu, but not women and children. The potlatch could involve either the public distribution of private wealth or its destruction. The lisudu involves only the public destruction of wealth, with the distribution of the destroyed mithan's flesh being incidental to the primary purpose of the competition. The potlatch distribution had elements of an investment which was returned with interest. The lisudu involves no such investment. In both institutions the wealth could be supplied not only by the competitors but by others who had a stake in maintaining the competitors' prestige. The lisudu may be started by a man whenever he chooses. The potlatch, while it might be undertaken on any occasion, was also expected on special occasions involving changes of name, at weddings, births, and such. The primary object destroyed in the lisudu is a domestic animal; the potlatch involved blankets, coppers, or other goods. (For a thorough functional and historical account of the Kwakiutl potlatch, see Helen Codere, *Fighting with Property* [Monographs of the American Ethnological Society, Vol. 18; New York: J. J. Augustin, 1950. 135 pp.]. For a general account of the potlatch in the Northwest, see H. G. Barnett, "The Nature of the Potlatch," *American Anthropologist*, 40 [1938]: 349–58.)

Appendix **B**

Free-ranging of Bovines in Southern Asia

The free-ranging form of bovine keeping, which has never been thoroughly investigated, occurs in scattered parts of Southeast Asia and adjacent India. In mithan country, the mithan is the most common free-ranging bovine. Elsewhere in Southeast Asia the water buffalo is. Common cattle are also reported as free-ranging in a few places.

Among the Eastern Rengma Naga, where buffaloes take the place of mithan as sacrificial animals, the buffaloes live semiferal in the forest and are fierce. The Chang Naga regard it as normal for a man to be killed when a group rounds up an old bull buffalo. The Western Rengma turn their common cattle loose when the harvest is in, permitting them to wander unattended until the next sowing season (Mills, 1937: 91–92). Free-ranging is also mentioned for buffaloes among the Thadou Kuki (Shaw, 1929: 85); the Haka Chin (Carey and Tuck, 1896, 1: 181); Chakma, Magh, and Tippera of Chittagong (Hutchinson, 1906: 20); and the Kachin of Burma (H.-E. Kauffmann, 1934: 66). Farther afield, the Lamet of Laos permit their buffalo to run free without herdsmen in the woods. Should a buffalo become dangerous, it is enticed into an enclosure and allowed to starve until it is tame; then it is let out again to join the herd. The Lamet have zebu cattle in a few villages but always keep them in the village square overnight (Izikowitz, 1951: 200–202). In the Philippines common cattle were unknown in pre-European times, but on Luzon and perhaps certain other islands domesticated buffalo were permitted to live half-wild, though they were caught from time to time; they were not milked or used for plowing, but were primarily sacrificial animals (Fürer-Haimendorf, 1932: 66–72).

The Miao of Hainan Island are one group who have free-ranging common cattle. They permit them to wander in the mountains, where the cattle become wild and difficult to control; one Miao host is reported as sending men with guns to kill his animals for a feast (Wang, 1948: 26). Among certain Magh (Marma) of the Chittagong Hills common cattle range freely without herders and, in at least some instances, they stay out at night (pers. com., H.-E. Kauffmann, Oct. 10, 1966).

Some may be tempted to conclude that free-ranging bovine keeping developed first among the hill peoples of the region, since it is most common among such groups today. However, it occurs in certain lowland areas and may once have been widespread there, too. In the Kalè Valley of Burma, writes H. Fielding Hall (1917: 243–44), buffaloes are permitted to wander in the jungle for eight months each year, during which time they become quite wild. They are rounded up only when they are needed for plowing and carting. In some parts of Cambodia people permit both their common cattle and water buffalo to range free (Thompson, 1937: 337; anonymous, 1942: 231–32; J. Delvert, 1961: 44). According to Charles H. Wharton (1957: 6–7), moreover, the ancient Khmer used a free-ranging system with the domestic ox called *ko-khmer,* which some Cambodians believe to have been a hybrid of kouprey and common cattle. There are reports until quite recently that the ko-khmer were permitted to be free for about nine months each year; then some were recaptured to work in the rice fields. Thus free-ranging is not restricted to a particular environment, and is limited mainly by availability of grazing land.

Though the items above apply to Southeast Asia and adjacent India, a cursory search of the literature reveals additional cases of free-ranging bovines scattered across southern Asia. There is one report for the Asur, a tribal people of the Chota Nagpur area of India, that common cattle are permitted to roam unsupervised for most of the year, though they are brought to the village daily at midday for milking, and are herded when crops are in the fields (Ruben, 1939: 18). In Sikkim certain Lepcha send most cattle untended to the mountains from February until perhaps mid-June (Gorer, 1938: 100–101; J. Morris, 1938: 68). The people of Ishkoman in northwest Pakistan are reported to keep numerous yaks which they do not use for riding, loading, or milking. The yaks are permitted to wander semiwild in highland pastures, and are visited by their owners only to brand a calf or to kill an animal for meat. Free-ranging of yaks is reported, too, for certain districts neighboring Ishkoman (Schomberg, 1935: 93), and for the Pamirs.

Cattle Sacrifice, Sun and Moon, and Fertility among Mithan-keeping Peoples

Among the Naga and Chin peoples, the sun and moon are not regarded as deities today. There are hints that this was not always so, for J. Rawlins, writing of the Kuki of Tripura (1790: 187), reported that the sun and moon were gods; and S. R. Tickell (1852: 211) noted for another Kuki (Lakher) group, living north of Arakan, both the divinity of sun and moon and the sacrifice of pigs and cattle to them at the start of the rains. This suggests that the sacrifice was made to assure fertility. There are also other fragments that suggest a tie among cattle sacrifice, the moon and sun, and fertility. Among them are the Y-shaped memorial posts erected by the Sema Naga in connection with mithan sacrifice; many of these posts are ornamented with carvings, including circles said to represent the moon (Hutton, 1921a: 48; 1922: 58, 60). There are also the circular representations observed by Hutton on the boards of an Angami Naga house in Kohima village, also said to represent the moon. H.-E. Kauffmann (1955: 91) believes that sun and moon representations, like certain other Naga symbols, represent fertility and abundance. Circular carvings of what is probably the sun or moon appear on the ancient stone monoliths of Dimapur (Figure 23), which so closely resemble the memorial posts of the present-day Angami, Sema, and Ao.

The Ao Naga, according to W. C. Smith (1925: 87 ff.), sometimes "sacrifice cows and pigs to the ruling spirits of the Sun and Moon" in the belief that if this is not done their cattle and pigs would die and their crops fail. Ao priests, at times of inclement weather, break eggs—a universal fertility symbol—and eat them, then hang up the shells for the sun deity and ask him to provide good weather lest people suffer from food shortage. The next day men rest and the priests go from house to house drinking beer and "singing praises to the Sun." Verrier Elwin, basing his opinion on Smith's account, views the Ao as approaching closer to sun worship than any of the hill peoples of Assam (excluding NEFA). Smith's account, however, does not fit with J. P. Mills's statements about the sun and moon among the Ao. Mills says that the sun and moon play no role in the life of men and are not deities; that no ceremony is performed to honor them, though prayers at large sacrifices are introduced with an appeal to them. But in the preliminaries of one Ao Feast of Merit, writes Mills, when a man brings home a common cow or bull he says "I have bought a present for the sun and moon" (1926: 215–16, 388).

C. R. Stonor (1950: 11–12) contends that in the Feasts of Merit (with their concern, as we have seen, with fertility) the Northern Sangtam Naga introduce a strong note of sun worship; among the elements he mentions are the lighting of "a sacred fire" at the sacrificial place, exactly at sunrise; arrangement of the heads of the sacrificed mithan on the posts so as to catch the first light of sun; the setting aside of a portion of meat specifically for sun and moon; the addressing of invocations to sun and moon before dancing and feasting begin; and the wearing, by Sangtam women, of necklaces made of large shell discs, which are connected with and may represent the sun. There is the custom, too, among various mithan-keeping groups, of swearing oaths on the sun and moon.

Verrier Elwin (1958: 29 ff.), writing of the NEFA groups, argues that there, outside of the Naga and Buddhist areas, "there is a strong cult of the great luminaries right through the central mountains, in the Lohit, Siang and Subansiri Divisions, and eastern Kameng." He cites as an example the Adi of Siang, who view the Great Mother, Kayum, as the creator, but look on Doini-Polo (Donyi-Polo), the sun-moon, as the most powerful deity. Doini-Polo is not given special sacrifices, for he does not need them, but he is "the unifying force behind all Adi theology." According to one Minyong Adi myth (see pp. 218–19), Doini-Polo created the mithan. Fürer-Haimendorf (1954: 593) mentions the slaughter of mithan by a Minyong man guilty of clan incest, at a feast at which Doing-Angung (the supreme sky god), the sun and moon, and other deities were asked to condone the crime. Finally there is the story of the Bugun or Khowa, narrated previously (pp. 219–20), about the origin of the mithan among their neighbors, the Aka: that the mithan is the offspring of incestual intercourse between the son and daughter of the sun and moon.

Despite such examples as these, "cult of the great luminaries" seems too strong a term to apply to NEFA beliefs, in view of the rich and varied group of deities and spirits found among the Adi and other peoples of that region.[1] At most among mithan-keeping peoples the sun and moon

1. See Fürer-Haimendorf, 1962: 132 ff., for information on Apa Tani deities and spirits; Baruah, 1960: 69 ff., on the Idu Mishmi; Sinha, 1962: 111 ff., on the Aka; S. Roy, 1960: 236 ff., and Fürer-Haimendorf, 1954: 593–94, on the Adi. For brief

or supernatural beings identified with them are part of that large body of deities and spirits; and among many of them they are not deified at all. Thus we come to the conclusion that though the sun and moon do figure in religion and ritual among various mithan-keeping peoples, they are simply part of a far broader religious world; and, as H.-E. Kauffmann observes for the Naga (1955: 90–91), a sun or moon cult does not form one of its central points.

There are indications, nevertheless, that to some extent the sun and moon are involved with man's efforts to assure fertility, abundance, and well-being. This suggests that, *if* a fertility cult involving bovines did indeed spread from the Near East to the Assam hills, either it did so before sun or moon deities were prominent in it or the Assam hill tribes took it over in a much-modified form or later altered it, without the sun or moon in prominent positions.

---

statements about the sun and moon in the life of the Assam hill groups, see H.-E. Kauffmann, 1955: 89–91, and V. Elwin, 1958: 29 ff. A lengthy account that we were not able to consult is the Ph.D. dissertation in anthropology by Alois N. Bucher, "Sonne und Mond in Mythus und Kult bei den Völkern Assams, Burmas und Benachbarter Gebiete," University of Fribourg, 1963.

Some Parallels and Differences among the Kafirs, the Naga, and the Ancient Near East

By 1889–91, when Sir George Scott Robertson visited the Kafirs, they seemed to know little about the meanings of their traditional religious practices, or, if they did, they were unwilling to explain them to him. The practices themselves include some striking parallels with Naga religious practices. There are also parallels in the position of cattle in religion, as well as in society and economy. Notable differences occur, too, which tie the Kafirs to the peoples of the early Near East rather than to those of the Assam hills. Significant among the parallels and differences are:

1. Common cattle were the most important bovine of the Kafirs, as for the peoples of the early Near East; for the Naga the mithan or buffalo is more important.

2. Common cattle were milked by the Kafirs, and used in plowing. This too was true of the early Near Easterners but not of the Naga.

3. Like the Naga and other mithan-keeping peoples, the Kafirs conducted business among themselves by barter; the "cow" (presumably Robertson means the female of common cattle, though one cannot be certain whether he used the term for common cattle in general) was a standard of value; according to Robertson, one cow was worth twenty Kabuli rupees; a goat, three rupees; and a sheep, two.

4. "Cows" were used in payment of fines, as mithan are among the Naga and other Assam hill groups.

5. There is no evidence that the Kafirs had a cult of skulls, as did certain early Near Eastern peoples. Nor, unlike the Naga, were they headhunters. There is nevertheless one hint that they shared the view of those

Source: This discussion is based on the account of the Kafirs by George Scott Robertson, 1896: especially 87, 151, 376–477, 542–43, 549–50, 554–55, 589–90, 630–51.

273

groups that the head is the principal repository of certain valuable qualities. Robertson wrote that if a raiding party was defeated and unable to bring its dead back, it tried at least to bring back the heads of the dead, which were treated with ceremony and disposed of in the cemetery of the home village.

6. Like both the Naga and early Near Eastern peoples, the Kafirs had a pantheon including many deities and spirits, to whom animals were sacrificed at times.

7. For the Naga, the early Near Eastern peoples, and the Kafirs, bovines were the sacrificial animals of highest standing, and served at the more important ceremonies. On lesser occasions, the Kafirs sacrificed goats and sheep.

8. Both bulls and cows were sacrificed by the Kafirs, but for the war god Gísh male animals, either bulls or male goats, were required.

9. Cows (females of common cattle?) were sacrificed throughout Kafiristan to the great god Imrá, the creator of all things on earth and in heaven. Sometimes this was done in "simple and general piety . . . , sometimes for particular reasons, such as recovery from sickness, thanksgiving for seasonable weather, and for other material benefits" (388–89). The concern here seems to be with well-being like the Naga and early Near Easterners.

10. Though every Kafir village had a temple to Imrá, there was one of extraordinary size and elaborateness in Kstigigrom, the most sacred village in Kafiristan. Each of the wooden pillars that supported the roof on the east side of the temple, and formed a square portico there, was carved in one of three designs. One was a basket design. Another was composed of two vertical rows of rams' heads extending from the base of the pillar to the top, on opposite sides of the pillar. The third consisted of the head of a horned animal, not identified by Robertson. The head was carved at the base of the pillar; the horns extended to the top, crossing and recrossing at intervals; and at the top, between the horns, was carved a grotesque head, and hands which grasped the horns near their tips. On the wall of the temple where the portico was were seven huge doors, only two of which could be opened. All seven doors and one space between were carved in relief with large images of Imrá seated and preparing butter in a goatskin churn. Between some of the images were vertical rows of what Robertson thought were cows' or rams' heads. Above the large images was a board decorated with small figures and horns. On the portico was a sacrificial stone, and a large pile of offal nearby showed that cattle were the offerings. Though the above observations are vague and fragmentary, the rows of cows' or rams' heads, the depiction of Imrá churning butter, and the clear evidences of cattle

sacrifice suggest that the cow and ram occupied a special position in
Imrá's most important shrine. Certain attributes of the mother-goddess
and male god of the early Near East may be recognized in Imrá and Gísh,
but the identification is not clear or consistent. Nor is there anything in
Robertson's account to indicate, for this or other Kafir shrines, that
bucrania were displayed or that the bucranium design was prominent, as
among the Naga and in the early Near East.

11. Cows were sacrificed to Imrá when peace was made between
individuals; each participant placed his foot in the blood of the sacrificed
animal. Sacrifices of mithan on similar occasions are reported for the Naga.

12. Cows were sacrificed when an individual was buried, as mithan are
sometimes sacrificed for wealthy individuals among the Naga.

13. Among some Kafir groups wooden effigies, carved from the trunk
of a tree and often life-size, were set up near the grave of an adult, one
year after the death. The relatives of the deceased earned this privilege
by feasting the community at the time the effigy was erected; the amount
of food distributed determined the style and elaborateness of the effigy.
Thus a viewer could tell at a glance the effort made by the relatives.
There are suggestions that the effigies were not solely memorials. For
example, sacrifices were sometimes made, at the effigy, by descendants
who were ill, and the pedestal of the effigy was sprinkled with blood.
It seems likely that the descendant was attempting to make contact with
the dead person or his spirit to obtain a cure for his illness. Possibly the
effigy itself was the means of transmission for the life-force of the dead
person to his living relatives. Another suggestion that the images were
more than memorials is the Kafir belief that if an effigy were removed
from the country adverse natural conditions would follow. Thus while
Robertson was having some effigies carved to take to India, the bad
weather that occurred was blamed on this fact.

Wooden images of the dead are put up by certain Naga groups, too,
notably certain Angami and Konyak. For these Naga, in contrast to the
Kafirs, the images are temporary.

14. In some areas of Kafir country, warriors are commemorated at
death with special structures on which are tallied the "number of
homicides the man committed in his lifetime" (648). Many Naga and
Chin, too, at the time of death exhibit tallies of various sorts which
inform passersby of the accomplishments and the wealth of the dead
person. There is great variation in where the tallies are set up (whether
at the grave or elsewhere) and in the activities that are recorded; performance of the mithan sacrifice and the number of enemy heads taken
are two achievements frequently noted.

15. At various spots the Kafirs erected sacred stones—some set up by

men especially to be worshiped, and others erected as memorials to ancestors. There were regular sacrifices of animals at the stones. The Naga, too, have such stones, which are tied to a fertility cult.

16. In one place in Kafir country Robertson saw what apparently was another form of memorial. A detached piece of rock in the open had been surrounded by piled stones to form a narrow oblong structure, whose flat surface was about two and a half feet above the ground. He was told that the structure was intended for coolies to rest their burdens on. Robertson wrote that there were no coolies in Kafir country, and no loads to warrant such an effort. Such structures, he noted, were common in the neighboring regions of Astor and Chitral. In Naga country, too, somewhat similar-appearing memorials are built by a man before he dies. They serve as resting places for people on their way to the fields; and the Naga believe that the dead person's fertility is dispensed by means of the stone to those who rest there.

17. The Kafirs had an institution similar to the Feasts of Merit of the Naga. For the Kafirs, the inner circle of the tribe was the Jast, and Jast position could be attained only through the performance, over a period of years, of a series of feasts, both for the Jast and for the tribe at large. Included in one series of feasts was the sacrifice of bulls and male goats to the war god Gísh, at his shrine. There were also sacrifices at the feast giver's house. At a side ceremony, at which a bull and some goats were sacrificed, Robertson once observed arrows dipped in the flowing blood of the animals. At the end of the ceremony the arrows "were fired away promiscuously" (468). Also two containers of blood and water were poured ceremoniously on the ground by the ladleful. Though the Kafirs denied knowing the meaning of these acts, they suggest to us a desire to disperse the fertility of the sacrificed animals widely to the village and its soil.

The Kafirs who gave feasts enjoyed rights of display, like the Naga; but apparently did not erect wooden sacrificial or memorial posts which they permitted to remain standing.

Glossary, References, Index

Glossary

agam: an Adi generic word used for those spirits associated with domestic animals.

banteng: *Bos banteng* or *Bos sondaicus,* a wild bovine found throughout Southeast Asia from the Assam-Burma border to the Indonesian islands.

bibovine: a member of the bovine subgenus *Bibos;* the bibovines include gaur, mithan, banteng, kouprey, and Bali cattle.

dao: a machete, used both as an agricultural implement and a weapon.

dapo: a perpetual nonaggression pact found among Apa Tani, Dafla, and Hill Miri.

dzo: a yak/common cattle hybrid; *dzo-mo*: the female hybrid.

Feasts of Celebration: an institution described for the Chin in which a man gives a feast when he has killed a wild animal, thereby gaining status among the village hunters.

Feasts of Merit: an institution in which a man gives an ordered sequence of feasts over a period of years; performance of the feasts, which includes animal sacrifice, gains for the giver status and rights; found in mithan country among the Naga and Chin peoples.

gaur: *Bos gaurus,* a wild bovine of India and mainland Southeast Asia, believed to be the ancestor of the mithan.

gayal: a Bengali word used sometimes for the mithan and sometimes for both mithan and gaur; also found in Hindi and English.

genna: a Naga-Assamese word used in various senses: 1) for a Naga ceremony; 2) for "forbidden"; and 3) for "tabooed."

gyall: see gayal.

jhum: slash-and-burn, shifting, or swidden cultivation; a field cultivated under that system.

kouprey: *Bos sauveli,* a wild bovine of Cambodia.

lisudu: an Apa Tani institution involving competition between individuals; one individual destroys mithan and other wealth in view of his rival, thus obligating him to do likewise or lose face.

merum: fireplace association formed in the Adi bachelors' dormitory.

mithan, mithun, metna: English versions of an Assamese word used sometimes for *Bos frontalis* and sometimes for that animal and the gaur; herein mithan is restricted to the domestic animal, *Bos frontalis.*

279

morung: Assamese word used in two senses: 1) the village men's house, often called "bachelors' dormitory"; 2) a men's political and social institution, associated with that house if one is present.

NEFA: the North-East Frontier Agency of India.

thumona: a formalized system of guest-visits, found among the Aka, in which the host proffers substantial gifts as well as hospitality. The guest must later reciprocate.

wiyu: a generic word meaning "spirit."

wokchung: literally "pig killer"; a Lhota Naga religious official who is responsible for sacrificing animals at ceremonies held by individuals.

References Cited

Albright, W. F., and P. E. Dumont. "A Parallel between Indic and Babylonian Sacrificial Ritual," *Journal of the American Oriental Society*, 54 (1934): 107–28.

Allchin, F. R. *Neolithic Cattle-Keepers of South India*. Cambridge: Cambridge University Press, 1963. 189 pp.

Andress, Joel M. "Culture and Habitat in the Central Himalayas." Draft of Ph.D. Diss., Department of Geography, University of California (Berkeley), 1965. 298 pp.

Anonymous. "Divers types d'élevage au Cambodge," *Annales de Géographie*, 51 (1942): 231–32.

Antonius, Otto. *Grundzüge einer Stammesgeschichte der Haustiere*. Jena: Gustav Fischer, 1922. 336 pp.

———. "Beobachtungen an Rindern in Schönbrunn. II. Banteng, Gaur, Gayal," *Zoologische Garten* [Leipzig], 5 (1932): 178–91.

———. "Über Symbolhandlungen und Verwandtes bei Säugetieren," *Zeitschrift für Tierpsychologie*, 3 (1939): 263–78.

Bailey, F. M. "Gayal or Mithan (*Bibos frontalis*)," *Journal of the Bombay Natural History Society*, 21 (1911–13): 1071–72.

———. *China-Tibet-Assam: A Journey, 1911*. London: Jonathan Cape, 1945. 175 pp.

Baker, E. C. Stuart. "The Gaur and the Gayal (*Bos gaurus* and *Bos frontalis*)," *Journal of the Bombay Natural History Society*, 15 (1903–4): 227–48.

Bartlett, A. D. "On Some Hybrid Bovine Animals Bred in the Society's Gardens," *Proceedings of the Zoological Society of London*, 1884, pp. 399–402.

Barua, Hem. *The Red River and the Blue Hill; or The State of Assam*. Gauhati, Assam: Lawyers' Book Stall, [1954]. 140 pp.

Baruah, Tapan Kumar M. *The Idu Mishmis*. Shillong: Adviser to the Governor of Assam, 1960. 110 pp.

Basham, A. L. *The Wonder That Was India*. London: Sidgwick & Jackson, 1954. 568 pp.

Baumgartel, Elise J. *The Cultures of Prehistoric Egypt*. Rev. ed. London: Oxford University Press, 1955–60. 2 vols.

————. *Predynastic Egypt*. Fascicle containing Chap. IX(a), Vol. 1 of the forthcoming *Cambridge Ancient History*. Rev. ed. Cambridge: Cambridge University Press, 1965. 39 pp.

Bennison, J. J. "The Pau Chin Hau Movement in the Chin Hills," pp. 166–67 in *Census of India, 1931*, Vol. 1 (India), Pt. III. Simla: Government of India Press, 1935. 245 pp.

Bishop, Carl Whitting. "The Ritual Bullfight," *China Journal of Science and Arts*, 3 (1925): 630–37.

Blackburn, H. V. "A Bull Gaur (*B. gaurus*) and a Tigress Fight to Death," *Journal of the Bombay Natural History Society*, 37 (1935): 950–51.

Blanford, William T., ed. *The Fauna of British India, Including Ceylon and Burma; Mammalia*. London: Taylor & Francis, 1888–91. 617 pp.

Blyth, E. "Catalogue of Mammals and Birds of Burma," *Journal of the Asiatic Society of Bengal*, 43, Pt. 2, Extra Number (1875): 1–167.

Bodenheimer, Friedrich S. *Animal and Man in Bible Lands*. Leiden: E. J. Brill, 1960. 232 pp.

Bökönyi, S. "A Maroslele-Panai neolitikus telep gerinces faunája," *Archaeologiai Értesitö* (Magyar Tudományos Akadémia, Budapest), 91 (1964): 87–93.

Boessneck, Joachim. "Zu den Tierknochen aus neolithischen Siedlungen Thessaliens," *36. Bericht der Römisch-Germanischen Kommission 1955* (1956): pp. 1–51.

————. "Zu den Tierknochenfunden aus der präkeramischen Schicht der Argissa-Magula," *Germania* (Archaeologisches Institut des Deutschen Reichs), 38 (1960): 336–40.

————. "Haustierfunde präkeramisch-neolithischer Zeit aus Thessalien," *Zeitschrift für Tierzüchtung und Züchtungsbiologie*, 76, No. 1 (1961): 39–42.

————. "Die Tierreste aus der Argissa-Magula vom präkeramischen Neolithikum bis zur mittleren Bronzezeit," pp. 27–99 in V. Milojčić, J. Boessneck, and M. Hopf, *Die deutschen Ausgrabungen auf der Argissa-Magula in Thessalien*, Vol. 1 ("Das präkeramische Neolithikum sowie die Tier- und Pflanzenreste"). Beiträge zur Ur- und Frühgeschichtlichen Archäologie des Mittelmeer-Kulturraumes, Vol. 2. Bonn: Rudolf Habelt, 1962. 119 pp.

Boettger, Caesar R. *Die Haustiere Afrikas*. Jena: Gustav Fischer, 1958. 314 pp.

Bohlken, Herwart. [1958] "Vergleichende Untersuchungen an Wildrindern (Tribus *Bovini* Simpson 1945)," *Zoologische Jahrbücher*, 68 (1958): 113–202.

————. [1958a] "Zur Nomenklatur der Haustiere," *Zoologischer Anzeiger*, 160 (1958): 167–68.

————. "Der Kouprey, *Bos (Bibos) sauveli* Urbain 1937," *Zeitschrift für Säugetierkunde*, 26 (1961): 193–254.

Bower, Ursula Graham. *Hidden Land*. New York: William Morrow, 1953. 260 pp.

Braidwood, Robert J. "Jericho and Its Setting in Near Eastern History," *Antiquity*, 31 (1957): 73–81.

————. "Comments on *Environment and Archeology*," *Current Anthropology*, 7, No. 4 (Oct. 1966): 504.

————, and Bruce Howe. "Southwestern Asia beyond the Lands of the Mediterranean Littoral," pp. 132–46 in Robert J. Braidwood and Gordon R. Willey, eds., *Courses toward Urban Life*. Viking Fund Publications in

Anthropology, No. 32. New York: Wenner-Gren Foundation for Anthropological Research, 1962. 371 pp.

————, and Charles A. Reed. "The Achievement and Early Consequences of Food-Production: A Consideration of the Archeological and Natural-Historical Evidence," *Cold Spring Harbor Symposia on Quantitative Biology,* 22 (1957): 19–31.

Brown, N. "Comparison of Indo-Chinese Languages," *Journal of the Asiatic Society of Bengal,* 6 (1837): 1023–38.

Brown, W. Norman. "The Sanctity of the Cow in Hinduism," *The Madras University Journal,* 28, No. 2 (Jan. 1957): 29–49. [Reprinted in *The Economic Weekly* (Calcutta), 16 (1964): 245–55.]

[Burma] *Union of Burma, First Stage Census, 1953,* Vol. 3. Rangoon: Superintendent, Government Printing and Stationery, Union of Burma, 1957. 78 pp.

Butzer, Karl W. *Environment and Archeology.* Chicago: Aldine Publishing Company, 1964. 524 pp.

Carey, Bertram S., and H. N. Tuck. *The Chin Hills: A History of the People, Our Dealings with Them, Their Customs and Manners, and a Gazetteer of Their Country,* Vol. 1. Rangoon: Superintendent, Government Printing, Burma, 1896. 236 pp.

Casal, Jean-Marie. *Fouilles d'Amri.* Publications de la Commission des Fouilles Archéologiques, Fouilles de Pakistan. Paris: C. Klincksieck, 1964. 2 vols.

Census of India, 1931, Vol. 1, Pt. I. Delhi: Manager of Publications, 1933. 518 pp.

Census of India, 1961, Vol. 1, Pt. II-C (ii), Language Tables. Delhi: Manager of Publications, 1964. 534 pp.

Chatterjee, Nilananda. *The Condition of Cattle in India.* Calcutta: All India Cow Conference Association, 1926. 647 pp.

Childe, V. Gordon. *The Most Ancient East.* London: Kegan Paul, Trench, Trubner, 1928. 258 pp.

Clark, Mary M. [Mrs. E. W.]. *Ao Naga Grammar with Illustrative Phrases and Vocabulary.* Shillong: Assam Secretariat, 1893. 181 pp.

Colebrooke, H. T. "Description of a Species of Ox, named Gayál," *Asiatic Researches,* 8 (1808): 511–27.

Conrad, Jack Randolph. *The Horn and the Sword; The History of the Bull as Symbol of Power and Fertility.* London: MacGibbon and Kee, 1959. 222 pp.

Coolidge, Harold Jefferson, Jr. "The Indo-Chinese Forest Ox or Kouprey," *Memoirs of the Museum of Comparative Zoology at Harvard College,* 54, No. 6 (1940): 421–531.

Coon, Carleton S. *Cave Explorations in Iran, 1949.* Museum Monographs. Philadelphia: University Museum, University of Pennsylvania, 1951. 125 pp.

Cooper, T. T. *The Mishmee Hills.* London: Henry S. King, 1873. 270 pp.

Dales, George F., Jr. "Mesopotamian and Related Female Figurines: Their Chronology, Diffusion, and Cultural Functions." Ph.D. Diss., University of Pennsylvania, 1960. 265 pp.

Dalton, Edward Tuite. [1845] "Report by Lieut. E. J. T. Dalton, Junior Assistant Commissioner of Assam, of his visit to the Hills in the neighbourhood of the Soobanshiri [sic] River," *Journal of the Asiatic Society of Bengal,* 14 (1845): 250–67.

————. [1845a] "On the Meris and Abors of Assam," *Journal of the Asiatic Society of Bengal*, 14 (1845): 426–30.

————. *Descriptive Ethnology of Bengal*. Calcutta: Office of the Superintendent of Government Printing, 1872. 327 pp.

Das, Jarak Chandra. "Some Notes on the Economic and Agricultural Life of a Little Known Tribe on the Eastern Frontier of India," *Anthropos*, 32 (1937): 440–49.

Das, N. K. "Assam," *Indian Farming*, 6 (1945): 421–22.

————. "Agricultural Economy of the Apa Tanis," *Indian Farming*, 8 (1947): 294–98.

Das, Tarakchandra. *The Purums: An Old Kuki Tribe of Manipur*. Calcutta: University of Calcutta, 1945. 336 pp.

Dash, Arthur Jules. *Darjeeling*. Bengal District Gazetteers. Alipore, Bengal: Bengal Government Press, 1947. 294 pp.

Delougaz, Pinhas, and Seton Lloyd. *Pre-Sargonid Temples in the Diyala Region*. Oriental Institute Publications, Vol. 58. Chicago: University of Chicago Press, 1942. 320 pp.

Delvert, Jean. *Le Paysan cambodgien*. Le Monde d'outre-mer passé et présent, Études, X. Paris-The Hague: Mouton, 1961. 740 pp.

de Planhol, Xavier. *De la plaine pamphylienne aux lacs pisidiens: nomadisme et vie paysanne*. Bibliothèque Archéologique et Historique de l'Institut Français d'Archéologie d'Istanbul, III. Paris: Librairie Adrien–Maisonneuve, 1958. 495 pp.

————. *Recherches sur la géographie humaine de l'Iran septentrional*. Mémoires et Documents, Vol. 10, Pt. 4. Paris: Centre National de la Recherche Scientifique, 1964. 78 pp.

Dewar, T. P. "Naga Tribes and Their Customs," pp. 267–95 in *Census of India, 1931*, Vol. 11 (Burma), Pt. I. Rangoon: Office of the Superintendent, Government Printing and Stationery, 1933. 306 pp.

Dobzhansky, Theodosius. *Genetics and the Origin of Species*. 3rd ed. New York: Columbia University Press, 1951. 364 pp.

Downs, James F. "Domestication: An Examination of the Changing Social Relationships between Man and Animals," *Kroeber Anthropological Society Papers*, No. 22 (Spring 1960), pp. 18–67.

Dunbar, George Duff-Sutherland. "Tribes of the Brahmaputra Valley," *Journal of the Royal Society of Arts*, 63 (1914–15): 290–99.

————. "Abors and Galongs: Part I. Notes on Certain Hill Tribes of the Indo-Tibetan Border," *Memoirs of the Asiatic Society of Bengal*, 5, Extra Number (1915): 1–91.

————. *Frontiers*. London: Ivor Nicholson & Watson, 1932. 320 pp.

Dundas, W. C. M. *An Outline Grammar and Dictionary of the Kachari (Dimasa) Language*. Shillong: Eastern Bengal and Assam Secretariat, 1908. 170 pp.

Dupree, Louis. "Prehistoric Archeological Surveys and Excavations in Afghanistan: 1959–1960 and 1961–1963," *Science*, 146, No. 3644 (Oct. 30, 1964): 638–40.

Dutta, Parul. *The Tangsas of the Namchik and Tirap Valleys*. Shillong: North-East Frontier Agency, 1959. 98 pp.

Dyson, Robert H., Jr. "Archeology and the Domestication of Animals in the Old World," *American Anthropologist*, 55 (1953): 661–73.

Edmond-Blanc, François. "A Contribution to the Knowledge of the Cambodian Wild Ox or Kouproh," *Journal of Mammalogy*, 28 (1947): 245–48.

Ehrich, Robert W., ed. *Chronologies in Old World Archaeology*. Chicago: University of Chicago Press, 1965. 557 pp.

Ellerman, J. R., and T. C. S. Morrison-Scott. *Checklist of Palaearctic and Indian Mammals, 1758 to 1946*. London: British Museum (Natural History), 1951. 810 pp.

Elwin, Verrier. *Myths of the North-East Frontier of India*. Shillong: North-East Frontier Agency, 1958. 448 pp.

———. *India's North-East Frontier in the Nineteenth Century*. London: Oxford University Press, 1959. 473 pp.

———. *Nagaland*. Shillong: Research Department, Adviser's Secretariat, 1961. 108 pp.

Emery, Walter B. *Great Tombs of the First Dynasty, II*. London: Egypt Exploration Society and Oxford University Press, 1954. 171 pp.

Epstein, H. "Domestication Features in Animals as Functions of Human Society," *Agricultural History*, 29 (1955): 137–46.

Evans, J. D. "Cretan Cattle-Cults and Sports," pp. 138–43 in A. E. Mourant and F. E. Zeuner, eds., *Man and Cattle*. Royal Anthropological Institute, Occasional Paper No. 18. London: Royal Anthropological Institute of Great Britain and Ireland, 1963. 166 pp.

Fairservis, Walter A., Jr. "The Harappan Civilization—New Evidence and More Theory," *American Museum Novitates*, No. 2055 (Nov. 17, 1961): pp. 1–35.

Fielding Hall, Harold. *The Soul of a People*. London: Macmillan, 1917. 314 pp.

Flannery, Kent V. "The Ecology of Early Food Production in Mesopotamia," *Science*, 147, No. 3663 (March 12, 1965): 1247–56.

Frankfort, Henry [1936]. "A New Site in Mesopotamia: Tell Agrab," *Illustrated London News*, Sept. 12, 1936, pp. 432–36.

———. [1936a] "The Oldest Stone Statuette Ever Found in Western Asia, and Other Relics of Ancient Sumerian Culture of a Period Probably before 3000 B.C.: New Discoveries in the Earliest Temple at Khafaje, in Mesopotamia," *Illustrated London News*, Sept. 26, 1936, pp. 524–27.

Frankfort, Henry. *Cylinder Seals*. London: Gregg Press, 1965. 328 pp. [Reprinted; originally published in 1939.]

Fraser, A. F. "The State of Fight or Flight in the Bull," *British Journal of Animal Behaviour*, 5 (1957): 48–49.

Frechkop, Serge, and R. Lavocat. "Sous-ordre des Ruminants ou Sélénodontes," pp. 568–693 in Pierre-P. Grassé, ed., *Traité de Zoologie*, Vol. 17. Paris: Masson, 1955. 1170 pp.

Friederichs, Heinz F. "Zur Kenntnis der frühgeschichtlichen Tierwelt Südwestasiens," *Der Alte Orient*, 32, Nos. 3 and 4 (1933): 1–45.

Fürer-Haimendorf, Christoph von. "Zur Frage der Herkunft der Büffelhaltung auf den Philippinen," *Biologia Generalis*, 8 (1932): 66–72.

———. "Through the Unexplored Mountains of the Assam-Burma Border," *Geographical Journal*, 91 (1938): 201–19.

———. [1939] *The Naked Nagas*. London: Methuen, 1939. 243 pp.

———. [1939a] "The Megalithic Culture of the Naga Tribes of Assam," *Research and Progress*, 5, No. 2 (March-April 1939): 95–100.

―――. [1946] "Agriculture and Land Tenure among the Apa Tanis," *Man in India,* 26 (1946): 19–49.

―――. [1946a] "Culture Types in the Assam Himalayas," *Indian Geographical Journal,* 21 (1946): 49–57.

―――. "The Tribes of the Subansiri Region," *Royal Central Asian Journal,* 35 (1948): 238–48.

―――. [1950] *Ethnographic Notes on the Tribes of the Subansiri Region.* Assam, Miscellaneous Official Publications. Shillong: Assam Government Press, 1950. 61 pp.

―――. [1950a] "Youth-Dormitories and Community Houses in India," *Anthropos,* 45 (1950): 119–44.

―――. "The After-Life in Indian Tribal Belief," *Journal of the Royal Anthropological Institute of Great Britain and Ireland,* 83 (1953): 37–49.

―――. "Religious Beliefs and Ritual Practices of the Minyong Abors of Assam, India," *Anthropos,* 49 (1954): 588–604.

―――. *Himalayan Barbary.* London: John Murray, 1955. 241 pp.

―――. *The Apa Tanis and Their Neighbours.* London: Routledge & Kegan Paul, 1962. 166 pp.

―――. "The Social Background of Cattle-Domestication in India," pp. 144–49 in A. E. Mourant and F. E. Zeuner, eds., *Man and Cattle.* Royal Anthropological Institute, Occasional Paper No. 18. London: Royal Anthropological Institute of Great Britain and Ireland, 1963. 166 pp.

Gadd, C. J. *History and Monuments of Ur.* London: Chatto & Windus, 1929. 269 pp.

―――. *The Cities of Babylonia.* Fascicle containing Chap. 13, Vol. 1 of the forthcoming *Cambridge Ancient History.* Rev. ed. Cambridge: Cambridge University Press, 1964. 60 pp.

Galton, Francis. "The First Steps towards the Domestication of Animals," *Transactions of the Ethnological Society of London,* N.S., 3 (1865): 122–38.

Gans, Heinrich. "Banteng (*Bibos sondaicus*) und Zebu (*Bos indicus*) und ihr gegenseitiges Verhältnis, nebst Ausführungen über den Einfluss der Domestikation beim Banteng, Gaur, Ur und Yak," *Kühn-Archiv,* 6 (1915–16): 93–152.

Gordon, D. H. *The Pre-Historic Background of Indian Culture.* Bombay: N. M. Tripathi, 1958. 199 pp.

Gorer, Geoffrey. *Himalayan Village; An Account of the Lepchas of Sikkim.* London: Michael Joseph, 1938. 510 pp.

Goswami, Binod Behari. "System of Bride-Price in the Lushei Tribe," *Journal of Social Research* (Ranchi, Bihar), 3, No. 1 (March 1960): 44–47.

Gray, Annie P. *Mammalian Hybrids.* Technical Communication No. 10 of the Commonwealth Bureau of Animal Breeding and Genetics, Edinburgh. Farnham Royal, Bucks, England: Commonwealth Agricultural Bureaux, 1954. 144 pp.

Gray, I. Errol. "Mr. Errol Gray's Journey from Assam to the Sources of the Irawadi," *Geographical Journal,* 3 (1894): 221–28.

Grierson, George Abraham. *Linguistic Survey of India.* Calcutta: Office of the Superintendent of Government Printing, 1903–28. 11 vols.

Griffith, William. "Visit to the Mishmee Hills in Assam," *Asiatic Journal and Monthly Register for British and Foreign India, China, and Australasia,* N.S., 25 (1838): 233–44.

————. "Journal of the Mission Which Visited Bootan, in 1837–38, under Captain R. Boileau Pemberton," *Journal of the Asiatic Society of Bengal,* 8 (1839): 208–91.

Guthrie, W. K. C. *The Religion and Mythology of the Greeks.* Fascicle containing Chap. 40, Vol. 2 of the forthcoming *Cambridge Ancient History.* Rev. ed. Cambridge: Cambridge University Press, 1964. 55 pp.

Hafez, E. S. E., and M. W. Schein. "The Behaviour of Cattle," pp. 247–96 in E. S. E. Hafez, ed., *The Behaviour of Domestic Animals.* Baltimore: Williams and Wilkins, 1962. 619 pp.

Hahn, Eduard. *Die Haustiere und ihre Beziehungen zur Wirtschaft des Menschen.* Leipzig: Duncker & Humblot, 1896. 581 pp.

Haldane, J. B. S. "Sex Ratio and Unsexual Sterility in Hybrid Animals," *Journal of Genetics,* 12 (1922): 101–9.

Hamilton, R. C. *An Outline Grammar of the Dafla Language as Spoken by the Tribes Immediately South of the Apa Tanang Country.* Shillong: Assam Secretariat, 1900. 127 pp.

Harper, Francis. *Extinct and Vanishing Mammals of the Old World.* Special Publication No. 12. New York: American Committee for International Wild Life Protection, 1945. 850 pp.

Harris, David R. "New Light on Plant Domestication and the Origins of Agriculture: A Review," *Geographical Review,* 57 (1967): 90–107.

Hauxwell, T. A. "Tsine (*Bibos sondaicus*) Found with Village Cattle," *Journal of the Bombay Natural History Society,* 21 (1911–13): 1072–73.

Hays, H. R. *In The Beginnings; Early Man and His Gods.* New York: G. P. Putnam's Sons, 1963. 575 pp.

Heine-Geldern, Robert. "Kopfjagd und Menschenopfer in Assam und Birma und ihre Ausstrahlungen nach Vorderindien," *Mitteilungen der Anthropologischen Gesellschaft in Wien,* 47 (1917): 1–65.

————. "Südostasien," pp. 689–968 in Vol. 2, Pt. 1, of Georg Buschan, *Illustrierte Völkerkunde.* Stuttgart: Strecker & Schröder, 1923. 1078 pp.

————. "Die Megalithen Südostasiens und ihre Bedeutung für die Klärung der Megalithenfrage in Europa und Polynesien," *Anthropos,* 23 (1928): 276–315.

————. "Das Megalithproblem," pp. 162–82 in Emil Breitinger, Josef Haekel, and Richard Pittioni, eds., *Beiträge Österreichs zur Erforschung der Vergangenheit und Kulturgeschichte der Menschheit.* 1958 Symposion der Wenner-Gren Foundation, Burg Wartenstein bei Gloggnitz, Austria. Horn, Austria: Ferdinand Berger, 1959. 238 pp.

Hermanns, Matthias. *Die Nomaden von Tibet.* Vienna: Herold, 1949. 325 pp.

————. "Were Animals First Domesticated and Bred in India?" *Journal of the Bombay Branch of the Royal Asiatic Society,* 27, Pt. II (1952): 134–73.

————. *The Indo-Tibetans.* Bombay: K. L. Fernandes, 1954. 159 pp.

Herskovits, Melville J. *Economic Anthropology.* New York: Alfred A. Knopf, 1952. 547 pp.

Hertwig, Paula. *Artbastarde bei Tieren.* Handbuch der Vererbungswissenschaft, Lieferung 21 (II,B). Berlin: Gebrüder Borntraeger, 1936. 140 pp.

Hesselmeyer, C. H. "The Hill-Tribes of the Northern Frontier of Assam," *Journal of the Asiatic Society of Bengal,* 37, Pt. II (1868): 192–208.

Higgins, J. C. "The Mithun," *Journal of the Bombay Natural History Society,* 35 (1931): 444–45.

Hodgson, B. H. "On the Aborigines of the Sub-Himalayas," *Journal of the Asiatic Society of Bengal,* 16 (1847): 1235–44.

———. [1849] "On the Aborigines of Nor-Eastern India," *Journal of the Asiatic Society of Bengal,* 18 (1849): 451–60.

———. [1849a] "On the Aborigines of the Eastern Frontier," *Journal of the Asiatic Society of Bengal,* 18 (1849): 967–75.

———. "On the Indo-Chinese Borderers and Their Connexion with the Himalayans and Tibetans," *Journal of the Asiatic Society of Bengal,* 22 (1853): 1–25.

Hodson, T. C. "The Native Tribes of Manipur," *Journal of the Anthropological Institute of Great Britain and Ireland,* 31 (1901): 300–309.

———. *The Naga Tribes of Manipur.* London: Macmillan, 1911. 212 pp.

Hole, Frank. "Investigating the Origins of Mesopotamian Civilization," *Science,* 153, No. 3736 (Aug. 5, 1966): 605–11.

———, and Kent V. Flannery. "Excavations at Ali Kosh, Iran, 1961," *Iranica Antiqua,* 2 (1962): 97–148.

———, Kent Flannery, and James Neely. "Early Agriculture and Animal Husbandry in Deh Luran, Iran," *Current Anthropology,* 6, No. 1 (Feb. 1965): 105–6.

Hooke, S. H. *Babylonian and Assyrian Religion.* London: Hutchinson, 1953. 128 pp.

Hubback, Theodore. "Malayan Gaur or Seladang (*Bibos gaurus hubbacki*)," *Journal of the Bombay Natural History Society,* 40 (1939): 8–19.

Hughes, W. Gwynne. *The Hill Tracts of Arakan.* Rangoon: Government Press, 1881. 55 pp.

Hutchinson, R. H. Sneyd. *An Account of the Chittagong Hill Tracts.* Calcutta: Bengal Secretariat Book Depot, 1906. 202 pp.

Hutton, John H. [1921] *The Angami Nagas.* London: Macmillan, 1921. 480 pp.

———. [1921a] *The Sema Nagas.* London: Macmillan, 1921. 463 pp.

———. [1922] "Carved Monoliths at Dimapur and an Angami Naga Ceremony," *Journal of the Royal Anthropological Institute of Great Britain and Ireland,* 52 (1922): 55–70.

———. [1922a] "The Meaning and Method of the Erection of Monoliths by the Naga Tribes," *Journal of the Royal Anthropological Institute of Great Britain and Ireland,* 52 (1922): 242–49.

———. [1922b] "Divided and Decorated Heads as Trophies," *Man,* 22 (1922): 113–14.

———. "The Significance of Head-Hunting in Assam," *Journal of the Royal Anthropological Institute of Great Britain and Ireland,* 58 (1928): 399–408.

———. [1929] "Outline of Chang Grammar," *Journal and Proceedings of the Asiatic Society of Bengal,* N.S., 25 (1929): 1–101.

———. [1929a] "Diaries of Two Tours in the Unadministered Area East of the Naga Hills," *Memoirs of the Asiatic Society of Bengal,* 11, No. 1 (1929): 1–72.

———. [1929b] "Assam Megaliths," *Antiquity,* 3 (1929): 324–38.

———. "Races of Further Asia," *Man in India,* 12 (1932): 1–18.

———. "The Mixed Culture of the Naga Tribes," *Journal of the Royal Anthropological Institute of Great Britain and Ireland,* 95 (1965): 16–43.

Imperial Gazetteer of India. Provincial Series: Burma. Calcutta: Superintendent of Government Printing, 1908. 2 vols.

————: Eastern Bengal and Assam. Calcutta: Superintendent of Government Printing, 1909. 663 pp.

[India. Indian Council of Agricultural Research]. *First Indian Dairy Year Book,* 1960. New Delhi: Indian Council of Agricultural Research, 1961. 115 pp.

Inverarity, J. D. "The Indian Bison, with Some Notes on Stalking Him," *Journal of the Bombay Natural History Society,* 4 (1889): 294–310.

Isaac, Erich. "On the Domestication of Cattle," *Science,* 137, No. 3525 (July 20, 1962): 195–204.

Izikowitz, Karl Gustav. *Lamet; Hill Peasants in French Indochina.* Etnologiska Studier, 17. Göteborg: Etnografiska Museet, 1951. 375 pp.

Jacobsen, Thorkild. "Ancient Mesopotamian Religion: The Central Concerns," *Proceedings of the American Philosophical Society,"* 107 (1963): 473–84.

James, E. O. *The Cult of the Mother-Goddess.* New York: Barnes & Noble, 1959. 300 pp.

————. *The Ancient Gods; The History and Diffusion of Religion in the Ancient Near East and the Eastern Mediterranean.* London: Weidenfeld & Nicolson, 1960. 359 pp.

————. *The Worship of the Sky-God.* London: Athlone Press, University of London, 1963. 175 pp.

Kauffmann, Hans-Eberhard. "Landwirtschaft bei den Bergvölkern von Assam und Nord-Burma," *Zeitschrift für Ethnologie,* 66 (1934): 15–111.

————. "Züchtungsbiologische Beobachtungen in der Schweinezucht bei den Naga und Thadou-Kuki in Assam," *Biologia Generalis,* 14 (1938): 284–95.

————. "Kurze Ethnographie der nördlichen Sangtam-Naga (Lophomi), Assam," *Anthropos,* 34 (1939): 207–45.

————. "Die Bedeutung des Dorftores bei den Angami-Naga," *Geographica Helvetica,* 10 (1955): 84–95.

————. "Formes et motifs d'art dans la culture mégalithique ancienne," *Actes du VIe Congrès International des Sciences Anthropologiques et Ethnologiques,* Paris, 1960, Vol. 2, Pt. 1: 415–18.

————. "Observations on the Agriculture of the Chittagong Hill Tribes," pp. 111–34 in John E. Owen, ed., *Sociology in East Pakistan.* Occasional Studies of the Asiatic Society of Pakistan, I. Dacca: Asiatic Society of Pakistan, 1962. 275 pp.

Kauffmann, Oscar. *Aus Indiens Dschungeln,* Vol. 1. Leipzig: Klinkhardt & Biermann, 1911. 192 pp.

Keith, Arthur Berriedale, trans. *The Veda of the Black Yajus School Entitled Taittiriya Sanhita.* Harvard Oriental Series, Vols. 18 and 19. Cambridge: Harvard University Press, 1914. 2 vols.

Kenyon, Kathleen M. "Jericho and Its Setting in Near Eastern History," *Antiquity,* 30 (1956): 184–95.

————. *Digging Up Jericho.* New York: Frederick A. Praeger, 1957. 272 pp.

————. *Archaeology in the Holy Land.* New York: Frederick A. Praeger, 1960. 326 pp.

Kingdon-Ward, Frank. *In Farthest Burma.* London: Seeley, Service, 1921. 303 pp.

————. "The Seinghku and Delei Valleys, North-East Frontier of India," *Geographical Journal,* 75 (Jan.–June 1930): 412–32.

————. *Plant Hunter's Paradise.* New York: Macmillan, 1938. 347 pp.

————. *Burma's Icy Mountains*. London: Jonathan Cape, 1949. 287 pp.

————. "The Mishmis of Assam," *Geographical Magazine*, 24 (1951–52): 579–85.

————. *Plant Hunter in Manipur*. London: Jonathan Cape, 1952. 254 pp.

————. *Return to the Irrawaddy*. London: Andrew Melrose, 1956. 224 pp.

Kirkbride, Diana. "Five Seasons at the Pre-Pottery Neolithic Village of Beidha in Jordan," *Palestine Exploration Quarterly* (Jan.–June 1966), pp. 8–72.

Konow, Sten. "Note on the Languages Spoken between the Assam Valley and Tibet," *Journal of the Royal Asiatic Society*, 1902, pp. 127–37.

Koppers, Wilhelm. "Zentralindische Fruchtbarkeitsriten und ihre Beziehungen zur Induskultur," *Geographica Helvetica*, 1 (1946): 165–77.

Kramer, Samuel Noah. *Sumerian Mythology*. Rev. ed. New York: Harper & Brothers, 1961. 130 pp.

————. *The Sumerians: Their History, Culture, and Character*. Chicago: University of Chicago Press, 1963. 355 pp.

————. "The Indus Civilization and Dilmun, the Sumerian Paradise Land," *Expedition*, 6, No. 3 (Spring 1964): 44–52.

Kühn, Julius. "Bastard zwischen Gayal und Zebu," *Der Zoologische Garten* (Frankfurt), 24 (1883): 126–27.

————. "Fruchtbarkeit der Gayalbastarde zu Halle a. S.," *Der Zoologische Garten* (Frankfurt), 26 (1885): 59–61.

Lambert, Aylmer Bourke. [1804] "Description of Bos Frontalis, a New Species, from India," *Transactions of the Linnean Society of London*, 7 (1804): 57–59.

————. [1804a] "Further Account of the Bos Frontalis," *Transactions of the Linnean Society of London*, 7 (1804): 302–5.

Lambert, E. T. D. "From the Brahmaputra to the Chindwin," *Geographical Journal*, 89 (1937): 309–23.

Leach, E. R. *Political Systems of Highland Burma*. Cambridge: Harvard University Press, 1954. 324 pp.

Lehman, F. K. *The Structure of Chin Society*. Illinois Studies in Anthropology No. 3. Urbana: University of Illinois Press, 1963. 244 pp.

Lewin, T. H. *Wild Races of South-Eastern India*. London: William H. Allen, 1870. 352 pp.

Lhote, Henri. "Faits nouveaux concernant la chronologie relative et absolue des gravures et peintures pariétales du Sud Oranais et du Sahara," pp. 191–214 in Luis Pericot Garcia and Eduardo Ripoll Perello, eds., *Prehistoric Art of the Western Mediterranean and the Sahara*. Viking Fund Publications in Anthropology, No. 39. New York: Wenner-Gren Foundation for Anthropological Research, 1964. 262 pp.

Livesey, T. R. "The Gayal, or Mithan (*Bos frontalis*)," *Journal of the Bombay Natural History Society*, 35 (1931): 199–202.

Löffler, Lorenz G. "Zur sakralen Bedeutung des Büffels und Gajals für Ahnenkult, Ernteriten und soziale Feste im Gebiet Südostasiens." Ph.D. Diss., Johannes-Gutenberg-Universität, Mainz, 1954. 247 pp.

————. "Khami/Khumi–Vokabulare," *Anthropos*, 55 (1960): 505–57.

Lorrain, J. Herbert. *A Dictionary of the Abor-Miri Language, with Illustrative Sentences and Notes*. Shillong: Eastern Bengal and Assam Secretariat, 1907. 572 pp.

————, and Fred W. Savidge. *A Grammar and Dictionary of the Lushai Language (Dulien Dialect)*. Shillong: Assam Secretariat Printing Office, 1898. 346 pp.

Lotsy, J. P. "Die Aufarbeitung des Kühn'schen Kreuzungsmaterials im Institut für Tierzucht der Universität Halle," *Genetica*, 4 (1922): 32–61.

Lus, J. "Sovremennoe sostojanie otdalennoĭ gibridizacii životnyh i perspektivy daljneĭšeĭ raboty" [Distant hybridization of animals—present status and future prospects], *Izvestiia*, Akademiia Nauk SSSR, Otdelenie mat. i est., Seriia biologicheskaia (1938), Pt. 1, pp. 775–852.

Lydekker, Richard. *Wild Oxen, Sheep, and Goats of All Lands*. London: Rowland Ward, 1898. 318 pp.

————. *The Game Animals of India, Burma, Malaya, and Tibet*. London: Rowland Ward, 1907. 409 pp.

————. *The Ox and Its Kindred*. London: Methuen, 1912. 271 pp.

————. *Wild Life of the World*, Vol. 2. London and New York: Frederick Warne, [1916]. 440 pp.

McCall, Anthony Gilchrist. *Lushai Chrysalis*. London: Luzac, 1949. 320 pp.

Macdonell, Arthur Anthony. *A Practical Sanskrit Dictionary*. Oxford: Oxford University Press, 1929. 382 pp.

————. *The Vedic Mythology*. Varanasi: Indological Book House, 1963. 189 pp. [Reprint of an earlier work.]

————, and Arthur Berriedale Keith. *Vedic Index of Names and Subjects*. London: John Murray, 1912. 2 vols.

Macgregor, C. R. "Notes on the Akas and Akaland," *Proceedings of the Asiatic Society of Bengal*, 1884, pp. 198–211.

Mackay, Ernest J. H. *Further Excavations at Mohenjo-Daro*. Delhi: Manager of Publications, 1937–38. 2 vols.

————. *Chanhu-daro Excavations, 1935–36*. American Oriental Series, Vol. 20. New Haven, Conn.: American Oriental Society, 1943. 338 pp.

Majumdar, Surendra Nath. "The Ao Nagas," *Man in India*, 4 (1924): 41–82.

Majumder, Surendra Nath. *Ao Nagas*. Calcutta: Sailen Majumder, [1925]. 58 pp.

Mallowan, M. E. L. *Early Mesopotamia and Iran*. New York: McGraw-Hill, 1965. 142 pp.

————, and J. Cruikshank Rose. "Excavations at Tall Arpachiyah, 1933," *Iraq*, 2, Pt. 1 (1935): 1–178.

Malten, Ludolf. "Der Stier in Kult und mythischem Bild," *Jahrbuch des Deutschen Archäologischen Instituts*, 43 (1928): 90–139.

Maringer, Johannes. *The Gods of Prehistoric Man*, trans. by Mary Ilford. London: Weidenfeld & Nicolson, 1960. 219 pp.

Marshall, John. *Mohenjo-Daro and the Indus Civilization*. London: Arthur Probsthain, 1931. 3 vols.

Mayrhofer, Manfred. *Kurzgefasstes etymologisches Wörterbuch des Altindischen*, Vol. 1. Heidelberg: Carl Winter, 1956. 569 pp.

Mellaart, James. [1961] "By Neolithic Artists of 7500 Years Ago—Statuettes from Hacilar, Unique for Quantity, Variety, Beauty and Preservation," *Illustrated London News*, 238, No. 6341 (Feb. 11, 1961): 229–31.

————. [1961a] "Two Thousand Years of Hacilar—Starting from over Nine Thousand Years Ago: Excavations in Turkey Which Throw Light on the

Earliest Anatolia," *Illustrated London News*, 238, No. 6349 (April 8, 1961):
588–91.

———. [1962] "The Beginnings of Mural Painting," *Archaeology*, 15, No. 1
(Spring 1962): 2–12.

———. [1962a] "A 7th-6th Millennium Township of Southern Anatolia, Larger
Than Pre-Pottery Jericho: First Excavations at Catal Huyuk—Part I," *Illustrated London News*, 240, No. 6410 (June 9, 1962): 934–36.

———. [1962b] "The Earliest Frescoes Yet Found on a Man-Made Wall:
Remarkable Discoveries in the Excavations at Anatolian Catal Huyuk—
Part II," *Illustrated London News*, 240, No. 6411 (June 16, 1962): 976–78.

———. [1962c] "Man's First Murals," *Horizon*, 5, No. 1 (Sept. 1962): 10–13.

———. [1962d] "Excavations at Çatal Hüyük. First Preliminary Report, 1961,"
Anatolian Studies, 12 (1962): 41–65.

———. "Excavations at Çatal Hüyük, 1962. Second Preliminary Report,"
Anatolian Studies, 13 (1963): 43–103.

———. [1964] "Earliest of Neolithic Cities: The Third Season of Excavations
at Anatolian Chatal Huyuk. Part I—Shrines and Images of 9000 Years Ago,"
Illustrated London News, 244, No. 6496 (Feb. 1, 1964): 158–60.

———. [1964a] "Earliest of Neolithic Cities: Delving Deep into the Neolithic
Religion of Anatolian Chatal Huyuk. Part 2—Shrines of the Vultures and
the Veiled Goddess," *Illustrated London News*, 244, No. 6497 (Feb. 8,
1964): 194–97.

———. [1964b] "In the Dawn of Religion: A Reconstruction of a Funerary
Rite, Nearly Nine Thousand Years Ago, At Chatal Huyuk, in Anatolia,"
Illustrated London News, 244, No. 6510 (May 9, 1964): 728–29.

———. [1964c] "Excavations at Çatal Hüyük, 1963. Third Preliminary Report," *Anatolian Studies*, 14 (1964): 39–119.

———. *Earliest Civilizations of the Near East*. New York: McGraw-Hill, 1965.
143 pp.

———. "Excavations at Çatal Hüyük, 1965. Fourth Preliminary Report,"
Anatolian Studies, 16 (1966): 165–91.

Millington, Powell. *On the Track of the Abor*. London: Smith, Elder, 1912.
218 pp.

Mills, J. P. *The Lhota Nagas*. London: Macmillan, 1922. 255 pp.

———. *The Ao Nagas*. London: Macmillan, 1926. 500 pp.

———. "Notes on a Tour in the Chittagong Hill Tracts in 1926," pp. 118–23
in *Census of India, 1931*, Vol. 1 (India), Pt. III. Simla: Government of India
Press, 1935. 245 pp.

———. *The Rengma Nagas*. London: Macmillan, 1937. 381 pp.

———. "A Brief Note on Agriculture in the Dirang Dzong Area," *Man in
India*, 26 (1946): 8–11.

———. [1947] "Tours in the Balipara Frontier Tract, Assam," *Man in India*,
27 (1947): 4–35.

———. [1947a] "Headhunting among the Mishmis of the Lohit Valley,
Assam," *Man in India*, 27 (1947): 74–75.

———. "The Mishmis of the Lohit Valley, Assam," *Journal of the Royal
Anthropological Institute of Great Britain and Ireland*, 82 (1952): 1–12.

Milroy, A. J. W. "The Preservation of Wild Life in India. No. 3. Assam,"
Journal of the Bombay Natural History Society, 37 (1934–35): Supplement

(The Wild Animals of the Indian Empire and the Problem of Their Preservation, Pt. III), 97–104.

Molz, P. Marcellinus. "Ein Besuch bei den Ao-Nagas in Assam (Indien)," *Anthropos*, 4 (1909): 54–70.

Mongait, Alexander. *Archaeology in the U.S.S.R.*, trans. from the Russian by David Skvirsky. Moscow: Foreign Languages Publishing House, 1959. 429 pp.

Monier-Williams, Monier. *A Sanskrit-English Dictionary*. Oxford: Clarendon Press, 1899. 1333 pp.

Mori, F. "Some Aspects of the Rock-Art of the Acacus (Fezzan Sahara) and Data Regarding It," pp. 225–51 in Luis Pericot Garcia and Eduardo Ripoll Perello, eds., *Prehistoric Art of the Western Mediterranean and the Sahara.* Viking Fund Publications in Anthropology, No. 39. New York: Wenner-Gren Foundation for Anthropological Research, 1964. 262 pp.

Morris, John. *Living with Lepchas; a Book about the Sikkim Himalayas.* London: William Heinemann, 1938. 306 pp.

Morris, R. C. "The Vernay-Hopwood Upper Chindwin Expedition," *Journal of the Bombay Natural History Society*, 38 (1935–36): 647–71.

Nathusius, Simon von. "Die bisherigen Ergebnisse der Kreuzungsversuche mit dem Gayal (*Bibos frontalis*) im Haustiergarten des Landwirtschaftlichen Instituts der Universität Halle," *Kühn-Archiv*, 1 (1911): 61–105.

―――. *Der Haustiergarten und die dazu gehörigen Sammlungen im Landwirtschaftlichen Institut der Universität Halle.* Hannover: M. and H. Schaper, 1912. 77 pp.

Neighbor, R. E. *A Vocabulary in English and Mikir.* Calcutta: Baptist Mission Press, 1878. 84 pp.

Newland, A. G. E. *The Image of War, or Service on the Chin Hills.* Calcutta: Thacker, Spink, 1894. 90 pp.

Ogilvie, C. S. "The Behaviour of Seladang (*Bibos gaurus*)," *Oryx*, 2 (1953–54): 167–69.

O'Malley, L. S. S. *Darjeeling.* Bengal District Gazetteers. Calcutta: Bengal Secretariat Book Depot, 1907. 231 pp.

―――. *Bengal, Bihar and Orissa, Sikkim.* Cambridge: Cambridge University Press, 1917. 317 pp.

Parry, N. E. *The Lakhers.* London: Macmillan, 1932. 640 pp.

Parsons, James J. "The Acorn-Hog Economy of the Oak Woodlands of Southwestern Spain," *Geographical Review*, 52 (1962): 211–35.

Paul, Gemini. "Sherdukpens. IV. Village Council, Land, Taxes and Food," *Vanyajati*, 6 (1958): 153–56.

Peal, S. E. "Notes on a Visit to the Tribes Inhabiting the Hills South of Síbságar, Asám [sic]," *Journal of the Asiatic Society of Bengal*, 41, Pt. 1 (1872): 9–31.

―――. "The Mithun," *Nature*, 33 (Nov. 1885–April 1886): 7.

―――. "On the 'Morong' as Possibly a Relic of Pre-Marriage Communism," *Journal of the Anthropological Institute of Great Britain and Ireland*, 22 (1893): 244–61.

Pemberton, R. Boileau. "Report on Bootan," pp. 1–123 in Ashley Eden, R. B. Pemberton, W. Griffiths, and Kishen Kant Bose, *Political Missions to Bootan.* Calcutta: Bengal Secretariat Office, 1865. 343 pp.

Perkins, Dexter, Jr. "Prehistoric Fauna from Shanidar, Iraq," *Science,* 144, No. 3626 (June 26, 1964): 1565–66.

Perrot, Jean. "Palestine-Syria-Cilicia," pp. 147–64 in Robert J. Braidwood and Gordon R. Willey, eds., *Courses toward Urban Life.* Viking Fund Publications in Anthropology, No. 32. New York: Wenner-Gren Foundation for Anthropological Research, 1962. 371 pp.

Pettigrew, W. *Tangkhul Naga Grammar and Dictionary (Ukhrul Dialect) with Illustrative Sentences.* Shillong: Assam Secretariat, 1918. 476 pp.

Phillips, E. G. *Outline Grammar of the Garo Language.* Shillong: Assam Secretariat, 1904. 31 pp.

Pilgrim, Guy E. *The Fossil Bovidae of India.* Memoirs of the Geological Survey of India, Palaeontologia Indica, N.S., 26, Memoir No. 1 (1939): 1–356.

Pizey, R. M. "Sounds Made by Gaur or Indian Bison (*Bibos gaurus*)," *Journal of the Bombay Natural History Society,* 36 (1932–33): 243.

––––––. "On the Distinction between Indian and Malayan Gaur," *Journal of the Bombay Natural History Society,* 41 (1940): 657–59.

Pollok, F. T., and W. S. Thom. *Wild Sports of Burma and Assam.* London: Hurst & Blackett, 1900. 507 pp.

Prashad, B. *Animal Remains from Harappa.* Memoirs of the Archaeological Survey of India, No. 51. Delhi: Manager of Publications, 1936. 64 pp.

Prater, S. H. "Indian Domestic Cattle and Their Wild Ancestors," *Indian State Railway Magazine,* 10 (1937): 433–36. [Abstract in *Animal Breeding Abstracts,* 5 (1937): 264.]

––––––. *The Book of Indian Animals.* Bombay: Bombay Natural History Society, [1948]. 263 pp.

Rawlins, John. "On the Manners, Religion, and Laws of the Cúci's, or Mountaineers of Tipra," *Asiatick Researches,* 2 (1790): 187–93.

Reed, Charles A. "Animal Domestication in the Prehistoric Near East," *Science,* 130, No. 3389 (Dec. 11, 1959): 1629–39.

––––––. "A Review of the Archeological Evidence on Animal Domestication in the Prehistoric Near East," pp. 119–45 in Robert J. Braidwood and Bruce Howe, *Prehistoric Investigations in Iraqi Kurdistan.* Studies in Ancient Oriental Civilization, No. 31. Chicago: University of Chicago Press, 1960. 184 pp.

––––––. "Osteological Evidences for Prehistoric Domestication in Southwestern Asia," *Zeitschrift für Tierzüchtung und Züchtungsbiologie,* 76, No. 1 (1961): 31–38.

Report on the Marketing of Cattle in India. Agricultural Marketing in India, Marketing Series No. [83?]. Delhi: Manager of Publications, 1956. 235 pp.

Report on the Marketing of Milk in the Indian Union. Agricultural Marketing in India, Marketing Series No. 64. Delhi: Manager of Publications, 1950. 214 pp.

Riasanovsky, Valentin Aleksandrovich. *Fundamental Principles of Mongolian Law.* London: Kegan Paul, Trench, Trubner, 1937. 338 pp.

Riebeck, Emil. *Die Hügelstämme von Chittagong.* Berlin: A. Asher, 1885. 5 sections.

Risley, H. H. *India. Ethnographic Appendices.* Census of India, 1901, Vol. 1. Calcutta: Office of the Superintendent of Government Printing, India, 1903. 251 pp.

Robertson, George Scott. *The Káfirs of the Hindu-Kush.* London: Lawrence & Bullen, 1896. 658 pp.

Robinson, William. "Notes on the Languages Spoken by the Various Tribes Inhabiting the Valley of Asam and Its Mountain Confines," *Journal of the Asiatic Society of Bengal,* 18, Pt. I (1849): 183–237.

———. "Notes on the Dophlás and the Peculiarities of Their Language," *Journal of the Asiatic Society of Bengal,* 20 (1851): 126–37.

———. "Notes on the Languages Spoken by the Mi-Shmis," *Journal of the Asiatic Society of Bengal,* 24 (1855): 307–24.

Rockhill, William Woodville. "Notes on the Ethnology of Tibet," pp. 665–747 in *Report of the U. S. National Museum for 1893.* Washington: Smithsonian Institution, 1895.

Rodden, Robert J. "Excavations at the Early Neolithic Site at Nea Nikomedeia, Greek Macedonia (1961 season)," *Proceedings of the Prehistoric Society,* N.S., 28 (1962): 267–88.

———. "An Early Neolithic Village in Greece," *Scientific American,* 212, No. 4 (April 1965): 82–92.

Ross, E. J. "A Chalcolithic Site in Northern Baluchistan," *Journal of Near Eastern Studies,* 5, No. 4 (Oct. 1946): 284–316.

Rowlatt, E. A. "Report of an Expedition into the Mishmee Hills to the Northeast of Sudyah," *Journal of the Asiatic Society of Bengal,* 14 (1845): 477–95.

Roy, Nilima, "Habitations of the Adis of the Siang Frontier Division," *Vanyajati,* 5 (1957): 125–33.

Roy, Sachin. "Domestic Animals and Their Role in the Life of the Adis," *Vanyajati,* 6 (1958): 146–52.

———. *Aspects of Padam-Minyong Culture.* Shillong: North-East Frontier Agency, 1960. 315 pp.

Ruben, Walter. *Eisenschmiede und Dämonen in Indien.* Internationales Archiv für Ethnographie, Vol. 37, Supplement. Leiden: E. J. Brill, 1939. 306 pp.

Rütimeyer, L. "Versuch einer natürlichen Geschichte des Rindes, in seinen Beziehungen zu den Wiederkäuern im Allgemeinen, Zweite Abtheilung," *Neue Denkschriften der Allgemeinen Schweizerischen Gesellschaft für die Gesammten Naturwissenschaften,* 22 (1867): 1–175.

St. John, R. F. St. Andrew. "A Short Account of the Hill Tribes of North Aracan," *Journal of the Anthropological Institute of Great Britain and Ireland,* 2 (1873): 233–46.

Sanderson, G. P. *Thirteen Years among the Wild Beasts of India.* 7th ed. Edinburgh: John Grant, 1912. 387 pp.

Śāstri, Mādhava, ed. *Kāṇva-Saṁhita.* Kashi Sanskrit Series No. 35. Benares: Chowkhamba Sanskrit Series Office, 1915. 194 pp.

Sauer, Carl O. *Agricultural Origins and Dispersals.* New York: American Geographical Society, 1952. 110 pp.

Savidge, Fred W. *A Grammar and Dictionary of the Lakher Language.* Allahabad: Pioneer Press, 1908. 210 pp.

Schaller, George B. *The Deer and the Tiger; A Study of Wildlife in India.* Chicago: University of Chicago Press, 1967. 370 pp.

Schloeth, Robert. "Cycle annuel et comportement social du Taureau de Camargue," *Mammalia,* 22 (1958): 121–39.

——. "Das Sozialleben des Camargue-Rindes," *Zeitschrift für Tierpsychologie*, 18 (1961): 574–627.

Schomberg, Reginald C. F. *Between the Oxus and the Indus*. London: Martin Hopkinson, 1935. 275 pp.

Schumann, Hubert. "Gayal und Gaur und ihre gegenseitigen Beziehungen," *Kühn-Archiv*, 3 (1913): 7–80.

Scott, J. George, and J. P. Hardiman. *Gazetteer of Upper Burma and the Shan States*, Pt. I, Vol. 1. Rangoon: Superintendent, Government Printing, Burma, 1900. 727 pp.

Sen Gupta, P. N. "Investigations into the Dietary Habits of the Aboriginal Tribes of Abor Hills (North-Eastern Frontier), Part II, Minyong and Pangi," *Bulletin of the Department of Anthropology* [Government of India], 3, No. 2 (July 1954): 155–73.

——. "Investigations into the Dietary Habits of the Aboriginal Tribes of Abor Hills (North-Eastern Frontier), Part III, Galong Tribe," *Bulletin of the Department of Anthropology*, 4, No. 2 (July 1955): 69–95.

Sentsi, P. "The Rengma Nagas Today," *Journal of Social Research* (Ranchi, Bihar), 8, No. 1 (March 1965): 44–49.

Shafer, Robert. "Classification of the Sino-Tibetan Languages," *Word*, 11 (1955): 94–111.

Shakespear, J. *The Lushei Kuki Clans*. London: Macmillan, 1912. 250 pp.

Sharma, R. R. P. *The Sherdukpens*. Shillong: Research Department, Adviser's Secretariat, 1961. 101 pp.

Shaw, William. *Notes on the Thadou Kukis*. Calcutta: Asiatic Society of Bengal, 1929. 175 pp. [Also appeared in *Journal of the Asiatic Society of Bengal*, N.S., Vol. 24 (1928).]

Shrode, Robert R., and Jay L. Lush. "The Genetics of Cattle," pp. 209–61 in Vol. 1 of M. Demerec, ed., *Advances in Genetics*. New York: Academic Press, 1947. 458 pp.

Shukla, Bramha Kumar. *The Daflas of the Subansiri Region*. Shillong: North-East Frontier Agency, 1959. 139 pp.

Simoons, Frederick J. *Eat Not This Flesh: Food Avoidances in the Old World*. Madison: University of Wisconsin Press, 1961. 241 pp.

Simpson, George Gaylord. *The Principles of Classification and a Classification of Mammals*. Bulletin of the American Museum of Natural History, Vol. 85. New York: American Museum, 1945. 350 pp.

Sinha, Raghuvir. *The Akas*. Shillong: Research Department, Adviser's Secretariat, 1962. 144 pp.

Smith, William Carlson. *The Ao Naga Tribe of Assam*. London: Macmillan, 1925. 244 pp.

Solecki, Ralph S. "Prehistory in Shanidar Valley, Northern Iraq," *Science*, 139, No. 3551 (Jan. 18, 1963): 179–93.

Sopher, David E. "The Swidden/Wet-Rice Transition Zone in the Chittagong Hills," *Annals of the Association of American Geographers*, 54 (1964): 107–26.

Soppitt, C. A. *An Historical and Descriptive Account of the Kachari Tribes in the North Cachar Hills, with Specimens of Tales and Folk-Lore*. Shillong: Assam Secretariat Press, 1885. 35 pp.

Spearman, Horace Ralph, comp. *The British Burma Gazetteer*. Rangoon: Government Press, 1879–80. 2 vols.

Spencer, Joseph E. *Shifting Cultivation in Southeastern Asia*. University of California Publications in Geography, Vol. 19. Berkeley and Los Angeles: University of California Press, 1966. 247 pp.

Spöttel, W. "Ein Beitrag zur Vererbung der Körperformen und des Skeletts," *Züchtungskunde*, 7 (1932): 296–308.

Srivastava, L. R. N. *The Gallongs*. Shillong: Research Department, Adviser's Secretariat, 1962. 128 pp.

Stanford, John Keith. *Far Ridges*. London: C. and J. Temple, [1946]. 208 pp.

Steen, Charlie R. "Material Culture of the Langsing Nagas, Northern Burma," *Southwestern Journal of Anthropology*, 4 (1948): 263–98.

Stevenson, H. N. C. *The Economics of the Central Chin Tribes*. Bombay: The Times of India Press, [1943]. 200 pp.

Stewart, R. "Notes on Northern Cachar," *Journal of the Asiatic Society of Bengal*, 24 (1855): 582–701.

Stonor, Charles R. "The Feasts of Merit among the Northern Sangtam Tribe of Assam," *Anthropos*, 45 (1950): 1–12.

———. "The Mithans of Assam," *Geographical Magazine*, 26 (1953–54): 332–35.

———. "Notes on Religion and Ritual among the Dafla Tribes of the Assam Himalayas," *Anthropos*, 52 (1957): 1–23.

———. "Indian Bison of the Naga Hills," *Country Life*, Dec. 17, 1964, p. 1697.

Stronach, David. "Excavations at Ras al 'Amiya," *Iraq*, 23 (1961): 95–137.

Thévenin, René. *Origine des animaux domestiques*. Paris: Presses Universitaires de France, 1947. 126 pp.

Thom, W. S. "Some Notes on Bison (*Bibos gaurus*) in Burma," *Journal of the Bombay Natural History Society*, 37 (1934–35): 106–23.

Thompson, Virginia. *French Indo-China*. New York: Macmillan, 1937. 517 pp.

Tickell, S. R. "Notes on the Heumá or 'Shendoos,' a Tribe Inhabiting the Hills North of Arracan," *Journal of the Asiatic Society of Bengal*, 21 (1852): 207–13.

———. "Extracts from a Journal up the Koladyn River, Aracan, in 1851," *Journal of the Royal Geographical Society*, 24 (1854): 86–114.

Todd, Burt Kerr. "Bhutan, Land of the Thunder Dragon," *National Geographic Magazine*, 102, No. 6 (Dec. 1952): 713–54.

Turner, Samuel. *An Account of an Embassy to the Court of the Teshoo Lama, in Tibet; Containing a Narrative of a Journey through Bootan, and Part of Tibet*. London: G. and W. Nicol, 1800. 473 pp.

Urbain, A. "Le Kou Prey ou boeuf sauvage cambodgien," *Mammalia*, 1 (1936–37): 257–58.

Van Buren, E. Douglas. *The Fauna of Ancient Mesopotamia as Represented in Art*. Analecta Orientalia, 18. Rome: Pontificium Institutum Biblicum, 1939. 113 pp.

van Loon, Maurits. "Pre-Neolithic Village," *Scientific American*, 214, No. 5 (May 1966): 53–54.

Vats, Madho Sarup. *Excavations at Harappa*. Delhi: Manager of Publications, 1940. 2 vols.

Wackernagel, Jacob. *Altindische Grammatik*, Band 2, 2 ("Die Nominalsuffixe," von Albert Debrunner). Göttingen: Vandenhoeck & Ruprecht, 1954. 966 pp.

Wang, Hsing-ju. *Hainan Tao chih Miao-jen* [The Miao People of Hainan Island]. Chung-kuo Pien-chiang Yen-chiu Shin [Institute for Chinese

Frontier Studies], Chu-hai University, Series B, No. 2. Canton: 1948. 146 pp. [Trans. from the Chinese by Te-Kong Tong for the Human Relations Area Files, New Haven, Conn.]

Watt, George. *The Commercial Products of India.* London: John Murray, 1908. 1189 pp.

Wehrli, Hans J. "Zur Wirtschafts-Geographie von Ober-Burma und den Nördlichen Shan-Staaten," *Jahresbericht der Geographisch-Ethnographischen Gesellschaft in Zürich,* 1905–6, pp. 41–154.

Weinberg, Saul S. "Neolithic Figurines and Aegean Interrelations," *American Journal of Archaeology,* 55, No. 2 (April 1951): 121–33.

——. *The Stone Age in the Aegean.* Fascicle containing Chap. 10, Vol. 1 of the forthcoming *Cambridge Ancient History.* Rev. ed. Cambridge: Cambridge University Press, 1965. 68 pp.

Wharton, Charles H. *An Ecological Study of the Kouprey, Novibos sauveli (Urbain).* Philippines (Republic), Institute of Science and Technology, Monograph No. 5. Manila: Bureau of Printing, 1957. 111 pp.

Wheatley, Paul. "A Note on the Extension of Milking Practices into Southeast Asia during the First Millennium A.D.," *Anthropos,* 60 (1965): 577–90.

Wilson, H. H., trans. *Ṛig-Veda Sanhitá,* Vol. 3. London: William H. Allen, 1857. 524 pp.

Winge, Herluf. *The Interrelationships of the Mammalian Genera,* Vol. 3 (Ungulata, Cetacea). Trans. from the Danish by E. Deichmann and G. M. Allen. Copenhagen: C. A. Reitzels Forlag, 1942. 308 pp.

Woodthorpe, R. G. *The Lushai Expedition, 1871–1872.* London: Hurst & Blackett, 1873. 338 pp.

Woolley, C. Leonard. *The Sumerians.* Oxford: Clarendon Press, 1928. 198 pp.

——. *Excavations at Ur.* New York: Thomas Y. Crowell, 1965. 262 pp.

Wright, Herbert E., Jr. "Climate and Prehistoric Man in the Eastern Mediterranean," pp. 71–97 in Robert J. Braidwood and Bruce Howe, *Prehistoric Investigations in Iraqi Kurdistan.* Studies in Ancient Oriental Civilization, No. 31. Chicago: University of Chicago Press, 1960. 184 pp.

Zaehner, R. C. *The Dawn and Twilight of Zoroastrianism.* London: Weidenfeld & Nicolson, 1961. 371 pp.

Zervos, Christian. *Naissance de la civilisation en Grèce.* Paris: Éditions 'Cahiers d'Art,' 1962–63. 2 vols.

Zeuner, Frederick E. [1963] *A History of Domesticated Animals.* London: Hutchinson, 1963. 560 pp.

——. [1963a] "The History of the Domestication of Cattle," pp. 9–15 in A. E. Mourant and F. E. Zeuner, eds., *Man and Cattle.* Royal Anthropological Institute, Occasional Paper No. 18. London: Royal Anthropological Institute of Great Britain and Ireland, 1963. 166 pp.

Index

Abo Teni (ancestor of the Dafla), 47, 219

Acculturation, xiv, 38, 155–56, 157, 183

Adi: domestic animals, 23n, 83–84, 170; origins and affinities, 63, 80; population, 80; groups of, 80; racial characteristics, 80; language, 80; settlement and house types, 81; landscape described, 81; social life, 81–82, 86–88, 99; political life, 82–83, 89–91, 99; trade, 83, 85–86, 100, 189; agriculture and crops, 83, 90, 99–100, 119; sacrifice of mithan, 83–96 passim, 168n, 179, 179n, 180; use of milk by, 84; care and economic uses of mithan, 84–86, 100, 154, 165, 192n, 197; religious beliefs, 88–89, 91–96 passim, 271–72; ordeals and oaths, 90–91; mentioned, xiv, 38, 199, 218

Adi Hills, 23n, 83, 219

Afghanistan: early domesticated cattle in, 239, 261; early cattle cults of, 257, 258; mentioned, 228. See also Ghar-i-Mar

Afterworld: ancestral spirits return from, 55, 69, 177; position of men in, and its improvement, 69, 70, 88–89, 137–59 passim, 173–77 passim, 248, 258, 260; mithan in, 69, 89, 130, 137, 152, 158, 173, 174, 177, 182; Plain of Heaven as, 137, 145, 148, 149, 153, 159; souls of ill visit, 178; con-

cern with as motive for bovine domestication, 263

—Adi, 88, 89

—Apa Tani, 69–70, 176, 178

—Chin, 137–53 passim, 158, 159, 173

—Dafla, 55

—Naga, 110, 124, 125, 129–30, 158, 159, 173, 174, 177, 182

—Sumerian, 248

—Zoroastrian, 258

Agam, 279

Agrab, Tell, 254

Agricultural implements: plow, 23, 44, 78, 83, 97, 122, 134–35, 190n; digging stick, 83; dao, 83, 134, 144, 279; hoe, 97, 134, 144; ax, 134, 144; mithan shoulder blades as, 196. *See also* Ax; Dao; Hoe; Plowing

Agriculture: and suitability for mithan keeping, 11, 166–67, 188–89, 229; and gaur numbers, 22; rites and festivals, 58, 76, 92, 94–95, 96, 109, 117, 129, 178; origins of, 234–37, 237n, 240. *See also* Agricultural implements; Crops; Shifting cultivation

—of Adi, 83, 94–96, 99–100

—of Apa Tani, 64, 69, 76, 78

—of Chin, 134–35, 140, 144–45

—of Dafla, 47, 48, 58, 98, 219

—of Naga, 107, 117, 119, 129, 188–89

—of NEFA, 43

299